Algrove Publishing Limited
1090 Morrison Drive
Ottawa, Ontario
Canada K2H 1C2

Canadian Cataloguing in Publication Data

Main entry under title:

Popular mechanics shop notes for ...

(Classic reprint series)
Includes indexes.
Originally published: Chicago : Popular Mechanics Co., 1905-
"Compiled from the "Shop notes" department of Popular mechanics
    magazine, and "Written so you can understand it;" tells easy
    ways to do hard things" --Added t.p., v. 1.
Contents: v. 1. 1905 - v. 2. 1906 - v. 3. 1907 - v. 4. 1908 - v. 5. 1909 - v. 6. 1910 - v. 7. 1911 -
    v. 8. 1912 - v. 9. 1913 - v. 10. 1914 - v. 11. 1915 - v. 12. 1916 - v. 13. 1917 - v. 14. 1918 -
    v. 15. 1919 - v. 16. 1920 - v. 17. 1921 - v. 18. 1922 - v. 19. 1923.
ISBN 0-921335-87-3 (v. 11) - ISBN 0-921335-91-1 (v. 12) - ISBN 0-921335-94-6 (v. 13) -
ISBN 0-921335-96-2 (v. 14) - ISBN 0-921335-98-9 (v. 15) - ISBN 0-921335-93-8 (v. 16) -
ISBN 0-921335-95-4 (v. 17) - ISBN 0-921335-97-0 (v. 18) - ISBN 0-921335-99-7 (v. 19) -

    1. Do-it-yourself work. 2. Industrial arts. I. Title: Shop notes for ... II. Series: Classic
reprint series (Ottawa, Ont.)

TJ1160.P66 2000   600   C99-900763-7

Printed in Canada
#10800

Publisher's Note

Virtually every woodworking magazine in the English-speaking world has a shop notes section and has published an accumulation of them in book form. This was all started in 1905 with the first annual issue of *Popular Mechanics Shop Notes*, a compilation of advice on jigs, fixtures, methods of work, processes and projects. The earlier issues focussed primarily on metalworking, but with tips for a variety of other trades liberally sprinkled throughout. As years went by, the contents shifted more and more to woodworking and handyman projects. Each book is profusely illustrated. The line drawings of the earlier issues were supplanted by superb engravings until photographs started to creep in during the 1920s. Each year has its charm but all issues share the attribute of being clear, concise and widely informative.

Leonard G. Lee, Publisher
Ottawa
September, 1999

WARNING

This is a reprint of a book compiled in the early 1900s. The book describes what was recommended to be done in accordance with the knowledge of the day.

It would be advisable to treat all corrosive, explosive and toxic materials with much greater caution than is indicated here, particularly any materials that come in contact with the body.

Similarly, some of the recommended projects were dangerous then and remain so now. All of this material should be regarded with a judicious eye and necessary precautions taken.

POPULAR MECHANICS

SHOP NOTES

FOR

1918

———

EASY WAYS TO DO HARD THINGS

———

OF DAILY USE
TO EVERY MECHANIC

———

Vol. XIV—Table of Contents, Pages 2887-2893

———

POPULAR MECHANICS, CHICAGO

Shop Notes

Time Variations of a Watch Explained

By EDWIN L. POWELL

COMPLAINT that a watch varies in timekeeping apparently without special cause is quite common. The series of experiments outlined herewith may be performed readily at home, and will demonstrate that a watch of substantial quality will keep time correctly if properly handled. It should be apparent also, that a reason may be found for each of these ordinarily unaccountable variations in the performance of a watch.

The record of a watch from the first of one month to the 15th of the following month, illustrated graphically, is shown in the diagram. It was a seven-jeweled instrument, cost $8, and had been in use four years.

The watch was carried upright during the day in the upper vest pocket, and placed, not suspended, on a dresser or shelf in the same position at night.

Two windings every 24 hours were found to give the steadiest results; one at 8 o'clock each morning and the other at 10 o'clock each night. The watch was usually carried between these hours in the day, and left on the dresser during the night. Skipping a winding or permitting the watch to remain on the shelf longer than usual caused a perceptible slowing up, which is shown in the chart.

The record was begun shortly after the watch had been repaired and regulated by a jeweler. It kept time to within one-quarter second a day while hanging upright on his desk. Note the variation of four seconds each day as soon as it was carried in the pocket. This condition was permitted to continue for nine days to ascertain if the gain was consistent. This proved to be the case, with an exception when

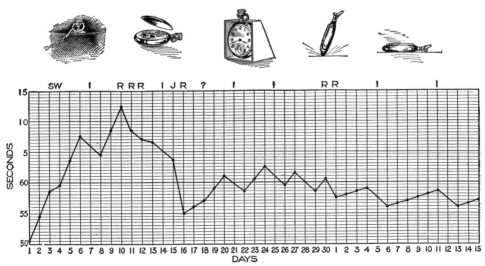

Nearly All of the Variations Shown in the Diagram were Traced to Definite Causes, as Regular Position in Pocket, Permitting Dust to Enter, in Holder Overnight, Shock, and Placed Horizontal

one of the regular windings was skipped, as indicated on the chart by the letters SW.

Regulation was then begun, each adjustment being indicated on the diagram by the letter R. No screw set was attached to the regulator, as the watch was an inexpensive one. Even with the aid of a glass, minute adjustment of the controlling arm was difficult, and usually resulted in moving it too far. This caused a rapid variation of the record, and a great number of adjustments was necessary before a satisfactory result was obtained.

Of the other letters used, J stands for a slight jar, which the watch received on the 15th, resulting in a loss of 8½ seconds. Irregularity of treatment, which occurred on Sundays and holidays when the watch remained on the shelf until past the noon hour before being placed in the pocket, is indicated at I. No check was made on these days, but readings on the following days showed a loss of from 2½ to 3 seconds, in each instance the variation being recorded at nearly the same angle. It will be noted that the adjustment finally obtained nearly compensates for this loss for the rest of the week, thus keeping the watch almost correct on the average. One unaccountable variation occurs in the record, indicated by the question mark on the 18th day. This was caused probably by a jar too slight to have been noticed at the time. Readings were taken at noon, United States Naval Observatory time at Washington, D. C.

Hydroplane for Carrying a Line across a Stream

The simple hydroplane shown in the illustration was the means of carrying

The Swift Current Drove the Hydroplane Onward and the Tension on the Line Forced It to the Bank

a line across a swollen stream after bridges and telephone wires had been torn away, in an Arizona valley. Cannon and rockets failed to carry a line over and two swimmers gave up the task. When a light line had been taken across by the hydroplane, rigged as shown in the sketch, a cable was drawn over and a ferry attached to it. In a short time reconstruction work was under way.

An Inexpensive Universal Joint

In the case of light and medium-heavy machinery, a very cheap, durable, and efficient universal joint may be made from three straight chain links of round section. In connecting this form of a joint, one end of each shaft, the driving and driven, must be slotted, to receive the end link, and a bolt put through the shaft to prevent the link from pulling out. A reinforcing collar is shrunk over the end of the shaft to strengthen the slotted part.

Such a joint will drive at almost right angles and with very little friction. It is especially recommended for mining, lumbering, agricultural, and similar classes of machinery.

℄Aluminum castings may be ground on a disk grinder without filling the abrasive material if a coat of paraffin is applied to the wheel.

A Farm Shop and Garage
by W. E. Frudden

AUTOMOBILES and other self-propelled machines are almost indispensable to modern farming and are in general use. Proper equipment for their storage and repair is not so common, hence the farm shop and garage described should prove suggestive as a means of economy in the maintenance and housing of these valuable machines. They will be good investments only if proper care is given them. The plant described is in use on a farm in Iowa and was designed to fit the particular needs of the owner. It has a number of features that are adaptable to similar buildings, of various sizes and materials, and in other climates.

The construction of the building is standard and may be carried out in frame with a rough cement exterior finish, as shown in the illustration, or in a variety of materials. Clapboards, shingles, sheet metal, or a prepared sheet-roofing material may be used. The walls may be built up of concrete blocks or brick, and the upper portion finished in less substantial material. No details are shown for the framing and the general finishing of the openings and trim, as they are standard. The roof is of the hip type, with a shortened ridge.

The building is set on a slight knoll so that good drainage is afforded. Light is available from all sides, as shown in the ground-floor plan, and the window openings are distributed to give adequate light in all parts of the interior, particularly at the workbench, where a double window is shown. The entrances are large, giving easy access for the machines, and aiding in lighting the interior. The doors at each end of the building make it possible to drive through, avoiding the necessity of backing out in some instances. The double sliding doors in the center partition shut off the garage from the workshop, which may be used for general farm repair and construction work.

The garage will house three cars, and the large doors, extending almost the full width of the building, afford easy ingress and egress. Floor drainage is not shown in the ground-floor plan but should be installed to conform to the disposal facilities available. For washing the machines a concrete area, on a level with the floor and extending in front of the large doorways, will be found convenient. This may be built when the concrete foundation is made.

It is important that the doors be hung strongly, as they are of considerable width and height. The main doors should all be swung outward so as not to use interior space unnecessarily. The sliding doors in the partition will be found to have an advantage over other types in ease of construction and economy of space. The center partition may be made lightly and only high enough to separate the garage and shop, or built up into the roof structure. In the latter case it will be found convenient to heat the shop for winter use, when the garage is not so much used, except for storage.

It is intended that practically all repair work on the machines is to be done in the shop rather than in the garage. The car on which the work is to be done may be moved into the shop, where the arrangement of the machinery, workbench, and tool and supply cupboards is such that a minimum of effort is necessary to reach them. This practice also tends to keep the garage unlittered, and in the best condition for the proper storage of the cars or other machines, such as a farm tractor.

The lighting and interior arrangement of the shop should be noted par-

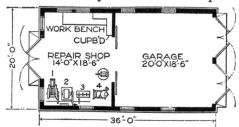

I-GAS ENGINE 2-ELECTRIC GENERATOR 3-EMERY
4-FORGE

Ground-Floor Plan, Showing the Well-Lighted Shop and Garage, the Workbench, Cupboards, and Machinery Arranged Compactly

ticularly, as these features offer valuable suggestions. The windows are arranged to advantage in that the workbench is afforded light from two windows on the rear and from another window at the vise end, where most of the close work is done. Two windows on adjacent walls afford plenty of light for the machinery, and by opening the doors additional light may be permitted to enter.

Machinery essential to a shop of this type is included in the equipment. A gas engine produces power for driving the electric generator, from which current is derived for a lighting system, and also drives a line shaft, from which belts are carried to the emery grinder and to a fan for the forge. Storage of current is also provided for, so that when the gas engine is in use, primarily to drive the machinery, its excess power may be applied to the generation of current. Other machines may be substituted for those shown in the illustration, to meet the particular needs of the owner, and to conform to the facilities.

Compactness, simple construction, and utility are the considerations in the designing of the workbench and the cupboards, shown in detail in the upper sketch. The close proximity of the cupboards and bench will be found especially convenient. The storage

space is inclosed with doors, or made in the form of drawers, as far as is practicable, for proper care and storage of tools and materials demand that they be inclosed. This adds to the orderliness of the shop and is conducive to better care of the tools and supplies, as well as affording security by locks, when desired.

The workbench is built up of frames of 2 by 4-in. stock, supporting a top of 1¾-in. planks. A floor shelf braces the supports 3½ in. from the shop floor, and is fitted between the frames, flush with their front edges, to form the lower casing of the doors and lower drawers. A baseboard, 3 in. wide, trims the bench at the bottom, and a narrower strip, together with a cove molding, finishes the joint between the top and the framework. A variety of cupboards and drawers is shown in the sketch, but these are suggestive only and may be arranged to suit individual needs.

Instead of extending the bench to the wall at both ends, the working end was provided with a 3½-ft. space, affording access from the end as well as the front. This will be found convenient, as often work can be handled readily only at parts inaccessible from the front of the workbench. Jobs of this type are the cutting and threading of pipes, and the handling of long pieces of stock, at the end of which joints are to be made, or fittings attached.

Two vises are provided, and these may be arranged to suit the individual convenience. The machine vise shown is of the pivot type, which will be found useful, since it may be set to face on the front or the end of the bench. The other vise is of the cabinetmaker's type, and is for use in woodworking. With the arrangement of the vises as shown, two persons may work at them conveniently and with a minimum of interference.

Other features, which may not have a general appeal but which will be found desirable in some instances, may be added. If the roof and headers over the doors are built heavily enough,

SIDE VIEW

DOOR TO GARAGE

FRONT VIEW

3'-8"

9

3'-6"

10"

3'-0"

12"

2'-8"

10'-4"

The Farm Shop and Garage is Designed to Care for Two Automobiles and a Small Tractor. It is Built with Standard Framing and Finished on the Exterior in Rough Cement, Although a Variety of Other Materials may be Used. Its Features Are Compactness of Storage and Equipment, Well-Lighted Rooms, Ease of Ingress and Egress, Separate Use of the Shop for General Farm Construction, and Suggestiveness in Designing Buildings for Similar Purposes

arrangement may be made to suspend blocks and tackle so that a car chassis may be raised at one end to permit work under it. This rigging may be used also in lifting heavy parts of the motor from the chassis. A turntable may be built into the floor of the garage or into the washing platform, suggested as an outdoor feature to be an extension of the garage floor, in front of the main entrance.

Watering Trough Made of an Old Boiler

A substantial watering trough was made by a California farmer of an old boiler fitted to the side of the barn, as

A Discarded Kitchen Boiler was Made into a Substantial Watering Trough

shown in the sketch. The openings were plugged and a section was cut on three sides and bent back to form a support, giving an opening at which the animals could drink.—Contributed by John Hoeck, Alameda, Cal.

To Prevent Flash Lamp from Short-Circuiting

It was not long after purchasing a small flash lamp before I learned a few interesting facts about them. After using it in the basement one morning to locate some misplaced articles, the lamp was carelessly placed on the top of a cast-iron radiator. The construction of the majority of these lamps is such that if a circuit is made by any conductor touching the two metallic ends of the lamp, the light will burn and the battery be taxed just as if the circuit had been made by pushing forward the contact button. As it was daylight and the room brightly illuminated, the burning of the lamp was not noticed, and when it was picked up that evening the battery was exhausted.

To prevent a recurrence due to thoughtlessness, I procured two short and heavy rubber bands and stretched them around the lamp, one over each end. It was an easy matter to remove them for renewal of the battery and it safeguarded the lamp from short-circuiting when the circuit snap was not applied.

Before retiring I usually laid the torch down by the bedside to have it handy for finding the switch of the electric lamp; for, being a railroad man, calls for duty during the night are frequent. Sometimes I had to grope around on the floor before laying hold of the torch, so I decided to make a permanent place for it where it could be easily found. A few pieces of fairly heavy brass wire were bent and soldered, as shown. The device was hung over the head end of the side spring support of the bed, which made the lamp easy to find and take hold of in a dark room. The arrangement was wrapped on the lower end with a tape

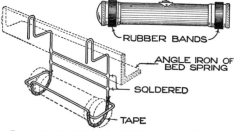

Protecting the Ends of a Flash Lamp to Prevent Short-Circuiting, and a Holder for the Lamp

to prevent it from short-circuiting in any way. The shape and size of the hanger were such that during the day the bedspread covered it.—Contributed by F. W. Bentley, Jr., Missouri Valley, Iowa.

Automobile Spring Inserts to Prevent Squeaking

Lubricated inserts between the leaves of automobile leaf springs will prevent squeaking when traveling over rough roads. The motorist may prepare the inserts by cutting strips of light canvas, or similar material, and filling them with graphite grease, heated in a pan placed in another pan of boiling water. The strips should be immersed in the melted grease and permitted to absorb it until saturated. Lay them on a board to dry, and cut of a size to fit between the leaves of the spring.

To Prevent Dust Entering Flywheel Bearing of Marine Engine

Considerable trouble was experienced in the bearing of a marine gasoline engine. The trouble-some bearing was the one close to the fly-wheel, and the peculiar design of the crank case permitted dust and grit to enter. These particles of dust evidently played havoc with the 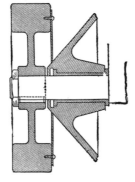 bearing, for it was found necessary to replace it quite often. The repair illustrated in the sketch was suggested and found to be entirely satisfactory when completed.

A piece of $\frac{1}{16}$-in. sheet metal was cut in the form of a ring, its outside diameter being almost that of the fly-wheel, and the inside diameter of sufficient size to fit easily the walls of the crank case when the engine was in operation. The disk was fastened to the inner face of the flywheel rim with machine screws. The disk prevented, to a great extent, the dust and grit from collecting on the inner side of the flywheel rim, and the trouble was entirely eliminated.

Brass Box Corners Made of Square Tubing

Attempts to make corners with which to reinforce boxes, or other constructions, usu-ally result badly when they are made of sheet metal bent from a flat piece. A better method is to obtain square tubing of the proper size and to cut off opposite corners, as shown in the il-lustration. When 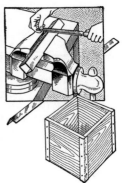 the cut edges are filed smooth and the corners fitted into place they will give strong reinforcement, since tubes of this kind are accurate in cross section and their corners are square without rounding at the angle.—Contributed by B. E. Dobree, Battleford, Sask., Can.

Removable Dock Railing

The illustration shows the method used for readily erecting and dis-mantling the railing on a yacht-club con-crete dock which was subjected to the force of severe winter storms. By un-screwing the right and left couplings the rail is easily taken as a unit from the brass-pipe stubs which are anchored in the concrete. Be- 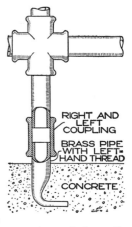 fore this scheme was adopted the railing required extensive repairs at the opening of each yachting season. The interior of the brass-pipe stubs were filled with concrete grout, which stiffened and strengthened them.—Contributed by J. J. O'Brien, Buffalo, N. Y.

Electric-Lamp Board of Sheet Metal

A substantial lamp bank may be readily made of a piece of sheet metal,

Various Groups of Connections may be Made on the Back of the Board

band iron, and a number of sign receptacles, as shown in the sketch.

The gauge and size of the metal will depend on the size of the bank desired. The metal should be cut to a size large enough to permit the bending over of its edges, ½ in. all around. This gives rigidity to the board and improves its appearance. Holes should be stamped out to fit the receptacles, which are of the ordinary type.

The supporting legs are made of ⅛-in. band iron, bent to fit under the board and drilled for rivets and bolts. Various groups of connections may be made on the back of the board. A crosspiece of metal or wood, drilled and insulated, should be riveted to the legs on one side as a support for the wires.—Contributed by H. W. Walter, Delaware, Ohio.

Pointers on Cleaning and Polishing an Automobile

High-polish finish on an automobile may be ruined by inexperienced persons in washing the car. The following suggestions will aid in producing good results and prolonging the wear of the finish.

Clear water should be used in washing a car, and when it is necessary to use soap, one that has no acid in it is best. Do not attempt to scrape off the mud and dirt, for the varnish surfaces may thus be scratched. Pour water over the dirty parts of the car from a small vessel or from a hose, in the latter case using no nozzle. The mud and dirt will be washed away slowly but without injury to the varnished surfaces. If water is not plentiful, a spray nozzle may be used.

The full force of the stream of water from a hose with a nozzle may be directed against the under side of the fenders, as this is not a highly finished varnished surface, but care must be taken that the nozzle does not strike the surfaces. After all the mud has been washed off, go over the car with a soft sponge, using plenty of water. Then dry it with a soft, clean chamois skin. It is best to use one chamois skin and sponge for the body, and another chamois skin and sponge for the running gear. The chamois skin should be rinsed frequently in clear water and wrung as dry as possible. If there is grease on any parts of the car, it should be removed first with a dry rag and then with soap and water.

The car must be wiped dry immediately after washing, as otherwise spots will appear as it dries. When a car has been out in the rain and the hood is hot, there will be more likelihood of spots forming on it. Wiping the car dry when it is taken in out of the rain will prevent such spots. They may be removed by applying a varnish polish.

Occasionally some of the openings in the radiator become filled with mud, decreasing its efficiency. This may be removed by forcing water through the radiator from the rear; otherwise the water may splash upon the engine and into the magneto.

Mohair tops should be brushed off frequently, and may be cleaned with a sponge dipped in a warm lather of Castile soap. Go over it several times with clear water so as to prevent alkali spots. Composition tops and curtains may be cleaned with water to which a little ammonia has been added. Leather tops may be washed and then treated with leather dressing. Never fold the top while it is wet, but stretch it in its raised position and permit it to dry.

The upholstering should be cleaned each time that the car is washed. If it is of leather, the dirt may be removed by rubbing it with a woolen or flannel cloth, dipped in water containing a small quantity of ammonia. Finish with leather dressing to insure pliability. Cloth cushions may be cleaned with a whisk broom and spots removed from them with soap and water.

The brass parts of the car may be cleaned with a brass polish. Do not permit the latter to come into contact with the varnished surfaces.

Lampblack, or silver polish, should be used in cleaning nickel parts. Rub all of the metal parts with an oily rag after they are polished. This prevents them from tarnishing easily in damp weather and also aids in cleaning them. —Contributed by P. D. Norem, Chicago, Ill.

Homemade Pipe Gauge

The standard pipe gauge shown in the illustration was made of a piece of sheet brass, $\frac{1}{16}$ in. thick. The various standard pipe sizes are represented and are indicated in figures beside the proper points on the gauge. It will be observed that the indications for

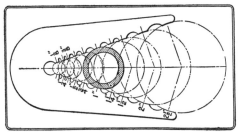

Standard Pipe Gauge Made of a Piece of Sheet Brass

the pipe sizes are opposite openings wider than the inside diameter of the pipes. It is necessary that the circles be laid out carefully to insure accuracy.

Hoop for One-Man Truck

Barrels or boxes containing heavy material may be handled easily on a truck by one man if the hoop shown in

The Hoop Prevents the Load from Tipping off the Truck

the sketch is attached. It may be made of heavy wire so that it can be released when not needed, or of band iron, permanently fixed to the sides of the truck and of a size to fit the barrels or other containers used. This simple device was found useful in a foundry and finishing room for castings, as it prevented undue effort on the part of men handling heavy loads on trucks and often saved the labor of an extra man. It may be adapted for use in stores or other places where crates or boxes are handled on a truck.—Contributed by Wilfred A. Cramer, Watertown, N. Y.

Painting an Automobile Radiator

Painting an automobile radiator quickly and thoroughly with a brush is difficult. A homemade spraying outfit similar to the one shown in the illustration made the job easy.

The outfit consists of a ½-gal. oil-can, made into an atomizer by attaching a tire pump to the end of the air pipe B. A piece of small brass pipe, A, was mounted in one side of the can, the upper end of it extending a short distance outside of the top. A second piece of pipe was mounted in a horizontal position in the top of the can, as shown at B. If a handle is attached to the can, as at C, the piece of pipe B may pass through it length-

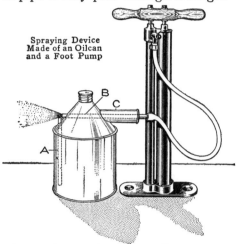

Spraying Device Made of an Oilcan and a Foot Pump

wise and extend a short distance beyond the end of the handle. Both pipes were soldered to the top of the can, and the screw top was provided with a gasket to make it tight.

When the air is forced through the horizontal tube B and caused to pass across the opening in the upper end of the vertical tube A, the liquid in the can is drawn up and forced out in a fine spray. A mixture for spraying the radiator may be made of lampblack and turpentine. A sheet of paper should be placed back of the radiator to protect the engine, and around the outer edge, to prevent the liquid from bespattering the brass finish.—Contributed by A. E. Andrews, Chicago.

Brush Finish for Brass

Brass and similar metals may be given a brush finish by rubbing them with steel wool. Care should be taken that the rubbing is done in one direction, otherwise a scratched surface will result. A lacquer should be applied to prevent tarnishing. A thin solution of white shellac in alcohol applied with a brush is satisfactory as a lacquer for large work, and small pieces may be dipped in the solution. —Contributed by Claude C. Soots, North Salem, Ind.

An Automatic Exhaust Heater

The heater consists of a pipe, about two-thirds the size of the exhaust pipe, but never larger, connected to the latter anywhere between the motor and the muffler by means of a tee fitting, which may be threaded or clamped in place. The back pressure from the muffler will cause the hot exhaust gases to pass through the heater pipe and out at the open end. To prevent the open end from being too noisy it should be swaged down, to make it smaller than the body of the pipe. The frictional resistance of the heating pipe is sufficient to muffle the noise to some extent.

The heat is regulated by means of an angle valve which should have a metal-to-metal seat. A discarded steam-radiator valve will answer the purpose well. The shield shown serves both as a protection for the shoes and as a flue to provide a circulation of air. The strip of asbestos acts as an insulator between the hot pipe and the floor board. The metal washers and clear-

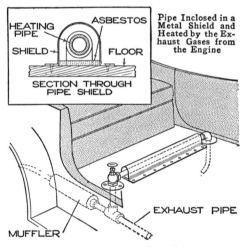

Pipe Inclosed in a Metal Shield and Heated by the Exhaust Gases from the Engine

ance space protect the floor board where the pipe enters.—Contributed by W. Burr Bennett, Bridgeport, Conn.

❡White woodwork may be kept fresh by rubbing it with a moistened cloth dipped in whiting. The surface should then be washed with clear water and dried.

Remedy for Overheating of Bearings

Persistent overheating of bearings which are in constant duty may be overcome by applying a mixture of flour of sulphur and lubricating oil to a consistency permitting use in an oil cup. This mixture will also be found useful on heavy-duty bearings in cam rolls, and similar machine parts.

Sootless Cap for Removing Stovepipes

Removing stovepipe was an exceedingly distasteful job, because of the

PIPE WITH CLOTH CAP

RUBBER BAND AND FASTENERS

soot and dirt that accompanied it, until I devised the cloth cap shown in the sketch. It is fitted over the end of the stovepipe and held in place by a piece of elastic provided with fasteners. The cap prevented the soot from falling out of the pipes while they were carried, and took most of the unpleasantness from the task.—Contributed by H. L. Schlegel, Birmingham, Alabama.

Load Scale for Trucks

Overloading, one of the severe abuses to which motor trucks are subjected, may be eliminated by the use of the device shown in the illustration. It consists of two vertical metal pieces, graduated and attached to the centers of the rear springs. They extend above the lower edge of the truck frame, by which the load is indicated on the scale, as shown by the dotted lines in the sketches. When the truck is empty the lower edge of the frame should register at zero, and when it is loaded to capacity it should be opposite the maximum-load indication, which is five tons in the device illustrated.

The scale markings are determined by placing the truck level and loading its platform evenly with loads of 1 ton, 1½ tons, etc., the indications on the scales being made at the lower edge of the frame. The graduations will not be spaced equally because of the

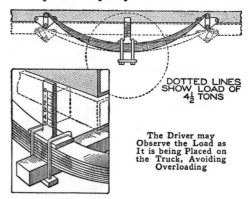

DOTTED LINES SHOW LOAD OF 4½ TONS

The Driver may Observe the Load as It is being Placed on the Truck, Avoiding Overloading

smaller spring deflection under light loads.—Contributed by Joseph Husson, New York.

A Temporary Shaft Coupling

It was necessary to connect two shafts for a temporary job, the ends of the shafts having a space of about 12 in. between them. One shaft was connected to an electric motor and the other to a centrifugal blower, and both machines were bolted permanently to the floor. A rough and ready form of coupling was rigged up in the following manner: Two pieces of cold-rolled steel, 14 in. long, 4 in. wide, and ⅜ in. thick, were procured and bent over at the ends as shown, after which

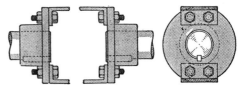

Connection Made of Two Bars between Two Flanges on Shaft Ends a Distance Apart

two holes were drilled in each end, equal in size to those in the flanges. The coupling was assembled, and needless to say it operated perfectly.

❰To obtain the distance between centers of two gears, add the number of teeth together and divide half the sum by the diametral pitch.

A Portable Keyseater

The main feature of the keyseating tool illustrated is the design of the ram. The ram, being round and extra-

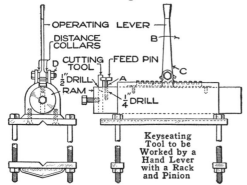

OPERATING LEVER
DISTANCE COLLARS
CUTTING TOOL
FEED PIN
B
D
$\frac{1}{2}$" DRILL
RAM
A
C
$\frac{1}{4}$" DRILL

Keyseating Tool to be Worked by a Hand Lever with a Rack and Pinion

long, presents a very large wearing surface, which greatly increases the durability of the machine. The "up and down" feed arrangement of the cutting tool is also very handy, though not new. The tool is round, with a flat surface ground on one side, against which the setscrew shown bears, to prevent it from turning. A notch is cut on the opposite side for the circular feed disk. This disk is 1⅛ in. in diameter and forms the head of the feed screw A. Further details of the feed device are shown in the illustration. The position of the ram is varied by pushing the operating lever down in the direction of the arrow B, and when the part C reaches the rack, the rack and pinion will be out of mesh. The ram may then be moved to any position by hand, and, when set as desired, an upward movement of the operating arm in the direction opposite to the arrow B reëngages the rack, and the stroke of the ram begins. As shown, the rack is set into the ram and securely bolted.

Bushings are not used because the very large surface reduces the wear to a minimum, and a little take-up is provided by tightening the nut D. The distance collars should be a loose fit for the reason that, as shown, the machine straddles the work and is securely clamped by the long bolts and straps.

Cleaning Paint on Engines

A compound with which engines or other oily machinery may be cleaned thoroughly is made as follows:

To one gallon of water add ¼ lb. of borax and ½ pint of lard oil. Mix them thoroughly, forming an emulsion. Rub the painted surfaces with the compound applied on waste or soft cloth, and with a clean cloth remove it before it dries.

Wrapping a Pair of Shoes

A neater package may be made in wrapping shoes without a box by placing the heels against the soles instead of placing the uppers together. The latter method exposes the heels, and, if they are high, may cause the wrapping to be broken.

Automatic Fire Damper in a Ventilating Duct

The illustration shows a damper for use in a ventilating duct which passes through a fire wall. As may be seen, a fusible link is incorporated in the actuating chain. This link will open when heated to about 140°, allowing the damper to be closed by the action of the weight which is attached to it. The damper may be locked in any posi-

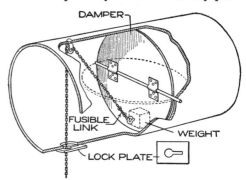

DAMPER
FUSIBLE LINK
WEIGHT
LOCK PLATE

A Fuse When Overheated Releases the Chain and the Weight Closes the Damper

tion by drawing the chain into the narrow end of the lock-plate slot which holds the chain from slipping.

Surface Whiting for Laying Out Work

In laying out work on structural iron or castings, chalking the surface is the usual method, but a better way is to mix whiting and benzine to the consistency of paint and apply the mixture with a brush. The benzine will soon evaporate and leave a fine white surface for the lines.

Screwdriver Grips Small Screws

The screwdriver shown in the sketch was devised when I found that I could 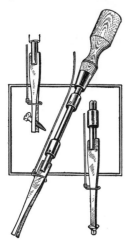 not reach into a corner of a cash register with an ordinary screwdriver. The tip was made from a pair of tweezers. The shank may be provided in various lengths, and the wire shown may be used to clamp the tweezers when it is desired to lift a screw out of an otherwise inaccessible place. If the strips of the tweezers are given the proper spring they will hold small screws firmly while they are put into place. The tips should be kept sharp and square. —Contributed by W. C. Loy, Rochester, N. Y.

A Belt Dressing

About as good a belt dressing as can be had is made by melting beeswax in neat's-foot oil in proportion of ½ lb. of wax to ½ gal. of the oil. To secure a good mixture, melt the wax first, then add the oil slowly, stirring constantly to get it thoroughly compounded.

❧Erasers may be kept in good condition by rubbing them on a piece of fine sandpaper provided for the purpose.

Outdoor Rack for Auto Tires

Motorcycle, bicycle, or other tires may be displayed to good advantage in front of motor-accessory shops by

The Tires are Displayed Out of Doors in the Rack

the use of the rack shown in the sketch. By extending the upper support, several tires of different size or style may be displayed. They are locked into place by the chain which closes the upper opening in the rack.— Contributed by Donald A. Kahn, South Bend, Ind.

To Prevent a Chain from Rattling

Where it is necessary to prevent a chain from rattling, as with those used on elevators, weave a rope into the links, as shown, and they will run noiselessly. The rope is woven in so that it will not get under or between the links where they bear on one another.

❧Small bulbs may be grown early in the spring by inserting them into holes in corks and floating them in a dish of water, in a shady place. As the roots sprout, moss and earth may be added, and the dish placed in a sunny spot.

Safety Boot Scraper for a Doorstep

The ordinary cast-iron blade boot scraper, located on or near the door-

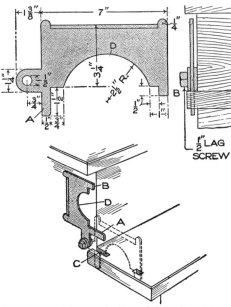

Boot Scraper That can be Turned Out of the Way When Not in Use

step, is a dangerous thing, and many a child bears a disfigured countenance as a result of falling over one of them. One placed on a step of a certain schoolhouse was responsible for injuries to three children during one term.

The sketch shows a good, substantial, and above all, a safety scraper that can be attached to a step. The detail of the blade is shown so that it can be easily cut out with a hacksaw from $\frac{3}{16}$ or $\frac{1}{4}$-in. sheet iron. It is fastened to the step so that it will drop readily into position. When not in use, it is pushed out of the way. When necessary to use it, the leg A is touched with the toe and the scraper drops down, the smaller leg B falling into a small ferrule sunk into the step. It may be necessary to cut a small piece out of the shelf, or footboard, if it projects over the frame, to let the small piece in, as shown at C. When the scraper has been used the toe is placed under the arch D, and the device is quickly thrown back into a safety position.

Corking Painted Ironwork

Sweating or condensation of vapor on the surface of ironwork is prevented on ships, and other structures which are in or near the water, by applying a layer of powdered cork over the paint. Several coats of red lead are first applied, and, while the last coat is still undried, finely ground cork is dusted on until the paint will absorb no more. When this is dry a coat of paint mixed with turpentine is applied. This process is also used in protecting iron or steel roofs from moisture on the under side.

Keeping a Record Map Up to Date

A wall map in the office of an electric-light company was used to indicate changes and extensions in the overhead lines. It was found difficult to make the alterations on the map satisfactorily. This was overcome by placing it in a picture frame having a glass front, and indicating the changes from time to time, on the surface of the glass, with several colors of waterproof ink.

Tamper Made of Concrete

A tamper for use in the garden or in home concrete construction may be made as follows: Procure a tomato can, about $4\frac{1}{2}$ in. in diameter, and remove the top. Drive nails part way into the end of a broomstick, or other round wooden rod, so as to form radiating projections. Insert the broomstick with the nails in it into the can and pour concrete around it. Care should be taken that the handle fits in the center of the can, and that its lower end does not touch the bottom while the concrete is being poured into place. Permit the mixture to harden, and a tamper that will be substantial will result.—Contributed by W. W. Baldwin, Washington, D. C.

⟨Several turns of tape around the middle of a pulley face will prevent a belt from working away from the center.

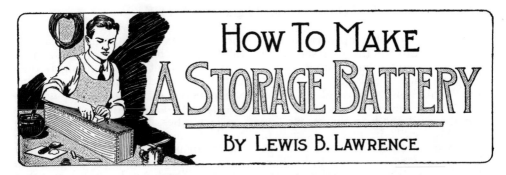

How To Make A Storage Battery

By Lewis B. Lawrence

IN the making, or handling, of a storage battery it must be understood that one cell will have an electromotive force of about two volts, and the length of time, or ampere-hours, it will run depends on the size of the cell and the surface of the plates. The description is for a 24-volt, 20 ampere-hour battery, which means that 12 cells are in the battery, and that they have such a size that they will deliver 20 amperes for one hour, or two amperes for 10 hours. It is of the lead-zinc type, the 12 cells being assembled in a box. To build the container, select the

stock of white pine, ⅜ in. thick, and cut one piece 21¼ in. long by 3⅝ in. wide, plane it, rabbet the edges and cut notches for an interlocking joint, as shown in Fig. 1. This piece is for the bottom of the box. The sides are made in a similar manner, the size of each being 21¼ in. long and 6 in. wide, as shown in Fig. 2, two pieces being required. Cut 11 pieces, 5⅛ in. long and 3⅜ in. wide, from ¼-in. stock, which form the separations in the box. The ends for the box are made as

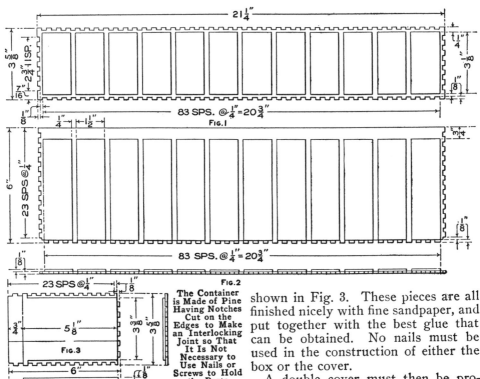

FIG.1

FIG.2

FIG.3

The Container is Made of Pine Having Notches Cut on the Edges to Make an Interlocking Joint so That It Is Not Necessary to Use Nails or Screws to Hold the Parts Together

shown in Fig. 3. These pieces are all finished nicely with fine sandpaper, and put together with the best glue that can be obtained. No nails must be used in the construction of either the box or the cover.

A double cover must then be provided, and this is cut from the ⅜-in. stock, which after planing will be reduced to ¼ in. The dimensions given in Fig. 4 are for the top part, and 12 pieces are cut like the one shown in Fig. 5 and mounted on the upper piece, Fig. 4, as shown in Fig. 6, with glue only. Drill ¼-in. holes and cut slots, ¼ in. square and ¼ by ⅜ in., ⁵⁄₁₆ in. from the edges and on the center line of the 1½ by 3⅛-in. pieces, as shown. A second cover is cut, as shown in Fig. 7, to form a water-tight box, which makes it possible to carry the battery around without spilling the acid. A few nails could be used in the construction of this cover, but it is best to put the whole box together with a good glue.

The mounting of the main box must be done carefully, and the parts fit snugly, so that when they are glued together the joints will hold water, if necessary. Join and glue together the bottom of the container and the two long sides; then, after applying glue to the edges of the 11 separators, slide these into their respective grooves and finish by gluing the two end pieces to the sides and bottom. The box is then bound tightly with strong cord and left to dry for about 12 hours. The mounting of the second cover is very similar to the making of the main box.

When the container and covers are dry, they must be immersed for about the acid. As an additional precaution the box may be painted inside with an acid-proof paint. The binding is then removed and the outside of the box sandpapered to remove all roughness left by the wax and rosin mixture.

Glass tubes, ¾ in. long, are fitted in the ¼-in. holes drilled in the cover, so that their upper ends will extend about ¼ in. above the surface, as shown in Fig. 6. The holes in the glass tubes allow the gases to escape without wasting the liquid. Two binding posts are fastened in a convenient place, Fig. 7 showing a good location for them.

The elements for each cell must now be constructed. Each one consists of five plates, three of them sheet zinc, and the other two of lead. The plates are cut from ³⁄₃₂-in. metal, 2½ by 4 in. in size, with a projection, 2 in. long by ¼ in. wide, on one corner of each as a connector, as shown in Fig. 8. The lead plates are roughened with vertical striations, by laying them on a soft piece of wood and hammering the teeth of a single-cut file into them. A ½-in. hole, A, is drilled through the center of each plate to allow for a free circulation of the electrolyte. The plates are mounted, as shown in Fig. 9, separating strips, about ¼ in. wide by ⅛ in. thick, being used between the plates. The

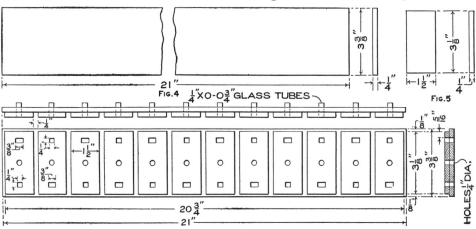

FIG.4   ¼"XO-0¾"GLASS TUBES
FIG.5
FIG.6

A Cover is Made to Fit over the Tops of the Cells to Prevent the Solution from Spilling When the Battery is Moved, and to Provide a Place for the Connections to the Plates

10 minutes in a boiling mixture of beeswax and rosin, 2 parts of wax to 1 part rosin, to make it impervious to best material to use for these strips is celluloid, but sheet rubber, such as is used for steam packing, will answer the

purpose quite well. Each element is held together with six clamps, made as shown in Fig. 10 and cut from hard

tank. Connect these plates together. Then connect the plates to be formed to the negative terminal, and the lead

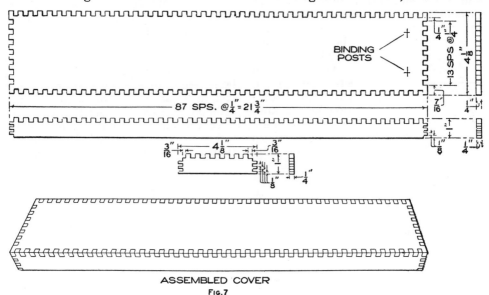

BINDING POSTS

87 SPS. @ $\frac{1}{4}$" = 21 $\frac{3}{4}$"

13 SPS @ $\frac{1}{4}$"

ASSEMBLED COVER

FIG.7

A Second Cover is Constructed the Same as the Main Container so That All Terminals, with the Exception of the Two Outlet Binding Posts, will be Covered and the Outside Present the Appearance of a Neat Box

rubber, the two at the bottom serving as feet upon which the element stands in the cell. Rubber bands, B, assist in holding the parts together firmly. The corner strips are bent together, as shown in Fig. 9, and brought out through the slots in the wood cover, Fig. 6.

The capacity of the battery will be considerably increased if the lead plates are made up electrochemically before being mounted, and this can be accomplished as follows: Make a small wood tank, 12½ in. long, 2⅝ in. wide, and 4½ in. deep, and place the 24 roughened plates in it so that they will be ½ in. apart, leaving a space of ½ in. between the first and last plates and the end of the tank. Steady the plates by means of small strips of wood, laid across the top of the tank, and connect them together in a strong but temporary manner. Cut 25 sheets of pure lead, using the pattern for the plates and not forgetting the ½-in. hole in the center, and place these "dummies" halfway between the plates to be formed, and one at each end of the

sheets to the positive terminal, of an electrical circuit, with a switch, rheostat, ammeter, and fusible plug in the line, as shown in Fig. 11. Next prepare a solution of distilled water, 2 qt., commercial sulphuric acid, 1 pt., and concentrated nitric acid, 1 pt. In preparing the solution, put the water in an earthen vessel, or porcelain basin, and add the sulphuric acid slowly while stirring the mixture constantly. This

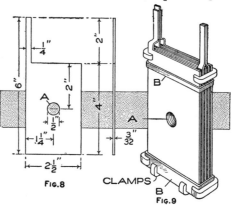

FIG.8

CLAMPS

FIG.9

Pattern for Cutting the Plates, and Location of Clamps to Hold Them Together in the Cell

mode of operation is important to avoid a sudden rise of temperature which will throw acid on the hands, or clothes, and the possible breaking of the vessel, or container, if glassware is used. Allow the mixture to cool, and then add the nitric acid slowly.

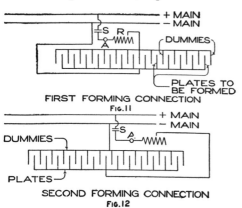

With the switch open, pour the solution in the tank —avoiding any drip or particles falling on the hands or clothes, as it burns very badly—until the surface of the liquid is about ¼ in. above the plates. Adjust the rheostat so that a very small current can pass; then close the switch, and decrease the resistance until the ammeter shows that a current of three amperes is flowing through the forming tank. Allow it to run for 10 hours, and then disconnect the plates from the source of energy. Remove the plates and dummies from the tank, taking care not to break their connections; then empty the tank and rinse it carefully. Set up the plates and dummies in the tank as before and pour in it the following solution: Distilled water 5 pt., and commercial sulphuric acid, 1 pt. This solution can be obtained already mixed from anyone recharging storage batteries, as it is the normal electrolyte

used for all lead storage batteries. Then connect up the plates to the positive terminal of the source of energy, and the dummies, to the negative terminal, as shown in Fig. 12, which is in the opposite direction of the connections made when the plates were in the former bath. Pass through them a current of three amperes until the liquid boils vigorously. This charge must last at least eight hours, and if the cells boil too hard before that time, reduce the current to two amperes by means of the rheostat. The connections can then be cut off, and the

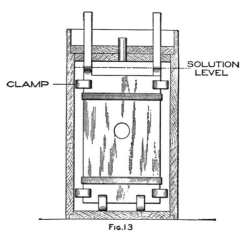

Pour In the Electrolyte Solution to the Depth Indicated, Just Covering the Plates

plates, which are now entirely formed, dipped for a few minutes in cold water, allowed to dry, and then mounted with the zinc plates to form the elements of the battery cells.

The corner strips of the elements, brought out through the slots in the cover, are connected together. These can be joined with lead, but the following plan is much better: The strips are bent over and interlaced, then wrapped with a few turns of small wire and thoroughly soldered. The surface of all the strips should be dusted with powdered rosin before they are interlaced, to facilitate the soldering, or a good soldering paste should be used. The soldering iron must not be too hot, for this will melt the terminals. Great care must be exercised in doing the soldering, to produce a good job. After soldering, the visible parts of the strips should be given a coat of good acid-proof paint, or a thick, black asphalt varnish.

The electrolyte solution for the cells is made as follows: Distilled water, 1 gal.; zinc sulphate, 2 lb.; cadmium sulphate, 2 lb., and magnesium sulphate, 4 oz. This fluid is poured into the cells until it stands about ¼ in. above the upper surface of the plates, as shown in Fig. 12.

If the lead plates, which are positives, have been formed by the process mentioned, a first charge, of about eight hours, will bring the cells to full capacity. If not, the plates have to be formed by successive charging and discharging. About 20 charges and discharges will be necessary to obtain the best working conditions, and even then the capacity of the battery will not be quite as large as if the positive plates had been formed before being mounted with the zinc plates.

In charging, a current of three amperes should be used, and the charge

kept up until the terminal pressure across the cells amounts to 28 volts. Never force it above this amount. Full

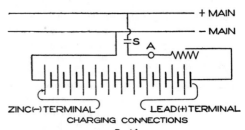

ZINC(—)TERMINAL   LEAD(H)TERMINAL
CHARGING CONNECTIONS
Fig.14
Wiring Diagram for Charging the Battery When It is Run Down by Use

charge is always indicated by a vigorous boiling in the cells. The current should never be kept on after the cells begin to boil.

The charging connections are shown in Fig. 14. For charging as well as for forming the plates, a resistance must be used in series with the battery, but on account of the great variation in voltages available, it is impossible to give any data regarding the proper size to use. A direct current is always used in charging.

File Used as Countersink

Satisfactory countersunk recesses for screws may be made in sheet metal by using a file, the thick portion of the tang where it meets the file being used to cut the recess. This will be found useful in an emergency, or when a countersink is not available.

A Dutch Clock

Those in charge of a number of workmen in a factory or shop will appreciate the device shown in the illustration and known as a "Dutch clock." It consists of a circular disk of stiff paper laid out in triangular portions radiating from the center. The names of the various departments are placed in these spaces and an indicator is fastened at the center. When the person at whose place the clock is, goes to any of the various rooms or departments he places the indicator on the appropriate space

on the dial. This informs others where he may be found.

The device has proved especially valuable to foremen or superintendents, but by inserting names instead of

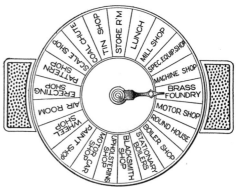

When the Foreman Leaves His Desk He Indicates Where He may be Found

places or otherwise varying the indications the clock may be adapted to a variety of uses.—Contributed by John F. Long, Springfield, Mo.

Reversing Automobile Brake Shoes for Wear

Brake shoes on old automobiles require relining oftener than those on new cars, and

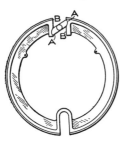

when the lining is taken out, it may be observed that although it is worn only slightly, the brake loses its power. This is caused by wear of the cam and the surface on which it operates. In a certain small car, which had been in use several seasons, and had been provided with a brake relining many times, it was noted that the surfaces AA were worn concave, so that the cam could be moved around to its full-pressure position without bringing much force on the brake drum. Turning the shoe over, causing the unworn surfaces BB to engage the cam ends, more than doubled the life of the lining.—Contributed by Morris G. Miller, New Rochelle, N. Y.

Removing Hard Spots on Lathe Spindle

Mechanics who have operated lathes with cast-iron headstock bearings appreciate the difficulty of dressing up a worn lathe spindle. The small particles of iron which adhere to the surface of

OIL STONE

HARD IRON SPOTS

the steel are so hard that a Swiss file cannot cut them. A small chisel is unsatisfactory for this work and grinding off the spots with a portable grinder gives poor results. A good method is to lap off the hard spots with a medium-grain oilstone. When almost down to the spindle surface use a fine-grain stone to finish. A fine bearing surface results, particularly if the stone is rubbed around the circumference, as shown in the sketch.

Curbing Borrowers of Electric Flatirons

To live agreeably among borrowing neighbors is a serious problem even for a good-natured housekeeper. One so situated experienced difficulty in keeping the electric iron at home. Its severe duties finally resulted in burn-

ing it out. A new one was about to be purchased, and in order to keep it at home the usual type of screw plug was removed from the end of the cord and replaced with a push plug. This necessitated a change in the wall outlet plate, but proved a great convenience. With this form of receptacle a connection may be made more quickly than with a screw plug. The first time the new iron was borrowed, it was promptly returned and not borrowed again by the same or any other neighbor.—Contributed by John D. Adams, Phoenix, Ariz.

Exit Lights That Illuminate

Red electric-light bulbs that were placed in the aisles and near the exits of the stock rooms of a large factory were found to cast annoying shadows and prevented the reading of orders without additional lights. I placed globes that were colored red on the upper portions only, in the sockets. This permitted the light to be given off from the lower part of the bulbs so that orders and papers might be read, and still provided the danger and exit lights required under the law. The expense of providing double lights was also overcome.—Contributed by F. W. Ward, Jersey City, N. J.

Gasoline Camp Stove

By R. S. MATZEN

AT the suggestion of an automobile owner, who is fond of jaunts into the woods and of fishing excursions, I devised the camp stove shown in the sketch. It is entirely self-contained, and may be filled with sufficient gasoline to provide a cooking fire for a considerable time. Its compact form and general usefulness was appreciated, and I have made several for persons who saw the original one in use. The large outer pipe is filled with fuel by removing the cap at the left. The pump on the opposite end provides pressure to force the vaporized gasoline from the burner at the center. The small valve is used to control the supply of fuel.

The stove is constructed as follows: Cut two pieces of 1-in. gas pipe, 14 in. long, for the sidepieces, and a 5-in. piece for the back end. Thread them, fit them with end caps and join the pipes in the U-shape shown, with elbows at the back corners. Tap the cap at the right for a bicycle-tire valve and fit the latter into place. A bicycle pump attached to it provides the pressure for the gasoline tank. Tap the back section of pipe for a ⅛-in. copper pipe, at the other end of which a valve is fitted. This completes the gasoline container from which the fuel is carried to the burner.

To make the burner, drill three rows of holes in the upper part of a piece of 1-in. pipe, 12 in. long, as shown in the illustration. The rows are ⅜ in. apart, and the holes, of ⅟₃₂-in. diameter, are also spaced ⅜ in. apart. Countersink each hole slightly with a ⅛-in. drill. Make two clamps, as shown, to hold the burner and the copper tube in the center of the tank. Plug the back end of the burner, and fit the other end with a cap, tapped to fit the valve with an elbow. Make a grate of heavy wire

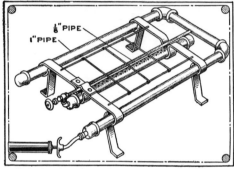

This Gasoline Camp Stove Is Compact and Self-Contained: The Fuel is Placed in the Outer Pipe and Kept under Pressure by the Pump

and fix it into the straps as shown. This completes the construction, and when the outer pipe, or tank, has been filled with fuel, pressure may be provided with the hand pump. The copper tube must be heated until the gasoline vaporizes. Then light the burner. The flame from the center row of holes keeps the generator tube hot, and the other holes provide for the heating of utensils.

Rigid Shear Made of Snips

Experiencing some difficulty in cutting a sheet of metal, I fixed one handle of an ordinary pair of snips in a vise, leaving the upper handle free. In this manner a powerful pressure was obtained by the use of one hand and the weight of the body thrown against it. The other hand was left free to hold the metal.—Contributed by W. W. Flanders, Everett, Wash.

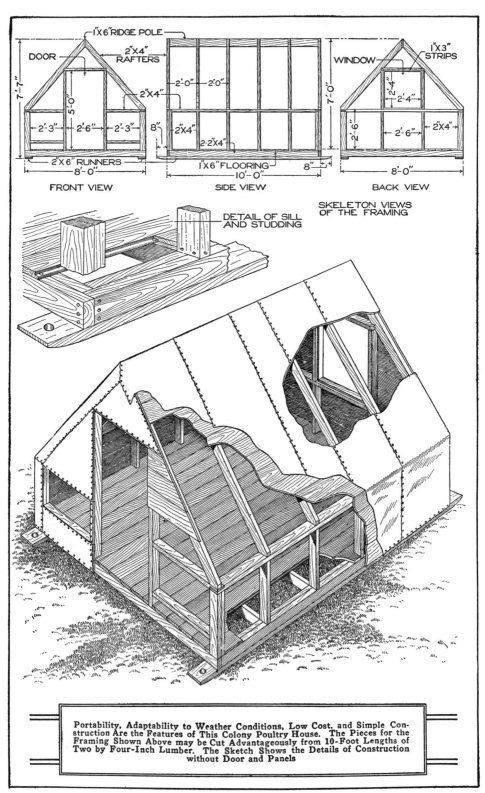

1"X6"RIDGE POLE

DOOR

2"X4" RAFTERS

2"X4"

7'-7"

5'-0"

2'-3" 2'-6" 2'-3"

2"X6" RUNNERS

8'-0"

FRONT VIEW

2'-0" 2'-0"

2"X4"

8"

2"X4"

2-2"X4"

1"X6" FLOORING

10'-0"

8"

SIDE VIEW

7'-0"

WINDOW

1"X3" STRIPS

2'-4"

2'-4"

2'-6"

2'-6" 2"X4"

8'-0"

BACK VIEW

SKELETON VIEWS OF THE FRAMING

DETAIL OF SILL AND STUDDING

Portability, Adaptability to Weather Conditions, Low Cost, and Simple Construction Are the Features of This Colony Poultry House. The Pieces for the Framing Shown Above may be Cut Advantageously from 10-Foot Lengths of Two by Four-Inch Lumber. The Sketch Shows the Details of Construction without Door and Panels

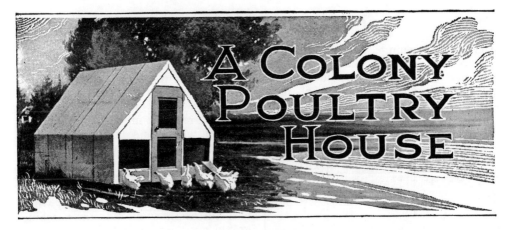

A Colony Poultry House

By W. E. FRUDDEN

PORTABILITY, adaptability to weather conditions, low cost, and simple construction are the features of the colony poultry house shown in the illustration. It is in use on a farm in Iowa and has been found satisfactory for 20 hens for the winter, and for the raising of chicks in flocks of over a hundred. It is built on skids so that it may be transported on rollers. Ventilation and shade are provided for with screens. For winter use, there are hinged doors, which may be lifted off easily in the summer.

The lumber for the house is all standard-size stock. The frame is built of 2 by 4-in. material, joined at the sill and corners to form 4 by 4-in. sections, and the skids are of 2 by 6-in. planks. The floor and sheathing boards are 6-in. shiplap. The house is covered with a prepared-roofing material.

Diagrams of the framing are shown in the upper figures of the plate of illustrations. The skids may be shaped first. Next spike together the sill of 2 by 4-in. material, as shown in the detail of sill and studding, and nail the skids in place.

Plan to cut all the pieces of the same size in a series, and make a measuring stick, or template, for each, particularly the rafters. Nail the floor joists into place, then the studding, door and window frames. The plate, which is nailed on top of the studding, should be fixed with a half-lap joint at the corners.

The floor should be nailed down next, as it is convenient to have it in place when the rafters are raised. The rafters are cut off flush with the sides of the house so that the siding and roofing material may be applied more easily. Nail the siding on the ends and sides, and on the rafters. The house may then be covered with roofing material.

The casements for the window openings should be made next. They are made of 7/8-in. material, 3 in. wide, one edge being nailed flush with the inner edges of the framing around the openings.

Details of the construction of the door are shown in the smaller illustration. It is built up of two thicknesses of boards, arranged so that the joints are reinforced, the horizontal rails on the inner side crossing the joints which appear on the front. Screws should be used to fasten together the pieces of the door, although properly clinched nails may also be used. The strips forming the inner side of the door are 1 in. narrower than those on the front, so that the 1/2-in. wire mesh may be fastened in place by quarter-round molding.

The panels in the door are similar in construction to those to be fitted into the other openings, at each side of the door and at the gable end of the rear of the house. The hinges are of the type used on storm windows, and permit the panels to be lifted off when raised nearly vertical. Oiled muslin may be fitted to hang by the upper edge in each of the openings, so that when the panels are removed shade from the summer sun may be provided. For purposes of ventilation the panels may

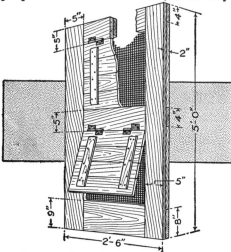

The Door is Built Up of Two Thicknesses Arranged to Reinforce the Joints

be opened or removed temporarily. If the window in the rear-gable end is not provided, a ventilator should be placed at the ridge. Roosts may be built in the rear part of the house, and nests arranged along the sides in the space adjoining the door, but not too close to the ventilating openings.

The stock bill for the construction of the colony poultry house is as follows:

2 pieces, 2 by 6 in. by 11 ft., 4 in., for skids.
1 piece, 1 by 6 in. by 10 ft., for ridge pole.
5 pieces, ⅞ by 3 in. by 10 ft., for casings, for openings.
2 pieces, ⅞ by 9 in. by 10 ft., for door.
30 pieces, 2 by 4 in. by 10 ft., for framing.
330 ft., ⅞ by 6 in. by 10 ft., shiplap flooring for floors, sides, and roof.
2 pieces, ⅞ by 10 in. by 10 ft., for nests and fittings.
250 sq. ft. roofing material for outer covering.

Improvised Buttonhook

Time, temper, and finger nails may be spared by using a string as an improvised buttonhook in emergencies. The twine should be fairly strong, and a loop should be pushed through the buttonhole, hooked around the button, and drawn through the hole, bringing the button into place easily and quickly.—Contributed by W. W. Baldwin, Washington, D. C.

Road Patching

The modern scheme of protecting road surfaces with sprayed oil has developed a new method of patching holes. Gravel is mixed with a heavy road oil, which acts as a binder. This is prepared in advance and carted to the place where the patching is to be done. Less gravel is needed than when it is used dry, because the hole need be filled only level and tamped, while with the ordinary method the patching gravel must be heaped above the normal surface of the road. Where patching on a large scale is to be done, a concrete mixer can be used to prepare the mixture.

Removing Steam-Gauge Dial-Glass Casings

Steam-gauge dial-glass casings are often hard to unscrew from the body of the gauge, due to the heat, and other influences, to which the gauge is continually subjected. This is aggravated by the fact that the covers are difficult to get hold of, and that it is not practical to apply any strong gripping device because of the danger of rupturing the material. The sketch shows how they can be removed with but very little trouble. One side of the gauge is lightly pinched between protected jaws of a vise, and the lower portion of the cover is set on a block of wood. Two bolts are placed in the holes in the back side of the body, and a narrow strip of metal is used as a lever. Any dial cas-

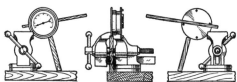

Removing a Glass-Cover Casing on a Steam Gauge with the Aid of a Vise

ing, after it has been turned one revolution, can be easily removed by hand. Getting it started is the difficulty. The most obstinate cover casing can be removed in this manner with no danger of disfiguring or rupturing it.

Preventing Rust under Molding on Screen Frames

Window-screen wire usually gives away near or under the small strip of molding that holds it to the frame. This is caused by the dampness retained in the joint after a rain, which results in the wire rusting. In placing new wire on a frame, be sure to paint it well on the edge after tacking it to the frame and before applying the molding.

Order Holder on an Expressman's Signal Flag

An expressman in a small city had the local druggist act as his agent. Orders received by the agent were written on slips of paper and placed in a pocket on the signal flag, which was placed in its socket beside the door to inform the expressman that he should call. Considerable delay in making inquiries for possible orders was thus avoided.—Contributed by Harry L. Dixson, Chicago, Ill.

Sharpening Scraper for Heavy Cut

Scrapers for finishing wood surfaces may be sharpened on their several edges for both light and heavy cuts, and this arrangement will be found more convenient than sharpening all the edges in the same manner. For light cuts, the edge of a scraper should be filed and honed square to the side of the scraper. For a heavy cut it is better to file the edge at a slight angle, and to turn over the acute corner with a round steel rod or a burnisher, rubbed along the edge with considerable pressure.—Contributed by L. E. Fetter, Portsmouth, N. H.

To Prevent Spilling Water on Automobile Radiator When Filling It

When filling an automobile radiator it is almost impossible to keep from spilling the water over the outside unless extreme caution and considerable time is taken at the end of the filling. The spilling can be prevented by making a stopper to fit the inside of the funnel in the small end. The stopper should be made of material that will not float. A cork will do, if a recess is formed in the center and filled with lead. A small wire, extending down from the lead and with the end turned, will provide a means of raising the stopper by pressing the bent end against the radiator filler. Just as soon as the funnel is lifted the stopper falls into place and prevents the water remaining in the funnel from spilling over the outside of the radiator.

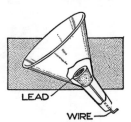

Straightening Small Rods in a Vise

Rods of some length and a diameter of an inch or even more may be straightened by the use of a comparatively light hammer, but the straightening of short rods is more difficult. This may be accomplished without marring the surface of the rods by the use of the grooved vise pads A, shown in the sketch. The pads should be made of copper or other moderately soft metal. The small strip riveted to the top of each pad will make it possible to use the three pads without using the hands to hold them in place.

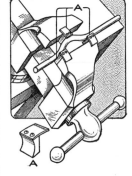

Simple Method of Bending Rails or Bars

An ordinary jackscrew, arranged with three posts sunk into the ground,

The Lifting Jack may be Used to Bend Bars or Rails by Rigging It between Posts Sunk into the Ground

may be used to bend heavy bars or rails, as shown in the illustration. The stakes must be heavy and set deep enough to stand the pressure. If necessary they may be braced. The bar, or rail, is set on blocks to make it level, and smaller blocks are fitted between it and the posts. The top of the jack is provided with a suitable block, to prevent slipping and to distribute the pressure evenly.

Truck for Baby Cab Indoors

A baby cab is usually convenient in which to place a child in order to have

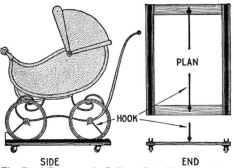

SIDE   END
The Truck Prevents the Soiling of the Floors by Dirt on the Carriage Wheels After Baby has been Given an Airing

it near its mother, who must work in various parts of the house. But after the carriage had been on the walk or street, we found it almost impossible to keep the wheels clean enough, and the result was that tracks marred the floors of our home. I constructed the carriage truck shown in the sketch, and the difficulty was remedied completely.

Now, on entering the house, the carriage is rolled on the truck, the brake is set, and the hooks at the front and back axles are put into place. The revolving casters make it possible to move the carriage more easily than on the wheels. The device was constructed of $\frac{7}{8}$-in. strips. Those for the end and sidepieces are $2\frac{1}{2}$ in. wide, and the small strips which guide the wheels are $\frac{3}{4}$ in. wide. Small channels of metal may be substituted for the wooden strips, as indicated in the end views.—Contributed by Charles P. Wiweke, Albany, N. Y.

Block Protects Sawyer's Hands from Splinters

Operators of cut-off saws, or other machinery on which rough wood is handled, will find a block fitted with a number of sharp steel points convenient in preventing splinters from entering the hands. In addition to the pain and annoyance of troublesome bits of wood which lodge in the flesh, there is the danger of infection. Such a block should be made to fit the hand, and a size of 2 by $3\frac{1}{2}$ by 6 in. will be found convenient. The steel points on one of the flat faces grip the lumber to be handled and the sawyer need not touch it with the hands except when the stock is to be lifted.

Making Smooth Castings in Babbitt Metal

Smooth castings may be made in babbitt metal if the following suggestions are observed: In constructing a wooden mold, permit the grain of the wood to run parallel with the pouring gate. The bottom of the mold should be "built up" out of the ends of boards, so that the grain runs at right angles to the surface of the bottom. This assists in venting the mold and prevents bubble holes. If the bottom is too large or difficult to construct in this fashion, use a sheet of dry blotting paper backed with wood. Cardboard and blotting paper are useful in constructing irregular parts of molds.

Dry the mold in an oven before casting. Place it in a box and pack sand around it to prevent leakage. Before pouring the metal into the mold, test the former by thrusting a wooden splinter into it, at intervals of a few seconds. When boiling and sputtering cease, it is ready to be poured. The straight edge of a piece of glass is an excellent instrument for finishing flat surfaces of babbitt metal.

Clip Board for Shop Orders

Each foreman's office in the repair and maintenance departments of a large manufacturing company is provided with a board for shop orders, as shown in the illustration. The board is studded with shoulder hooks numbered to correspond to the workmen, and orders for the men are placed in spring clips hung on the hooks.

The foreman arranges the orders in each clip as they are to be performed.

The Workmen Take Their Orders from the Clips Even in the Absence of a Foreman

If in the absence of the foreman a job is completed, the workman refers to his clip for another job.

Making a Waterfall for the Movies

Motion-picture operators devised an artificial waterfall over a dam in a landscape background for a scene, as shown

The Cameras were Set and at a Signal the Water was Released, Producing a Picturesque Waterfall

in the sketch, when weather conditions prevented a normal flow of water over the dam. The pond was small, the dam being only 50 ft. long, and the feeding streams were reduced to trickling rivulets.

Boards, set edgewise, were fitted to the planking on the inside of the dam, increasing its height 8 in. These boards were left in place and the water accumulated behind them in the pond. They were arranged to be pulled away quickly with wires run to the bank, as shown in the illustration. With cameras set, the boards were withdrawn. A waterfall the full length of the dam was produced and proved suitable for the desired purpose during a period of 10 minutes. This simple expedient averted a considerable loss and made results possible in spite of the perversities of the weather.—Contributed by Donald A. Hampson.

Oil-Well Pump Signal

The signal device to be fixed at the top of an oil-well pump frame, as

shown in the sketch, was devised by a well owner in Oklahoma and proved easily worth the effort of making it. The signal is attached to a cord fixed to the pump cable, and "wigwags" when the pump is in operation. The caretaker can thus see from a distance whether or not a well needs attention. —Contributed by Ray Colburn, Perry, Oklahoma.

Punch for Making Fiber Washers

The punch illustrated was designed for the cutting of washers out of sheets

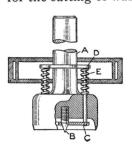

of fiber, $\frac{1}{32}$ in. thick. It is provided with springs which thrust the washer out when it is cut. The body of the punch A is counterbored in the lower face, and a sharp cutting edge is ground along the rim. The point B is threaded into the body, and extends slightly beyond the cutting edge. The spring device, at the lower end of which is a washer, C, operates in two holes drilled through the wider portion of the body. The washers C and D are riveted to the ends of the pins E, after the springs are inserted. The fiber is cut by placing the point B over the center of the desired disk and striking the shank of the punch with a hammer, or mallet. The cut washer is removed by pressing on the upper washer D. The center holes of the washers may be cut by a punch of suitable size. The body is made of tool steel, and drawn to a suitable temper at the cutting edge.—Contributed by C. H. Anderson, Worcester, Mass.

Safety-First Shaft Oiler

Accidents are not infrequent in shops from carelessness in oiling overhead shafting and machinery. Until recently this work was done in a large automobile plant by an oiler who carried a long ladder about the shop, with which to climb up among the whirling belts and pulleys. He not only endangered himself while at work, but the

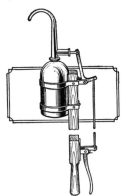

ladder was a nuisance to his fellow workers. By the use of the oiler shown in the sketch, the danger was removed, and it was seldom necessary to climb a ladder to reach the overhead machinery.

An oilcan of the force-pump variety was fitted to the end of a pole with straps, as illustrated. Its spout was lengthened and turned down at the front. A set of levers, controlled by a handle on the lower end of the rod, was attached. By shifting the lever handle, the pump is operated and oil forced from the can to the bearings overhead. —Contributed by J. S. Hagans, Toledo, Ohio.

An Emergency Funnel

If a funnel is needed for the pouring of gasoline into an automobile, or other motor vehicle, a glass bottle broken off near the bottom will provide a satisfactory substitute. Such a makeshift has saved tourists from inconvenience on several occasions. — Contributed by Calixte LeBeuf, Jr., West Mount, Quebec, Canada.

A GARDEN FOUNTAIN
AND BASIN OF CONCRETE

by Herman E. Nichols.

A SIMPLE home garden may be lifted out of the commonplace and given something of the atmosphere associated with the large estate or country place by the addition of a small fountain, in keeping with the surroundings. Spraying water and a glistening pool lend a charm to the home grounds, of which the householder may well avail himself, since the expense is comparatively inconsiderable, and the work may be undertaken, for the larger part, by the novice. A fountain and basin, designed with these considerations in mind, is shown in the illustrations, in actual use. It was constructed at a cost of $10 for materials and labor not performed by the owner.

Concrete is a substantial and economical material from which to construct a fountain, and has the added advantage that it may be handled with reasonable success by a careful person not specially skilled. It has possibilities of adaptation to a great variety of designs and methods of construction. This is a desirable feature, since many persons may wish to adapt the design shown to their own needs or artistic and constructive skill. The circle, square, diamond, oval, octagon, or more complicated figures, may be taken as the basis for a design, and "pick-up" materials about the home may be used to develop the forms for the concrete.

No attempt was made to finish the surfaces of the fountain, as the rough-cast effect is satisfactory and harmonizes well with the simple, substantial lines and construction. Other finishes, with inset designs, panels, etc., may be made to accord with the design and decoration of the home, or the formality of the garden.

A water supply is, of course, essential, but this should not offer serious obstacles, though it is a phase of the construction that had better be handled by a mechanic. A city water supply offers a ready solution. A spring with sufficient pressure to throw the water two feet above the upper surface of the fountain is also satisfactory. Where the fountain is to be connected with a private water-supply system, it is desirable to provide a tank set high enough to give the fountain-spray pressure. The quantity of water necessary for the fountain described is less than that used by the average lawn sprinkler, and like the latter, it may be turned on and off, or the size of the flow regulated, as desired. The water in the reservoir may in some instances be used for other purposes, such as watering flower beds or the garden. If the garden is protected, small fish may be kept in the reservoir.

The fountain, as shown in the illustration, consists of two main parts, the reservoir below and the dished bird basin, from the center of which the spray flows. The design is based on the octagon, the layout of which is shown in the small ground plan and elevation at the top. The details of the water supply, the casting and finishing of the reservoir, and the making of the basin are shown below in the sectional diagram and the sketch.

The water-supply pipes and the drain to remove the excess water from the reservoir should be provided and fitted into place before the construction of the fountain proper is begun. The supply pipe should be ½ in., and the outlet pipe ¾ in. The outlet pipe should extend to within an inch of the upper edge of the reservoir. It should be turned from time to time while the concrete is setting, in order that it may be removed when it is desired to drain the reservoir for cleaning or for the winter.

When the pipes are arranged, the foundation of grouting, B, may be laid. Care must be taken that the supply pipe is centered properly. The grouting should be about 10 in. in depth, and of a mixture of one part cement, three parts sand, and six parts gravel, or crushed rock. In order to make the foundation of the same shape and only slightly wider than the main portion of the fountain, it is desirable to make the frame for the outer faces of the reservoir, as shown in the ground plan and elevation, before laying the foundation. The frame may then be used as a guide, although the octagon may be laid out on level ground, and by careful digging, the sides of the hole may be used, without boards, as the foundation limits.

The form for the reservoir should be made very carefully, as upon its accuracy will depend the symmetry of the fountain. First make a frame of 6-in. boards, inclosing a 4-ft. square, as shown in the ground plan. At the middle of each of the sides lay off a distance of 20 in., centering it, and making the measurements on the inner sides of the frame. Fit pieces into the corners, having braced the square frame against being forced out of shape. Make three pieces of 1½-in. strips to form a mold for the inner octagon. The pieces are 16⅔ in. long on the outer surface, and should be mitered carefully, and nailed at the joints. To hold the form in its proper shape, place it inside of the

outer form, and set it to provide a space of 4 in. between them. Nail braces to the inner form, and when using the latter, separate it from the outer form the necessary distance with braces, and level its upper edge with that of the outer form.

Fix the outer form into place on the foundation. A mixture of one part cement to three parts of sand is used in all of the remaining concrete construction. Pour in the mixture, tamping it down, and shape the material roughly to the cross section shown in the sectional view. The thin part of the reservoir near the middle is 1½ in. thick. When the concrete has been heaped up sufficiently at the sides, set the three-section inner mold into place, and level off the upper surface of the sides, on the outer and inner molds, as at MN. Transfer the inner mold and complete the rim all around the reservoir. Smooth off the interior, sloping it evenly and making the floor flat. It is important that the outlet pipe be turned repeatedly at this stage so that it will be removable when the concrete is dry. The forms may be left in place temporarily as a protection.

The support for the bird basin may be poured next. Form a sheet of galvanized iron into a cylinder with an inside diameter of 6 in. and a height of 15 in. Set this over the center of the reservoir and pour the concrete into it, leveling the mixture off at the top of the cylinder. The supply pipe should be plugged during these operations in order to prevent particles from clogging it.

The bird basin should be made on a board table, as shown in the small sketch above the sectional view. It may be made by fixing the 3-in. pieces I, making up the form, to the table, or by building up a form similar to the outer form for the reservoir, as shown in the ground plan. The latter method is preferable, particularly for the novice. Pour the concrete into the form and smooth off the upper surface even with the upper edges of the mold. Form the dish in the top, 1 in. deep, with a trowel. The center hole,

ELEVATION

The Effectiveness of This Inexpensive Fountain for the Home Garden is Brought Out Strikingly in the Photograph Reproduced Above. The Ground Plan and the Elevation Present the General Dimensions and the Construction of the Forms for the Reservoir and the Bird Basin. The Small Sketch Shows the Use of the Forms I, for Shaping the Basin H, and the Plug J, Which Provides a Hole for the Pipe. The Sectional View Shows the Reservoir A, the Foundation B, the Post Form D, the Outlet Pipe F, and the Guide Boards M and N, for Leveling the Top Surface through which the supply pipe is to fit, should be provided for by inserting a wooden plug, or a short section of pipe of proper diameter, into the center of the mold, and turning it while the concrete is setting. When the proper time for drying has been allowed, the bird basin may be set into place and the molds removed. Rough corners or leakage roughnesses may be cut away.

It may be noted in the sectional view that the supply pipe was provided with

a stopcock, C, set into a chamber, G, so that the water may be regulated with the wrench E. A tap extending from the supply pipe may be used to supply water to a garden hose, at K.

The material and other costs for this fountain as constructed were as follows: screened sand, ½ yd., 75 cents; two bags cement, $1; piping, $2.25; labor, $6. Gravel for the concrete used in the foundation was obtained without charge.

Rapid Method of Labeling Bottles

Bottles, or similar receptacles, may be labeled rapidly and easily by hand. The method as illustrated is as follows:

FIG.3   FIG.4   FIG.5
Paste is Spread on the Stone, the Labels are Placed upon It, and Then Affixed to the Bottles

Fold the labels into the successive shapes shown at A, B, and C. Coat a piece of stone, or a sheet of heavy cardboard, with paste. Press a bunch of the bent labels upon the stone, as shown in Fig. 1. The lower label remains attached in the paste, when the bunch is lifted. Continue this operation rapidly until the stone is covered with labels. Pick up the labels one by one and affix them to the bottles in the manner shown in Figs. 3, 4, and 5.

This method is also cleanly, since the paste, instead of being squeezed out at the edges, is pushed toward the center

of the label by the movement used in affixing it. Two persons working together may accomplish relatively better results, the one applying paste and labels to the stone, and the other affixing the labels.

A Remedy for Carburetor Back-Firing

Back-firing of a gasoline engine through the carburetor can be, in a great many cases, traced to the excess air. On many of the carburetors a wire screen is usually provided for the purpose of allowing this air to enter in the form of line streams, which aids greatly in making the proper kind of mixture. The screen also serves another important purpose in that it prevents dirt from entering the carburetor.

In place of using only one screen, apply three, and by shifting them radially with respect to one another, the splitting up of the air is easily accomplished, and also increased or decreased as conditions warrant. The device works well, and the mere shifting of one or two of the screens quickly eliminates some of the troublesome cases of back-firing.

Coil Spring to Reinforce Rubber Tube

A coiled spring placed around, or inside of, rubber tubing will prevent the latter from collapsing in experiments, or other processes, in which there is less than atmospheric pressure within the tube, or a pressure greater than atmospheric pressure when the outer reinforcing is used.

Mirror as a Shop Tool

In many instances when a flash light was not at hand I have found a mirror of considerable aid in doing mechanical work upon which the light of a window or other source does not fall directly. Light may be reflected, by the use of a small mirror, into telephone boxes, engine cylinders, and other places difficult of access without special lighting. The mirror may be mounted so as to pivot in several directions, and fixed upon a small stand. In this form, it is especially convenient and often permits the workman the use of both hands.—Contributed by Roy B. Snow, Juddhaven, Ont., Canada.

Nonblister Screwdriver Handle

Blistering of the palms of the hands after considerable use of a screwdriver is a common experience, as well as a painful one. After one such instance I devised the revolving end for my screwdriver handle, shown in the sketch, with the result that I worked for hours without causing blisters. The disk was attached with a screw, countersunk slightly. The device is satisfactory only on handles having a fair diameter, since a screw strong enough to hold well will leave only a narrow end surface on which the hand may rest. The joint between the handle and

The Disk on the End of the Handle Prevents Blistering of the Palm

the disk should be smooth and oiled.—Contributed by D. R. Van Horn, North Loup, Neb.

Lean-Back Swing of Wood-Faced Angle Iron

Durability and comfort are the features of the lean-back swing, for use on the porch or other open-air spot, shown in the sketch. Adjustable brackets at the sides, fitted with wing nuts, make it easy to set the back at various angles, and the swing is so constructed

that the whole framework shifts to accommodate the angle of the back.

The frame is substantially built of riveted, or bolted, angle iron of 1-in. face. Wooden strips are used to face the metal frame, both for comfort and appearance. The smaller sketches

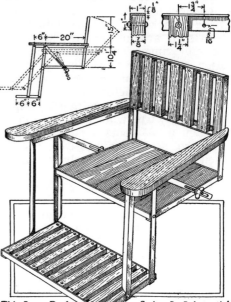

This Lean-Back Swing Is Substantial and Convenient for the Veranda, or Other Place Out of Doors. It is Built of Angle Iron Faced with Wooden Strips

above indicate the chief dimensions and the method of fixing the strips into place. The strips used for the footrest are $\frac{7}{8}$ by $1\frac{1}{4}$ in. and those in the back are $\frac{7}{8}$ by 2 in. Various sizes may be used for these strips, and the general dimensions of the swing may be altered to suit the individual needs. The bolts and rivets used were $\frac{5}{16}$ in. in diameter. Where a fixed joint was desired, it was riveted on the end so as to prevent the nut from becoming loose. Where loose joints are desired, it is best to fit the bolts with washers, and to place a second nut on the threads to act as a jam nut. The boards of the seat may be made of any convenient width, but it is best to set them apart slightly. — Contributed by Hubert Kann, Pittsburgh, Pa.

⟪A stick wedged into the slot will sometimes aid in starting machine screws.

Cable Clamp for Large-Conductor Terminations

By A. T. TALBOT

IT is not only difficult but uneconomical to "make up" heavy electrical conductors at termination points. By a termination point is meant a location where the conductor run ends or where it changes direction. If an endeavor is made to make up a large conductor on —twist it around—an insulator, considerable time is consumed in the operation, and furthermore, the copper that is wasted in making the short turns around the conductor represents a relatively considerable investment. This is particularly true when copper is quoted as high as 25 cents a pound. These end turns serve no purpose electrically, their function being merely to provide a mechanical attachment.

It is therefore usually considered good technical and economical practice to use a cable clamp, as suggested in the upper sketch, at such locations. The cable clamp, which is in electrical contact with the conductor, is insulated from adjacent members with a strain insulator, shown at the left. These strain insulators are usually of the type commonly applied in street-railway construction. Cable clamps of various designs may be made, or purchased in the open market. A clamp of the type illustrated, the details of construction of which are given in the following paragraphs, is cheap, effective, and readily made with reasonable shop facilities.

The upper sketch indicates how the conductor is fastened in the clamp by the binding section of the U-bolts. The end of the conductor at the right extends to an insulating support for the conductor run, while the other end may feed an energy-consuming device, connect to the terminals of a switch, or like appliance, or continue the run in a different direction, as shown in the lower sketch. The latter suggests the arrangement of a right-angle turn at the corner of a building in a heavy-conductor run. The conductors are held in the cable clamps. The strain insulators insulate them. Turnbuckles are provided so that the conductors may be drawn taut. The function of the tension rods, detailed in the small sketch, is to transmit the stress from the strain insulators to the turnbuckles. It is sometimes feasible to arrange a right-angle turn without using the tension rods, but as a rule their installation is justified because with them sharp bends in the conductor are eliminated, and furthermore, if they are used, the turnbuckles do not lie directly over one another. Where the turnbuckles are directly over one another, it may be difficult to turn them to adjust the tension. Eyebolts, inserted in holes drilled for them in the brick wall, support the entire arrangement. Cast-iron building washers should be used to distribute the pressure impressed by the bolts over an ample surface on the walls.

The diagram across the middle of the page shows a solution of a situation that is often encountered. That is, it is sometimes necessary to terminate conductors at a truss chord, or similar member, to provide for the insertion in the circuit of a cut-out, switch, or similar device. For such service an iron plate, having holes punched in it as suggested, may be bolted to the truss chord. The hooks of the turnbuckles may engage in holes provided for them in the plate. They may be procured with a hook at one end and an eye at the other, or with hooks or eyes at both ends.

The cable clamp proper consists of two parts, the plate and the U-bolts. The plate may be a piece of $2\frac{3}{4}$ by $\frac{3}{8}$-in. strap iron, cut and drilled as indicated in the illustration. U-shaped pieces of $\frac{1}{4}$-in. round iron stock are riveted to the lower face of the plate to provide "humps," so that the conductor, when it is clamped in position, may be more effectively restrained. The U-bolts are pieces of $\frac{1}{2}$-in. round iron stock, threaded at each end, provided with nuts, and bent into a U-shape, as detailed at the left of the lower sketch. They are shown clamping the cable, in the upper sketch.

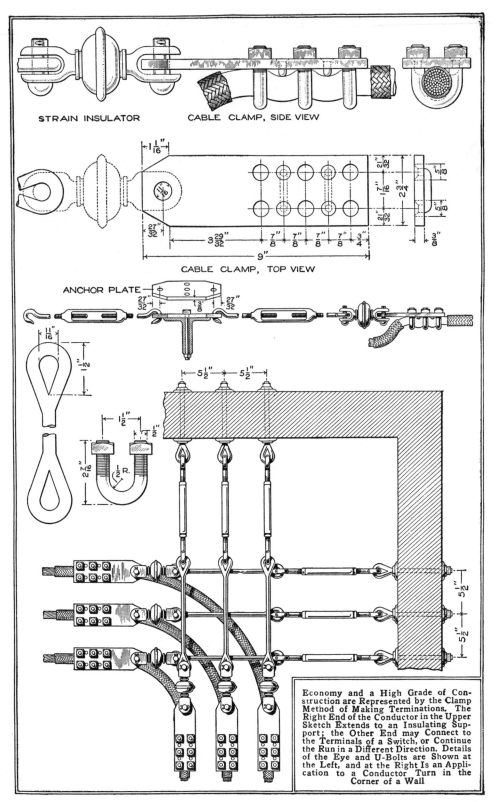

STRAIN INSULATOR

CABLE CLAMP, SIDE VIEW

CABLE CLAMP, TOP VIEW

ANCHOR PLATE

Economy and a High Grade of Construction are Represented by the Clamp Method of Making Terminations. The Right End of the Conductor in the Upper Sketch Extends to an Insulating Support; the Other End may Connect to the Terminals of a Switch, or Continue the Run in a Different Direction. Details of the Eye and U-Bolts are Shown at the Left, and at the Right Is an Application to a Conductor Turn in the Corner of a Wall

Reducing Size of Socket Wrench

Having broken a socket wrench of the size required to loosen a nut on an automobile and not knowing where I might obtain another, I devised a collar to fit into a wrench of larger size, as shown in the sketch. This method worked satisfactorily, and has been used to enable other wrenches to fit smaller-sized nuts.—Contributed by Percy L. Anderson, Wilmington, Del.

Detachable Lamp Hanging

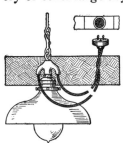

In shops or factories where machinery or other large objects are frequently moved and electric-light fixtures are endangered in the process, the detachable lamp hanging shown in the sketch will prove of service. The ceiling sockets of the fixtures should all be of the same type so that the hangings may be interchangeable. The lights are supported from rods or chains and may be released by the use of snap buckles.

One-Piece Razor Handle

When a razor handle broke I found that it was easier to make the new handle out of a single piece of wood than to fashion the halves separately and fit them together. The holes near the ends were bored first, and the slot was then sawed out and smoothed. The pin at the end A is not only for finish, but also prevents the handle from splitting at that point.—Contributed by James M. Kane, Doylestown, Pa.

Holder for Curtain Fixture

To avoid defacing the window trim in fastening brackets for roller shades or curtains, the fixtures may be secured to a strip of wood, as shown in the sketch, and suspended on screw eyes hooked over nails. This method causes no marring of the woodwork and, if the strips are finished to harmonize with it, makes a satisfactory device. There is an added advantage in that the strips with shades attached to them may be removed easily for cleaning, or for transfer to another location.—Contributed by Charles Schapmeier, Baltimore, Md.

Repairing a Valve Cage

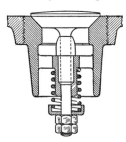

The automatic inlet valve on a motorcycle engine was not provided with a sufficient length of guide bearing. The constant shocks of the machine, together with the insufficient bearing length, caused the valve to vibrate laterally, and within a short time a poorly operated valve was the result. The illustration clearly shows the manner in which the trouble was eliminated. The repair consisted in merely inserting an additional bushing inside of the valve cage. The upper portion of the bushing was inserted as shown, a press fit being sufficient.

❡Piston rings should be left sharp on their edges, and rounded off only enough to remove a slight burr.

Time-Saving Kink in Bending Conduit Pipes

It is often difficult to draw wires through conduit pipes after they are in place, especially if the pipes are curved. By dropping a small weight attached to a cord through the pipe before it is bent, this difficulty is avoided. The cord is permitted to remain in the pipe while the bends are made in it and is used in drawing the wires through.— Contributed by D. B., Chicago.

Oiling Straddle-Milling Cutters

When two or more side-milling cutters are used in straddle-milling work the even oiling of each cutter is not infrequently a matter which keeps the operator busy with an oilcan. The sketch shows a little kink illustrating how a piece of wire can be bent and inserted in the mouth of a petcock in the large oilcan placed above the cutters, to run the oil evenly, drop by drop, on both cutters. Only a little adjustment will be necessary. A piece

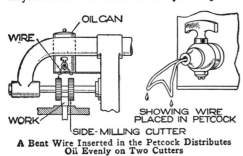

A Bent Wire Inserted in the Petcock Distributes Oil Evenly on Two Cutters

of $\frac{1}{16}$-in., or even smaller, wire can be utilized, and it will be found a very handy method of steadily oiling cutters on long pieces of work.

Oiling Sheet Metal for Stamping or Punching

A discarded wringer was used with satisfactory results for oiling sheet metal in the punch-press room of a large factory. The fittings which were added to the wringer may be seen in the sketch. The rubber was removed from the rollers A, and felt was substituted. The oil pan B was attached to the top of the wringer, and tubes, C, were fitted to carry oil to the rollers. A pulley, D, was fixed on the shaft in-

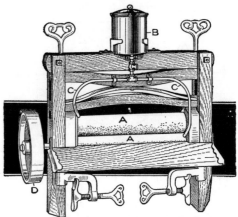

The Wringer was Converted into a Device for Oiling Metal in a Punch-Press Room

stead of a handle and a belt drive connected with it. A drip pan was placed under the wringer to catch the waste oil. The sheets of metal were fed between the rollers and were carried through by the friction. The adjusting screws at the top were used to produce the proper tension.

Odd-Sized Tubing Hammered from a Smaller Diameter

A piece of brass tubing, $3\frac{5}{16}$ in. in outside diameter and 6 in. long, was needed for an experimental job. No exact requirements as to finish were imposed, but the tube was to be seamless. The most desirable piece of tubing available was 3 in. in diameter with a wall of $\frac{3}{32}$-in. thickness. A piece, $5\frac{1}{2}$ in. long, was cut off and annealed by heating and plunging into water. It was then placed upon the anvil horn and hammered. After this treatment, the outside diameter was increased to that required, and the resulting tube was fairly round and smooth. Its length was increased to 6 in. by the hammering.

⊄Indications at intervals of 6 in. on the handle of a post auger will aid in determining the depth of the hole.

Vertical-Pull Windlass

Withdrawing of posts or small stumps from the ground may be accomplished readily by the use of the

The Windlass Exerts a Powerful Upward Pull and Is Useful in Removing Stakes or Small Stumps

device shown in the sketch. It consists of a box or other support for a strong plank, on which a roller provided with a chain operates. The chain is attached to the roller at each edge of the plank so that when pressure is applied on the handle, tending to roll the roller up the incline, the chain winds up and exerts a powerful pull on the stump, or other object, to be withdrawn. The slant of the plank aids in the action, since it causes the chain to wind up rather than the roller to move up on the incline.—Contributed by J. H. Moore, Hamilton, Canada.

Hollow Center for Re-Turning Spindles

The problem of accurately turning a number of small spindles, from which the end centers had been cut, was solved in the manner illustrated in the sketch. A soft center was obtained and bored out, as shown, in the tailstock center in which an oil hole is indicated. The small end of the

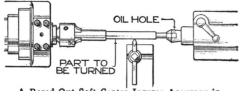

A Bored-Out Soft Center Insures Accuracy in Re-Turning without End Centers

spindle was inserted into this socket and the other was clamped in a three-way, draw-in chuck, placed in the headstock spindle. The oil hole shown should be turned so as to come at the top, but, for purposes of illustration, is shown in a horizontal position. This feature is necessary in order that the end of the spindle may not be damaged in wearing against its socket.

Preparing Sensitized Paper for Photography

A good quality of unwatermarked, unglazed paper, free from imperfection, should be used in the preparation of sensitized photographic papers. A dark room with red light should be used and the paper stored in the dark when completed. Distilled water is best for making the solutions, and the silver-nitrate solution should be protected from the light particularly. Great care must be used in their application to the paper, so as to make the film over the surface of even weight. The sensitized side of the paper should be marked at points which will not injure it in use.

Several kinds of paper in common use may be made by the following processes:

A nitrated paper is prepared by applying a solution of silver nitrate in water and alcohol to the surface of the paper. Brushing in one direction only, apply the solution with a sponge, or soft-bristle brush. The stronger the solution, the more sensitive the paper, the alcoholic solution giving the more sensitive surface. After drying, the paper may be printed, and is fixed by washing in water.

A muriated paper is prepared by soaking it in a water solution of sodium chloride, removing the excess with blotters and drying the paper. After drying, brush the surface with a solution of silver nitrate. For the sodium-chloride solution use 50 gr. of sodium chloride to each ounce of distilled water, and brush the surface with a silver-nitrate solution containing 120 gr. of silver nitrate to each ounce of water. The muriated papers are fixed by first washing in warm water, then dipping several times into a solution of 1 oz. of sodium hyposulphite in 1 pt. of water, and finally washing in water and drying.

A less sensitive muriated paper for copying engravings, drawings, botanical specimens, etc., may be made by using a sodium-chloride solution of 25 gr. to the ounce of water, and a silver-nitrate solution containing 90 gr. to each ounce of water.

An iodized paper may be made by first brushing the paper with a solution of 100 gr. of silver nitrate in 1 oz. of water and drying it, then dipping it into a solution of 25 gr. of potassium iodide in 1 oz. of water. Wash in water, drain off the excess water, and dry.

A bromide paper is made by soaking it in a solution of 40 gr. of potassium bromide in 1 oz. of water, and drying. When dry, brush over it a solution of 100 gr. of silver nitrate in 1 oz. of water. A compound chromatype paper may be made by washing the paper with a solution of 10 gr. of potassium dichromate and 20 gr. of copper sulphate in 1 oz. of water, and drying. After exposure, the paper is washed in the dark room with a solution of 40 gr. silver nitrate in 1 oz. of water, and then fixed by washing in water.

A rapid paper may be made by mixing 6 dr. of a saturated solution of bichloride of mercury with 1 pt. of water. Float the paper on this solution and then dry it. This may be done in the light. In a dark room, brush the surface of the paper with a solution of 38 gr. of silver nitrate in 1 oz. of water, and dry. Print the paper in bright sunlight, 2 to 10 seconds. Develop it in a solution of 15 gr. sulphate of iron, 25 gr. glacial acetic acid, and 1 oz. of water. The development must be watched closely, and when it reaches the desired point, wash the paper quickly in water and fix in a sodium-hyposulphite solution as given for muriated papers.

Ordinary blueprint paper for photographic work may be made by first preparing a solution of 1 oz. potassium ferrocyanide in 6 oz. of water and another solution of 1 oz. of ammonio-citrate of iron in 4 oz. of water. When ready to use, mix equal parts of each of these solutions and apply the mixture to the paper evenly with a brush or sponge. Fix by washing thoroughly in water.—Contributed by Charles E. Mullin, Huntingdon, Pa.

Tool Holder with Set of Cutters

A tool holder adapted for many uses in turning brass and other light metals,

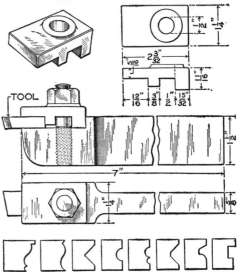

Various Types of Cutters may be Designed to be Clamped in the Holder

as well as the scraping of harder metals, is shown in the sketch. A series of specimen cutters, which may be shaped on both ends to give two cutting edges, are shown below. The main portion of the tool holder and the clamp are made of mild tool steel. The cutters are 1/4 in. thick and are made of high-speed steel.

The construction of the tool holder and clamp is such that it may be readily carried out by the average mechanic. The 1/2-in. screw and nut are of standard thread and size. The clamp is designed with two shoulder portions in order that the bit may be gripped firmly and not shift while the nut is being tightened with a socket wrench, part of the equipment of most lathes.—Contributed by Joe V. Romig.

Pulling Wires into Conduits

A very convenient and easy method for pulling wires into conduits is shown in the illustration. It often happens that

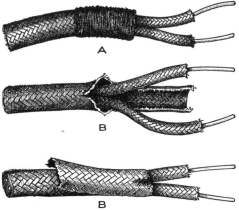

The Braiding as It Slips Back on the Wire, and How to Hold It at the End

the braiding on the wire slides back to such an extent that it is almost impossible to pull the wires into the conduit. The usual trouble is encountered as shown at A, and the way to prevent it is shown at B. The outer braiding is cut and folded back, preventing the covering from sliding back. — Contributed by E. Aultman, Jr., Haworth, New York.

Portable and Collapsible Bench

Observation of a plumber setting up a temporary workbench suggested the adaptation to a lawn bench, shown in

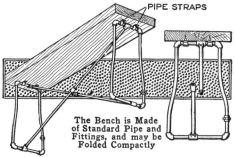

The Bench is Made of Standard Pipe and Fittings, and may be Folded Compactly

the sketch. Standard pipe fittings were used in its construction. The tee at the bottom of the upright is large enough to slide on the pipe. The bench

is "knocked down" by releasing the unions at the middle of the braces, permitting the supports to be folded compactly under the top.

By using pipes proportionately larger, heavy workbenches or tables may be made in the same manner. A collapsible back might be fitted to the bench, and folding arms placed at the end.

Keeping a Valve Lifter Clean

The cover illustrated was made for a valve lifter on an automobile engine.

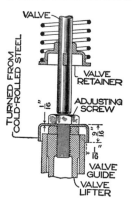

The design of the lifter made it easily exposed, and the grit and dust which found their way into the lifter rod caused a great deal of annoyance, necessitating frequent repairs and cleaning.

The device consisted of a cap, which was turned from a piece of bar stock, of the shape and dimensions shown in the sketch. It was placed between the adjusting screw and locknut, where it was securely held in place. The upper portion of the valve-lifter parts was completely protected by the cap, and no further trouble was encountered.

Obtaining Sharp Impressions from Dies

Die and tool makers often wonder why they do not get sharp and full impressions from dies, especially when the recesses are of unusual depth. If a small hole is drilled in the recess to permit the air to escape when the impression is made, the results will be gratifying.

Crude petroleum oil, diluted with gasoline, makes a good brown wood stain, resembling dark-oak finish.

Core-Drier Pattern for a Manifold

[The method by which a high-school boy made a successful pattern, after patternmakers had failed in several attempts, is set forth in this article. Doubtless the mechanics would have succeeded also, had they persisted, but the boy's success illustrates that intelligent effort is the basis for accurate workmanship, with the skilled workman as well as with the novice.—Editor.]

AMONG other things manufactured in a foundry were manifolds for the engine of a high-class automobile. It was a new job for the plant, and the core room was at first working with the temporary arrangement of a baked-sand drier for this manifold core. The task of making a pattern for a cast-iron drier devolved upon the pattern shop.

The castings from that pattern, when made, would treble the output of cores in the core room. The bunglesome sand drier weighed almost 100 lb., and was difficult to handle.

The patternmaker used the very latest methods to construct the core drier. A perfect core was secured and a plaster-of-paris cast made about it. This cast was to become the pattern. By removing the waste portions it was easily taken out. Two considerations were of main importance in the making of the pattern: shrinkage and a reduction of material that would give the least possible weight to the drier. It is, therefore, easy to see how delicate a performance it became. The three first casts were spoiled before the pattern went into the sand. The fourth, which was considered a finished pattern, was in wind and off on the shrink when the core was tried in the resulting casting. This pattern was thrown away. The last cast was worked up in an attempt to overcome the two points listed against the last pattern. It crushed in the ramming, and at this point the patternmaker gave it up as a bad job.

A high-school boy who studied patternmaking in school and had free entrance to the plant, had been watching the developments with growing interest, and when the regular workman gave up the job, he asked the owner of the foundry for the privilege of attempting to make the pattern, with the understanding that he was after

experience and not money. It was granted quickly. A blueprint of the manifold was provided, also one of the baked cores.

At the school shops the matter of

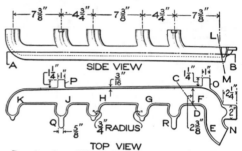

TOP VIEW
Drawing from Which the Pattern for a Core Drier was to be Made

making that pattern became, in a sense, an "acid" test. Its making was granted as a substitute for the regular pattern work. His observations had convinced the boy that the pattern should be made of wood, and the ultimate result showed that he was right. The patternmaker's drawing was made with the greatest possible care. The regular cast-iron shrinkage of one-eighth was allowed. All the measurements were derived from the blueprint of the manifold and the core. The distribution of the shrinkage varied only where the metal became less bulky, or where it ran slightly over the average in bulk, and there the dimension was recorded scant or full on the shrink rule, as the case demanded. It is evident that good judgment was most important here. The sketch shows the drawing from which the pattern was made.

The very best grade of straight-grain mahogany was used in making the pattern. A piece, 4 in. wide and 1½ in. thick, was trued up for the body. This is indicated in the sketch by the portion below the line AB. It was cut, and a half-lap joint with shoulders was made on the angle indicated by the line CD. The object of this was that the grain should not run short on the reverse curves of the discharge port. The outline of the valley was then laid out for the gouge work. This latter work was done to a series of templates that gave the proper width and depth at stated intervals.

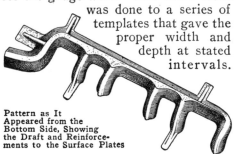

Pattern as It Appeared from the Bottom Side, Showing the Draft and Reinforcements to the Surface Plates

These points were taken just in front of the discharge point of each exhaust, indicated by the letters E, F, G, H, J, and K. The gouge work in the valley was not completed until after the extensions for the exhausts were placed. These were made of blocks of the right thickness, to bring the horns to the proper level, and were then glued to the body. The grain in these blocks ran crosswise to the body. When their shells became better established, the glue was reinforced with brads carefully placed. The outline of the shell for the horns was laid out as on the body piece, and the gouge work was then done in the rough. All the work, thus far, had been done on the valley. The table of a band saw was tilted to give the angle indicated by the line LM. This gave the pattern draft on the body, eliminated all surplus stock, and left a seat for the pattern. The sawing proved to be one of the most difficult operations of the job, on account of the frailness and clumsiness of the pat-

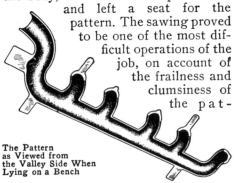

The Pattern as Viewed from the Valley Side When Lying on a Bench

tern. The outline of the top of the horns was next sawed, with the table only slightly tilted. The reduction of

the outside of the horns, from the outline of the top, had to be accomplished with care, as the saw left the surface that merged into the general contour of the body irregular in form. Draft had to be closely watched in this work.

The final dressing of the valley was next taken up. The core was sawed into sections, each containing one exhaust, making six parts in all. On each of the sections a white line, indicating just where the drier should come when the core was in place, was drawn. These sections became templates, to which the valley was made to conform with the proper amount of clearance. Establishing the floor of the valley was a vital point, for it was explained that when the drier was in use and was carrying a green core in the oven, during the process of baking, the core at a certain stage would "fall," if it did not have a perfect bearing on the floor of the drier. This would give a core out of true, and if used in making a casting, it would make a thin place in the walls.

The placing of the surface plates N, O, P, Q, and R, which served as bearings on the faces of the core box during the making of the green core, was the last operation in the construction of the pattern. They were housed into the edges of the body and supports placed below them. That marked N was used as a supporting platform for a pack of green sand around the last exhaust, this device taking the place of the horns used on the other exhausts.

The pattern was given its finishing sanding and was then shellacked. It is well to note that during the construction every possible precaution was taken to prevent warping. When the work was left, even for a short time, it was clamped to a stretcher. The new part, even though not entirely completed, was given a light coat of size. A high grade of shellac was used for the coating. Thus, when the pattern went to the sand, it had neither warped nor twisted.

The first casting proved that the young man had made good. The first core tried fell into place perfectly. The shrink had been gauged correctly, and that was the real test. Outside of a few minor changes for the sake of a better draft, the pattern was never altered and went its way to serve the purpose for which it was made.

Lettering for Curved Signs

Letters in curved signs may be laid out with the sides parallel, which is difficult for the novice, by the method shown in the illustration. The process is as follows:

Mark the line AB with a piece of crayon, or with a cord chalked and sprung. From the point C as a center, strike off the curves at the top and bottom of the lettering. Mark off the space, D, between the letters, and their width, E, along the upper curve. At A lay off the distance FG equal to the width of the letters. With a straightedge or a chalked cord strike off the lines for the sides of the letters, as shown, and complete them by drawing the other parts of the outlines with a straightedge and crayon. This will make the letters uniform in width, and

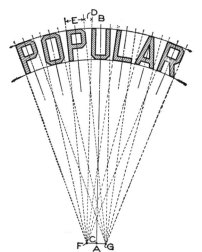

The Sides of the Regular Letters will Be Parallel if Laid Out as Shown

their sides will be parallel. In the illustration a letter comes at the line AB and the space for it must, therefore, be divided equally, and the other spaces and letters laid off from it.

Glass Panels in an Old-Style Closet Door

Replacing wooden panels in old doors with glass may be readily accomplished, as shown in the drawing.

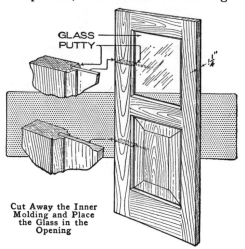

Cut Away the Inner Molding and Place the Glass in the Opening

In order to remove the old panels without altering the front of the molding portion, cut away the molding on the inside of the door. Clean the corner of glue and dirt, and place the glass in the opening. Three-cornered glazier's tacks are driven into the door frame to hold the glass, and the corner cut away is filled in on a bevel with putty, as shown in the upper cross-sectional view. Below is shown a sectional view of the door as originally constructed.

Securing Door with Loose-Pin Hinges

Loose-pin hinges on doors of cabinets and other similar constructions often permit intruders to gain entrance by removing the pins from the hinges and lifting the hinge edge of the door outward. This may be overcome by fixing pins cut from a wire nail into the edge of the casing above the upper and below the lower hinges. Holes drilled into the edge of the door to fit the pins prevent the withdrawal of the door even after the pins are removed from the hinges.—Contributed by George Niederhoff, St. Louis, Mo.

Homemade Bumper for Automobiles

Steel tubing forms the main portions of the automobile bumper shown in the sketch. It was designed with a

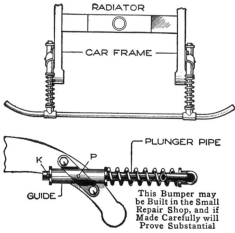

This Bumper may be Built in the Small Repair Shop, and if Made Carefully will Prove Substantial

minimum of special fixtures and is easily applied. The guide pipes are fastened to the side of the car frame by means of straps and are prevented from moving endwise by a pin, P. The plunger pipes are held in place by the washer and pin K. Strong helical springs were used. The fitting of the tubes and plunger parts must be done carefully to insure that the bumper will be substantial.

Crankshaft-Turning Fixture

A one-cylinder marine engine was being made in a small machine shop and the crankshaft-turning fixture,

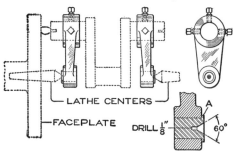

The Levers Taken from a Junk Heap Solved the Problem of a Turning Fixture in a Small Machine Shop

shown in the sketch, was quickly made and used successfully. Two old levers

taken from the junk heap were used. Their lower ends were plugged with steel, as shown at A, and centers made. The levers were then fixed to the main bearings of the crankshaft and the entire unit was held between the lathe centers. Three setscrews were provided for each lever, to insure rigidity.

Plumb-Bob Level Quickly Made

Often it is desired to level, or plumb, a surface when no spirit level or plumb is available. The devices shown in the sketch may be made quickly of materials usually at hand where construction is under way. The sketch at the left shows a level made of three strips or boards. Measure off a distance, C, on the lower strip. Mark the center point covered by the plumb line carefully. Cut two pieces, A, of exactly the same length and fit them to form an angle with their lower corners exactly over the marks limiting the distance C. When the lower piece is level a plumb line suspended from the point at the

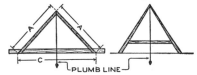

The Frames Are Convenient in Determining Levels When a Spirit Level Is Not Available

top will strike the mark at the center on the lower strip.

For use on irregular surfaces the device at the right is useful. Two poles of equal length are fitted together, and a piece braced across them forming a triangle having its two upper sides equal. Mark the center of the cross strip and attach the plumb line at the top of the frame. When the plumb line is exactly over the center mark on the cross strip, the points on which the lower ends of the poles rest are on a level.—Contributed by H. J. Cornthwaite, San Jose, Cal.

⟨The fine cutting edge of a tool should never be exposed to the hottest place in the fire; heat the heavy part first and allow the heat to run to the thin edge.

Shop Notes

A Self-Feeder for Hogs

By W. E. FRUDDEN

WHILE a self-feeder is not desirable for general use in swine feeding, it has been found practical in the quick fattening of nearly grown shoats or young hogs, and is a useful device where many hogs are to be fed. The feeder shown in the illustration is simple in construction and may be made in the farm workshop. At the left is a sketch with portions cut away, exposing the interior construction. The view at the right shows the end of the feeder, with the right half cut away to show the details of the framing. No length is given, as this may be varied to suit individual needs.

The framework consists of sections built up of 2 by 4-in. material and set on 18-in. centers. Fixed to them, at the bottom, are 2 by 4-in. supports for the ridge-shaped bottom of the feed bin. The sections are 5 ft. high to the upper side of the plate, as shown in the sectional view, and 4 ft. wide at the top and bottom. They are strongly braced, to resist the pressure of the contents, 2 by 4-in. braces being used at the top and 1 by 6-in. braces at the apex of the bottom of the bin.

Tongue-and-groove stock is best for the flooring and siding, as well as the roof, and should be not over 6 in. wide. The flow of the feed into the trough is regulated by an 8-in. board, 1 in. thick, fitted to slide vertically along the sides above the trough, behind cleats. The rafters are of 2 by 4-in. stock and may be set at a convenient pitch, one to three, as shown. The lids extend one-half the length of the feeder, but may be made the full length if not too heavy. They are supported on strap hinges and have sufficient overhang at the eaves and gables to protect the feeder from rain. Skids may be provided for transportation.

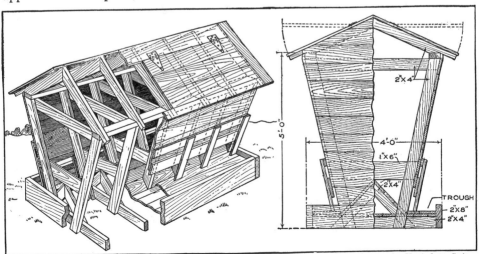

The Self-Feeder Saves Time in Feeding a Large Number of Hogs. Its Length may be Varied to Suit the Needs. The Quantity of Feed is Regulated by a Sliding Gate

Stream-Bank Protection

Protection against washouts on the outer side of a curve in a stream was afforded by building a slanting concrete wall at the point where the wear

The Reinforced-Concrete Bank Prevents the Wearing Away of the Earth at a Sharp Curve in the Stream

occurred. The sketch shows the concrete bank reinforced to withstand the heavy action of the water during freshets. Old steel hoisting cable was used to tie the various sections together. This was considered a good method of reinforcement in that it will hold the sections in place even after long wear and the action of the frost cracks them apart. Dangerous undercuts and cave-ins may be overcome by such a protection.—J. J. O'Brien, Buffalo, New York.

Spring-Cushioned Chair Legs

Coiled springs fixed to the legs of a chair or stool will give elasticity and prevent much of the discomfort ordinarily attendant to sitting on a chair or stool for hours at a time, as many workers must do. The springs should be fitted tightly over the bottom ends of the chair legs and should be of uniform height and tension. They must be strong enough so that the weight of a person will not cause them to collapse completely. A chair so fitted with springs permits the tilting of the seat backward or forward and gives much of the ease of a tilting-top chair. —C. M. Pfennig, Bristol, Conn.

Patching Veneer on Curved Surface

A small piece of veneering was broken from the front of a dresser drawer, the shape of which was such as to make clamping difficult. Several corks were placed against the curved surface to which the patch was to be fixed, and, when the clamp was applied from the inner surface of the drawer front, the corks gave a pressure along the sections of the curve. Their use had the added advantage that the front of the drawer was not marred. — Charles Fischer, Schenectady, N. Y.

Glass Prisms for Experimental Purposes

Glass prisms are sometimes desired for use in experiments, and the method of making them described is both practical and rapid. The process used was as follows: Two similar triangles, A and B, shown in the sketch at the left, having the desired angles and slightly smaller than the prism was to be, were cut from cardboard. Three pieces of window glass, having widths corresponding to the edges of the triangles and a length equal to the height of the prism, were cut. The triangle B was tacked to a block of wood, C. A coating of paraffin was applied to its upper surface and edges by using a heated rod, held in a pair of pliers and applied to a block of paraffin somewhat as when soldering. The surplus paraf-

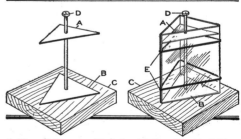

A Glass Prism was Made by Fitting Sheets of Glass around Triangles, and Binding the Joints with Paraffin

fin was scraped from the edges of the triangle, and a nail, D, was driven through the center of triangles A and

B, slightly into block C. The triangle A was adjusted as shown in the sketch at the left. The sheets of glass were then placed against the edges of the triangles and held in place by the rubber bands E. Paraffin was applied to the joints of the glass and around the lower triangle. The nail and the triangle A were removed carefully, and three coats of shellac were applied over the paraffin joints and the wooden base. The prism was then filled with water and was ready for use.—H. W. Offins, Grants Pass, Ore.

Drawing Pen Used as Emergency Forceps

A ruling pen of the double-nib variety may be used as an emergency forceps to remove slivers or other small substances which may find their way into the hand. The nibs should be cleaned in carbolic acid or otherwise made antiseptic. If the handle of the pen screws into place and has a sharp needle at the joint, as is common, this may be used to locate slivers and should also be made antiseptic.

Special-Size Thumbscrews Made Quickly

Requiring several thumbscrews of a special size, I devised the following method of making them: Ordinary fillister-head screws of a size to fit the work were used. A piece of sheet metal was driven tightly into the slot in the head and cut to the proper shape. The edges were filed and smoothed with emery cloth, and the screws proved satisfactory both as to appearance and use.—Monroe D. Dreher, Newark, N. J.

Blueprint Drier for Indoor or Outdoor Use

The case made of wooden strips fitted with panels of wire mesh, shown in the illustration, may be used on either the outer or inner sill of a window for the drying of blueprints. In warm weather it may be used in the position indicated, the prints being placed on

the screened surface of the bottom. A free circulation of air is afforded and the prints dry quickly. When weather conditions do not permit its use out-

Blueprints may be Dried Quickly in the Device Shown, Outdoors When Convenient, or Indoors over a Radiator

doors, the drier may be set on the inner window sill over a radiator. Snap hooks with appropriate attachments on the window frame on both the inner and outer side, must be provided.—John Havekost.

Paper Holder for Desk or Workbench

Papers or drawings on a desk or workbench, that must be referred to from time to time, may be cared for in the manner shown in the sketch. The device is made of a strip of sheet brass, or other metal, and clamps to the edge of the desk top, as indicated in the small sketch. The papers are held down by a flat disk attached to a rod around

The Holder Permits a Considerable Number of Papers to be Filed under It Temporarily

which a coiled spring is fixed to exert a pressure on the disk. A considerable number of sheets, or only a few, may be cared for in this way.

The Water Joy Wheel
A New Beach Device

By R. B. ALLEN

THRILLS in plenty are afforded visitors to a western beach park by the water joy wheel, installed in three feet of water primarily for the amusement of beach bathers. Onlookers enjoy the sport as well, and to see a group of bathers clinging desperately to the revolving wheel as it gains momentum, finally tumbling even the most adroit into the water, is not without thrills. The joy wheel in operation is shown in the upper sketch and below are given the details of the construction and operation of the device. The center table, over which a stream of water plays, is built up of hardwood flooring, carefully matched, and is connected to the driving mechanism. The slanting apron is stationary and protects the bathers as they are tossed from the rapidly revolving wheel. Constructions somewhat similar in principle have been in use as amusement devices, but the application to the beach, or a shallow pool, is interesting and novel.

The joy wheel was originally designed for use in a concrete basin and the working drawings give the details of construction for the installation of it under these conditions. The fitting of the device to a sand beach would not require the concrete floor shown outside of the cross section of the wheel foundation in Fig. 2, but the concrete base and circular wall to carry the steel ring, or plate, upon which the wheel revolves are necessary. The power could be applied in the manner indicated for the reservoir, and shown in cross section at the right of Fig. 2.

Mechanically the device is interesting, and by examining the detailed drawings, the construction may be understood readily. The wheel proper is 20 ft. in diameter and circular, as shown in Figs. 1 and 2. Its framework consists of wooden beams fitted at the center into a series of iron braces cast in the form of a ribbed, radiating flange. Its construction is shown in detail at the upper part of Fig. 2. It is 8 in. high and 18 in. in diameter. The beams are bolted to it and rest on roller bearings, similar to those of a center-pier drawbridge. The bearings are shown in Fig. 5. They have ball-bearing shafts, and brackets, 6 in. wide, with a 3½-in. opening to fit the beams, which are 3½ in. thick. The construction of the planking of the wheel is shown in Fig. 1, and in section at the top of Fig. 2. Two layers of flooring, pine below and maple above, very carefully laid and polished so as to avoid possible injury to the bathers, form the covering of the wheel as well as the apron. The latter is supported on brackets, fixed to the sides of the concrete wall which supports the circular steel plate, shown in Fig. 1, upon which the bearing wheels of the center table ride.

The general mechanical details may be best understood from the sectional views shown in Fig. 2. A motor, which furnishes the power, is mounted above a concrete manhole on the beach. A belt transmits the power to a counter shaft at the bottom of the manhole, and this is in turn connected with the long shaft which engages the main vertical driving shaft of the large wheel or revolving table. Stuffing boxes, indicated by the black sections where the long shaft passes through the concrete walls, prevent the water from entering the manhole at the right and the central pit under the table. Bearings for the shaft are also provided on the floor of the reservoir.

The main driving shaft of the table is 4 in. in diameter, and rests at its

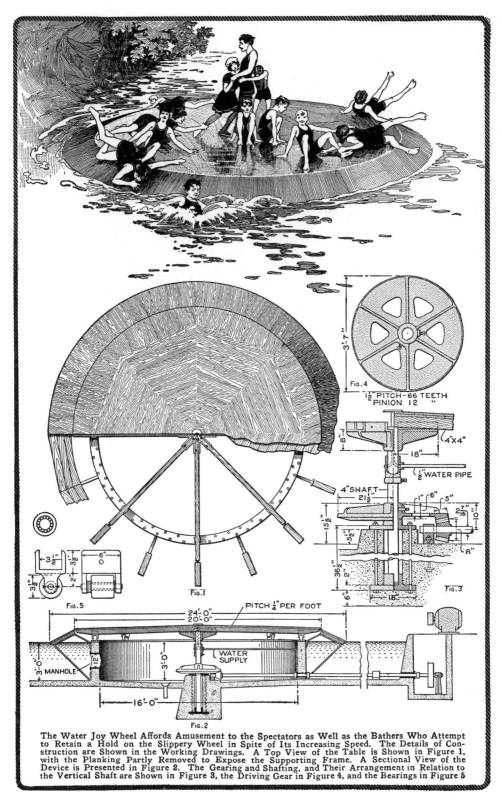

FIG. 4

1½" PITCH - 66 TEETH
PINION 12 "

8"

4"X4"

18"

½" WATER PIPE

4" SHAFT
21½"

15½"

1" 6" 5"

2 7/16" 10"

5½"

8"

FIG. 3

36½"

2"

6"

18"

FIG. 1

FIG. 5

3½"
3"
3½"
2"
6"

PITCH ¼" PER FOOT

24'-0"
20'-0"

WATER
SUPPLY

3'-0"

3'-0" MANHOLE

12"

16'-0"

FIG. 2

The Water Joy Wheel Affords Amusement to the Spectators as Well as the Bathers Who Attempt to Retain a Hold on the Slippery Wheel in Spite of Its Increasing Speed. The Details of Construction are Shown in the Working Drawings. A Top View of the Table is Shown in Figure 1, with the Planking Partly Removed to Expose the Supporting Frame. A Sectional View of the Device is Presented in Figure 2. The Gearing and Shafting, and Their Arrangement in Relation to the Vertical Shaft are Shown in Figure 3, the Driving Gear in Figure 4, and the Bearings in Figure 5

lower end in a steel-flanged concrete foundation, as shown in Fig. 2 and in detail in Fig. 3. Its upper end engages the radiating-brace flange at the center of the table. The end of the long shaft nearest the main driving shaft rests in a bearing, as shown in Fig. 3, and near it is fixed an 8-in. bevel-gear pinion of 12 teeth. This meshes with a pinion, 3 ft. 7 in. in diameter, and of 66 teeth, shown in detail in Fig. 4, and which is keyed to the main driving shaft.

The method of conducting the water supply to the center of the table is shown in Fig. 2, and in detail, as it reaches the outlet, in Fig. 3. The water is pumped into a tank set above the level of the outlet on the revolving table and is fed to it by gravity. By reference to the upper part of Fig. 3 it may be observed that the water-feed pipe is fitted to a collar having a hol-

low bead cast at its middle. The vertical shaft is bored to permit the water from this hollow bead to pass upward and out of the spout when the shaft is revolving. The continual flow of water over the surface of the table is essential to the proper operation of the device, as it is more difficult to retain a hold on the wet surface, and a dry surface might cause injury to the bathers.

The table is started slowly and controlled from the motor by the operator in charge. The speed is gradually increased with the result that the bathers find it difficult to remain on the wet surface. Their antics in attempting to retain a hold cause no end of amusement to both the participants and the spectators, and invariably result in the table being cleared as the speed is increased sufficiently.

A Locomotive Air-Pump Lift

The illustration shows a device for lifting air pumps from the floor to their place on the locomotive or for removing them, and also for carrying them from one place to another. The long part is placed under the upper, or steam, cyl-

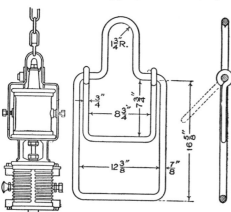

A Yoke to Slip on an Air Pump so That It can be Lifted with a Hoist

inder, and the part which turns on the main piece is thrown back and down over the valve chamber. In

this position the device is held in place with a piece of rope, tied in the back from side to side, to hold the lower part against the casting between the air and the steam cylinder, the top also being tied down for safety.—Joseph K. Long, Renovo, Pa.

Oiling an Automobile Cone Clutch

Cone clutches on motor cars are usually leather-lined, and in order to keep this leather in condition, it should be treated occasionally with neat's-foot oil. If it is permitted to become dry the clutch takes hold with a jerk, which is annoying to passengers and causes wear on the mechanism. This condition results in what is termed a "fierce" clutch.

Refacing is soon necessary, since the leather, being dry, wears rapidly. A squirt can should be used in forcing the oil between the parts of the clutch. If necessary its spout may be flattened slightly in order to reach the parts easily.—Donald A. Hampson, Middletown, N. Y.

⟮Scissors should be ground so that the points match precisely.

Removing Insulation Quickly

Insulation may be stripped from wire quickly by cutting rings around it with a knife at intervals of about 2 in. and tapping the wrapping with a hammer on a block of metal or hard wood. The sections of insulation may then be removed at the end of the wire. If the end of the wire is fixed, it may be necessary to cut the small sections longitudinally after they have been loosened.

Electromagnet Used to Place Letters in Score Board

Placing metal letters in bulletin or score boards, which are usually fixed at a considerable height, may be readily accomplished by the use of the electromagnet device shown in the sketch. It has other uses which will appeal to persons called on to handle metal material of small size in bins or compartments out of reach. The magnet is actuated by a battery which may be set into the handle if the articles to be handled are quite small. Otherwise, it may be attached to the handle. A push button controls the action of the magnet, and the letters or other articles may be released when in place by removing the thumb from the push button.—J. S. Hagans, Toledo, O.

Press Made of Pipe and Fittings

The illustration shows a press by means of which considerable force may be brought to bear in drying pasted articles or other material under pressure. It is made of standard pipe fittings supported on a board. The end supports are fixed into the base by means of hexagonal nuts fitted above and below. A board, or other con-

struction to distribute the pressure over a large area, may be fitted to the lower end of the screw. The thread in the cross fitting in which the screw

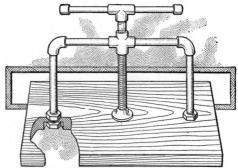

This Press is Made of Standard Pipe Fittings and may be Used for Various Purposes

operates should be run through in the vertical direction and of a size to give proper clearance for the threaded pipe.

Automobile Jacks Save Tires

The weight of an automobile on the tires, particularly when they are not fully inflated, as is often the case in a garage, is injurious. This may be counteracted by providing jacks of a type shown in the sketch.

They are made of heavy stock, hinged so that pressure on the bar will release the weight from them. A pipe may be used for the lifting bar or even

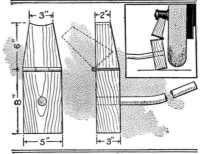

Removing the Weight of an Automobile from the Tires While in the Garage is Readily Accomplished with Jacks

a stout wooden rod. The small sketch shows the method of applying the jacks.

❡Putty should be stained to match the finish before applying it on high-grade work.

Cap Keeps Dust Out of Carburetor

Sticky needle valves are frequently causes of annoyance to motorists. Dust 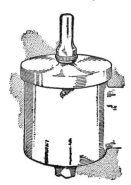 and grit enter the float chamber of a carburetor through the opening from which the stem of the valve projects. A cap fitted over the exposed end of the valve stem effectively overcomes this trouble. The illustration shows the cap knurled on one end so that it may be easily removed.

Safety Key for Faucets

Tampering with faucets on barrels of oil, molasses, and other liquids, may  be prevented by adapting the faucet handle to a pipe key, as shown in the illustration. The handle was cut off with a hacksaw to within ½ in. of the stopper, and the portion remaining was fitted to a piece of ½-in. pipe. The latter was placed on a shelf, inaccessible to children or others who might disturb the faucet.—Stanley Radcliffe, Laurel, Md.

Portable Pipe Rack

A contractor found the pipe rack shown in the illustration convenient  and economical, particularly in storing pipes in winter weather. Not a little damage is done to pipes that are permitted to lie in contact with water or snow, which is often the case when buildings are under construction. The racks were made of cast iron, and the flanges as well as the uprights are about ½ in. in thickness. The contractor transports them from place to place as they are needed, and they are strong enough to withstand rough usage.—A. E. Holaday, Naugatuck, Connecticut.

Holding a Water-Pump Gland Nut

The gland nut which held the piston-rod packing on a water pump 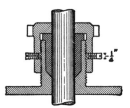 caused considerable trouble in constantly coming loose. This was due principally to the constant vibration, and also to the worn-out condition of the threads. A new nut was purchased, but the thread on the cylinder was found to be the one worn out, so this did not relieve the trouble. Two ordinary headless setscrews were then tried out with success and the trouble was eliminated.

Prevents Loosening of Tail Center in Lathe

The tailstock center of a lathe frequently is forced out of its spindle 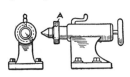 when the operator spins the handwheel in working rapidly. The falling out or loosening of the center causes delay, particularly when a large number of pieces are to be handled. This was overcome by placing a collar, A, on the spindle, and fixing it into place with a headless screw. The collar takes the thrust against the tailstock and prevents the center from being loosened. The collar may be removed easily when occasion requires.—C. Anderson, Worcester, Mass.

❡The parting tool used to cut off stock in a lathe should be set with its cutting edge at the center line.

Automatic Pressure Regulator

A maximum and a minimum pressure must frequently be maintained, and the device illustrated provides a method of regulating the pressure within such limits by the use of a pressure valve, M, working in combination with a safety valve, D, and a piston chamber, G. The rod I is connected to the toggle brace H, which in turn actuates levers regulating the increase or decrease of the pressure.

Normally the pressure in the pipe A operates on the safety valve D and the pressure valve M without any special result. Suppose that the minimum pressure to be maintained is 40 lb., and the maximum 100 lb. When the pressure has reached 50 or 60 lb., the shut-off between the tank and the regulator is opened. When the pressure has reached 100 lb., the safety valve D will blow off, permitting the air to pass into the chamber G against the piston F, forcing it to the opposite end of the chamber. The action is transmitted to the levers, by means of the toggle brace H, to shut off the pressure. If the pressure falls below the minimum, the spring in the valve M will act on the valve cap, opening it and permitting the air to pass through the nipple J into the chamber G and against the right face of the piston F.

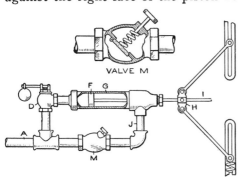

VALVE M

Pressure within a Maximum and a Minimum may be Maintained by the Installation of the Device Shown

The latter will be driven to the opposite end of the chamber, thus actuating the lever control to increase the pressure.—R. R. Rundell, Elmira, New York.

An Improved Tool Box for Mechanics

Some mechanic's tool boxes are provided with a sliding tray for small tools, and other articles. This may

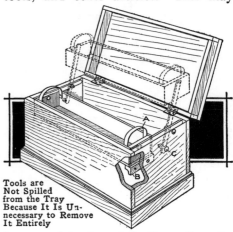

Tools are Not Spilled from the Tray Because It Is Unnecessary to Remove It Entirely

be moved back and forth so that the interior beneath the tray may be seen from both sides of it. The arrangement obstructs the full view of the inside of the tool box, and when it is desired to take a large tool therefrom the tray must be removed. It is often placed on the edge of the box and the contents are spilled accidentally. The illustration shows a tray mounted so as to give free access without removing it entirely.

The tray is carried by two strips of iron pivoted at the upper edge of the tool box. It swings with the strips of metal and retains its horizontal position. Handles A are provided to make raising it convenient. The tray rests normally on small strips, B. The pins C act as a stop when the tray is raised. —Joseph V. Gregorich, Chicago, Ill.

Trimming Belt Ends for Lap Joints

A broad wood chisel, the cutting edge of which has been ground to a convex shape, is a convenient tool for roughing out the end of a belt at which a spliced joint is to be made. The ends may be finished off with a sharp carpenter's block plane and then scraped to a smooth surface, with the edge of a piece of glass.

A Simple Combination-Lever Hoist

A handy homemade chain hoist may be made of a discarded automobile driving chain, or other link chain of this type, by rigging it with suitable levers to work in combination. The

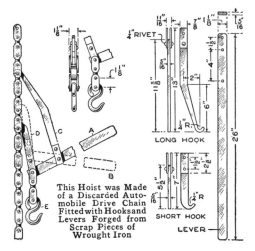

LONG HOOK

SHORT HOOK

LEVER

This Hoist was Made of a Discarded Automobile Drive Chain Fitted with Hooks and Levers Forged from Scrap Pieces of Wrought Iron

hoist shown in the sketch was constructed with such a chain and other fittings made of scrap metal in the machine shop. The device is easy to operate and handles a considerable load, depending on the strength of the chain and other parts used, as well as the force applied by the operator.

The parts are shown in detail in the sketches at the right. Their dimensions may be worked out to suit the individual requirements and are only for the construction of the particular hoist shown, which had a chain 1⅛ in. wide and 1⅛ in. from center to center of the pivot pins in the links, as indicated in the detail drawing of the chain. The arrangement and proportion of the levers must be worked out carefully for the particular chain used, and the longer the power arm A the greater the power to be derived, providing the lever is used to its fullest extent.

The illustration at the left shows the device in operation. When pressure is applied on the lever, or handle, A, with the hooks C and D in the position indicated, a pivoting action on the lower end of the hook C brings the power

arm to the position B. The lever hook D is carried upward, bringing the hook E, to which the weight is attached, with it. The hook on the end of D then engages the next higher link in the chain. The lever arm A is now lifted, which causes the pivoting action to take place at the lower end of the hook D; the hook C is carried upward and engages a new link. This process is repeated, the load at E being raised gradually, as with a differential hoist.

The levers and hooks are made of strips of wrought iron. The arm is 26 in. long and the holes bored in it are spaced carefully to fit the action of the lever arm and connecting parts, in operation. The spacing of the three holes indicated is determined in part by the size of the chain, and it is advisable to make a full-size diagram of the arrangement of the working parts, similar to the sketch at the left, and to test the operation by marking the path of the levers and hooks in engaging the chain. The hook C is 11⅝ in. long and provided with a fork at one end to fit over the lever arm at its pivot. The hook D is 5½ in. long and similarly fitted. The curved ends of the hooks must be made carefully and may require adjustment to make them operate smoothly in the links of the chain, and still retain their grip.—Paul A. Baumeister, Flushing, N. Y.

Bit Brace Used on Chuck Wrench

In operating the chuck on a bench lathe it was found that it took a good deal of time to change the jaws or to adjust them to the size of various pieces of work, when this was done by hand with an ordinary socket wrench. By placing the wrench in a brace it is gripped firmly by the small rod, which is provided as a handle, and much time may be saved in adjusting the jaws.—O. N. Webb, Nashville, Tennessee.

❡To place a valve in the line between the gasoline tank and the carburetor in a concealed place, will often prevent the theft of a car.

Renewing Cartridge Fuses

While cartridge fuses are convenient, they are expensive when burned out frequently, as is the case where experimental work is going on. When the wall cabinet is made for this form of fuse, it is impracticable to use the plain fuse wire or the screw-plug fuse to save the expense of frequent renewals, or even for emergencies. As the cartridge fuse is rapidly coming into general use, the following suggestions for renewing these fuses may be of interest.

In one form of cartridge fuse each of the brass end caps is held on by a small brass nail. To renew these, it is necessary only to pry up the nails a little, wrap the ends of a short piece of fuse wire around them and drive them in again, as illustrated in Fig. 1. If no fuse wire is at hand, a single strand of wire taken from a piece of drop cord will make a safe fuse, for a load of about 15 lamps. In using such a substitute too strong a fuse wire must not be provided, otherwise its failure to melt under an overload may endanger the wiring.

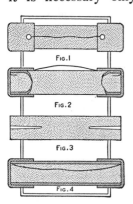

In the other form of cartridge fuse, the brass end caps are held on by deep punch marks. The caps may be pulled off easily by using the vise to hold one cap while the other is removed with a hammer and pliers. Take off both caps and file a slot in the fiber tube for about ½ in. at each end, Fig. 3, so that when a piece of fuse wire is laid along the tube and bent over at each end, the caps may be pushed on again and thus make a good connection, as in Fig. 2. When fine copper wire is used, it is not necessary to file the slots, and the wire may be placed inside, as in Fig. 4.

Adjustable Brake-Band Support

Dragging of the external brake bands on an automobile or motorcycle absorbs power that should be applied to

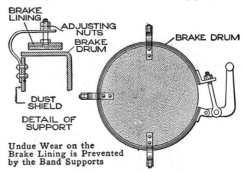

Undue Wear on the Brake Lining is Prevented by the Band Supports

the wheels, and causes overheating of the motor. Brake-band supports are not provided on many older cars. The device shown in the illustration has proven satisfactory for this purpose and can be made in the home shop. It consists of a flat spring having one end riveted to the brake dust shield, and the other drilled to fit a screw which is fastened to the brake band. The hole in the spring should be slightly larger than the screw. Adjustment is made with the nuts on the end of the screw, the second one being a locknut. Three springs will give proper support for the band.

Guard to Prevent Entangling of Reins

A guard that will overcome the annoyance and possible danger of the horses' reins becoming entangled in the draft rigging of a vehicle is shown in the sketch. It consists of an iron

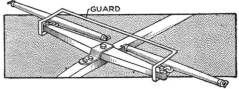

The Guard Prevents the Reins from becoming Entangled in the Draft Rigging

rod, fixed at either end to the lower side of the doubletree and shaped to prevent the reins from dropping under the ends of the singletrees.

Sanitary Clothes Washer

Often it is desired to wash clothing, or other articles, without bringing the hands into contact with the material, which may be infected. The sketch

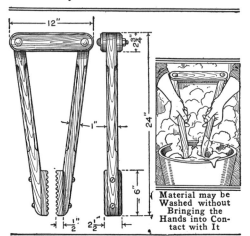

Material may be Washed without Bringing the Hands into Contact with It

shows a simple device that makes it unnecessary to use the hands directly in rubbing the cloth or other material. The washer is provided with two brushlike blocks on the lower end, by which the material is gripped. The upper joints of the frame are pivoted so that a free action of the brushes is permitted.—A. S. Thomas, Amherstburg, Ontario, Can.

Washer Makes Broken Spring Usable

The automobilist as well as the general mechanic will appreciate a kink by which broken valve springs, or other helical springs, may be used temporarily. A simple expedient by which a car was driven 40 miles without further trouble after a valve spring broke, was the insertion of a washer at the broken place in the spring. The two parts acted as two separate springs since the broken ends engaged the washer.—H. S. Wayne.

❏Windows in uncompleted buildings are whitened not only to prevent persons from looking in but also to prevent workmen from breaking the otherwise nearly invisible panes.

Cover for Mortar

When using a mortar and pestle for crushing hard substances there is a risk that some of the powder may be lost or possibly get into one's eyes. A good precautionary measure is to provide a disk of thick paper or cardboard to fit around the pestle. After the preliminary crushing the cover may be removed and the grinding continued in safety.

Ball-Bearing Tailstock Center

Working details of a ball-bearing tailstock center, which overcomes the objections to the ordinary dead center in an engine lathe, are shown in the illustration. Particularly when high-speed steel cutting tools are used and work is being rushed the common type of centers are often burned, causing delay and expense. The centers must be annealed, ground, or otherwise repaired frequently.

The center shown is fitted into the spindle of the tailstock, which is bored out to receive it. The thrust against the center is carried on the ball bearings, which operate in a ring, shown in

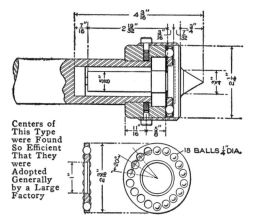

Centers of This Type were Found So Efficient That They were Adopted Generally by a Large Factory

18 BALLS ¼ DIA.

the lower sketch. This method gives the necessary freedom of action, and has been found to give such good results that in a large factory all of the manufacturing lathes are being fitted with centers of this type.—George P. Breitschmid, Arlington, R. I.

Eliminating Rattle of an Automobile Radiator

The radiator on an automobile truck was suspended by a hinge on each side made of two spiral-shaped pieces of spring steel. A space of approximately ½ in. had been provided between the lower edge of the radiator and the top flange of the front cross member, for the purpose of allowing the radiator a free up-and-down movement as the truck traveled over the irregularities encountered on the road. This often resulted in an almost continuous rattle whenever the radiator touched the cross member. To eliminate this noise a strip of rubber was inserted beneath the radiator and on top of the cross member. This acted as a shock absorber, and the trouble ceased.—Adolph Kline, New York City.

Economy in Platinum or Other Wiring

An electrical contractor doing some inside wiring, whose specifications called for the use of expensive platinum wire, was confronted with the following seemingly simple problem:

The laboratory in which the work was to be done was 30 ft. long, 12 ft. high, and 12 ft. wide. The strand of wire was to be carried from a point 1 ft. from the floor in the center of the end wall to a binding post 1 ft. below the ceiling in the exact center of the wall at the opposite end of the room. Under no circumstances could the wire be strung in the air between any two points. It had to be attached to a surface the entire distance—floor, walls, or ceiling.

To carry the wire down along the floor and then up the end wall he quickly calculated would require 42 ft. To go upward and across the ceiling would take just the same amount, and to follow the top of the baseboard around the side wall, and then up, would require more. So the contractor put in a requisition for 42 ft. of platinum wire, but the architects in charge of the work returned the requisition on the ground that he was using too much

material for the required distance. They sketched the laboratory walls, floor, and ceiling in a layout, as shown in the illustration, and then drew a

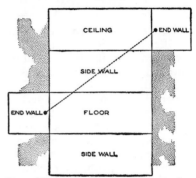

Two Feet of Expensive Platinum Wire was Saved by Making a Diagram to Determine the Best Method of Wiring

straight line between the two points. The distance was 40 feet.

An interesting feature of the problem is that in the architects' solution the contractor loses a foot at the outset by going down to the floor, and seemingly loses another when he carries the wire to the ceiling, which is a foot higher than his destination.—S. Dike Hooper, Eugene, Ore.

Finding the Capacity of a Wash Boiler

When asked to find the capacity of an ordinary wash boiler I found that the quickest and easiest way to solve the problem was to divide it into two figures—a box and a cylinder—find the

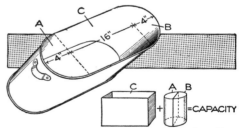

Dividing the Boiler into Two Parts Makes It an Easy Problem to Find the Capacity

cubical content of each, and add them together. The boiler is composed of the two ends A and B, making up the cylinder, plus the box C, which is the portion remaining.—James M. Kane, Doylestown, Pa.

A Farm Seed-Corn House

By E. L. Forrest

SELECTION of corn seed on a scientific basis is a generally recognized practice in corn raising and has proved its value. Carefully designed equipment is used by farmers who specialize in producing seed corn, particularly for the care and storage of the seed. Many farmers who do not make a business of seed-corn raising, but who require a considerable quantity of seed, will profit by the adoption of scientific methods in the care and selection of their seed, and a requisite is a properly constructed and ventilated storage house, where the corn may be tested, graded, and dried. In a number of farm communities several enterprising corn growers have joined in the building of a seed-corn house, and supply their neighbors with good seed. The details of such a house, that will care for about 90 bu., are shown in the upper sketches and below is a view of the exterior. It is 10 ft. wide, 16 ft. long, and 11 ft. high over all. The corn on the cob is placed on racks which are suspended from rafters by roller hangers. Space is provided for the testing of the corn and also for an oil stove, or other heater. Ventilation is afforded by the screened openings, covered with hinged doors and extending around the base of the house. Screened ventilating openings are also built into the roof.

The foundation is of concrete and designed to form a level surface with the floor. A mixture of one part of cement to three parts of clean, coarse sand, and six of crushed rock or gravel is suitable for the purpose. If the rectangular foundation is dug carefully to a depth of 12 in., only narrow guide boards need be used for the exposed edges of the floor surface. The guide boards must be leveled carefully so that the floor will be level. The exposed surfaces of the floor and foundation should be finished with a mixture

of sand and cement, and troweled smooth. The house is anchored to the foundation by bolts, which are set into the concrete and bolted through the two 2 by 4-in. pieces forming the sill. The studding for the sides and ends are cut 7 ft. long, as shown in the front view. Double 2 by 4-in. pieces are used for the plate, which holds the studding at their upper ends. The rafters are of 2 by 4-in. stuff, cut 7 ft. long and matched to the proper pitch. Lookouts of 2 by 2-in. stock are placed at the ends of the roof to support the 12-in. overhang.

The details of the side framing are shown in the side view. Double studs are placed at the corners, and the studding is set on 23-in. centers. The weight is carried largely by the uprights which extend to the sill, as the intermediate studs are fitted to crosspieces forming the upper sides of the ventilating-screen openings. The double plate is of sufficient strength so that this construction will carry the load satisfactorily. In regions where heavy snowfall makes the roof load considerable, or where, for any reason, extra strength is desired, it would be well to extend all the studs from the sill to the plate, and make ventilating openings between the studding.

The rafters are of 2 by 4-in. stuff and long enough to give wide eaves, affording the necessary protection to the ventilating openings. The openings in the roof are placed between two pairs of rafters and the hinged covers are fitted carefully, to make them weather-tight. The roof is covered with ship-lap boards, 6 in. wide, over which a composition roof is nailed. The joints in the roofing material may be run either vertically or horizontally, care being taken in either case to make proper laps and tight joints.

The sides are covered with matched siding, trimmed suitably at the cor-

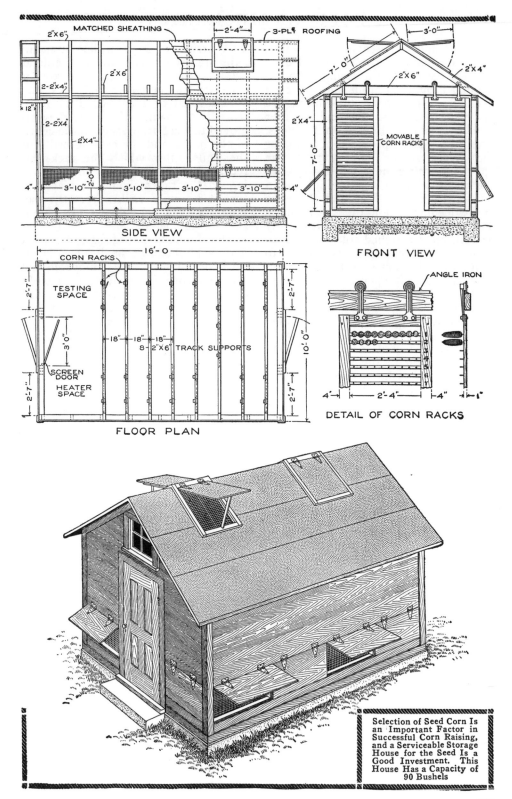

MATCHED SHEATHING
2"x6"
2'-4"
3-PLY ROOFING
2-2"x4"
2"x6"
2-2"x4"
2"x4"
12"
4"
3'-10"   3'-10"   3'-10"   3'-10"
4"
2'-0"

SIDE VIEW

3'-0"
7'-0"
2"x4"
2"x6"
2"x4"
7'-0"
MOVABLE CORN RACKS

FRONT VIEW

16'-0"
CORN RACKS
2'-7"
TESTING SPACE
3'-0"
18" 18" 18"
8-2"x6" TRACK SUPPORTS
2'-7"
10'-0"
SCREEN DOOR
HEATER SPACE
2'-7"

FLOOR PLAN

ANGLE IRON
4"   2'-4"   4"   1"

DETAIL OF CORN RACKS

Selection of Seed Corn Is an Important Factor in Successful Corn Raising, and a Serviceable Storage House for the Seed Is a Good Investment. This House Has a Capacity of 90 Bushels

ners and under the eaves. The ventilating openings in the sides and ends are fitted with a 2-in. casing strip extending around the four sides of each opening. The doors, or covers, are made of matched siding held together by cleats, and are hinged on T-hinges. The 2-in. casing provides a jamb for the covers on the outer edge of the openings. Wire mesh is fitted against the inner edge of the casing, and a 1-in. strip is nailed around the edge of the opening to hold the wire in place. The door may be of the stock variety or built up of matched stuff, cleated together. A screen door is hinged to swing into the house, so that the door may also be left open for ventilation. Small windows are fitted into the gable at each end.

The track supports for the racks are of 2 by 6-in. stuff, set on edge upon the plates. They are set on 18-in. centers, as shown in the floor plan, and provide for 16 racks, two on each track. The racks are suspended on heavy roller hangers so that they may be shifted for filling or examination. They consist of frames of 1-in. strips, 4 in. wide, and are 7 ft. long and 3 ft. wide. The corn on the cob is supported by

2-in. strips through which 10-penny nails are driven, as shown in the detail sketch of the corn racks. The rows of cobs are numbered so that they may be classified or identified after being stored. In loading the racks they are moved to the 3-ft. passage in the center of the house and the cobs forced onto the nails, after which the racks are returned to their places. The numbering on the racks should be placed so that it is easily visible from the passage, and the individual racks should also be numbered.

The fundamental design described may be applied to a smaller or a larger seed-corn house. The movable-rack arrangement is convenient for a smaller house, and the testing and heater spaces are also desirable. It would be well, therefore, to shorten the length of the house at the rear, under these conditions. For a larger house the same width might be maintained and the house extended, as required, at the rear. Double rows of racks might be installed, and, if the load became too great to be supported as in the house described, the racks could be rested on the floor and made to slide on a track, with guides at their tops.

Cross Disk on Faucet Stops Splashing

A piece of spring brass, about ¼ in. wide, bent into the form shown in the 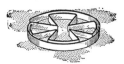 sketch and fitted to a faucet, will prevent the water issuing from it from splashing. The strip of brass is carefully bent to shape with pliers and inserted into the opening of the faucet. The diameter of the device, before being inserted, should be slightly greater than that of the opening, so that it will remain in place. High-pressure nozzles used by firemen are fitted with devices designed on this principle, and break up the stream of water so that one man can handle a hose that could not be handled otherwise by two men.

Safety Spring for Gas-Stove Burner

Danger of accidentally opening the burners on gas stoves by brushing against them may be overcome by attaching wire springs to the pipe which feeds the gas to the burners. The springs may be made of wire and should have about two coils around the feed pipe. The lower end of the spring is placed in contact with the front of the stove, below the feed pipe, and the upper end bears against the handle of the valve.—LeRoy Shenck, Mount Vernon, N. Y.

⟨Seams in concrete pavements are often run diagonally in order to prevent wear at the corners of the joints, which is severe if wagon wheels strike the edges.

Starting Large Gas Engines

By priming with ether instead of with gasoline it is possible to start heavy motors on the first quarter-turn. The ether should be used sparingly and in the usual manner. This method was employed with success on the engine of a large truck that would not start by spinning it.—Thomas W. Benson, Hastings-on-Hudson, N. Y.

Oil Tray for Screw Cutting

When considerable screw cutting is to be done in a lathe the oil tray shown in the sketch will be found convenient as an aid to first-class work. The box may be made of sheet metal, of a suitable size as indicated, or may be obtained from another source. It is fitted with a screen of sheet brass, cut to the shape indicated in the diagram and folded at A so that the portion B forms the bottom. The screen is suspended in the tray and catches the cuttings. The tray is partly filled with oil and rests on the lathe carriage when in

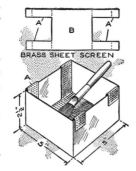

BRASS SHEET SCREEN

use. The brush is convenient in applying the oil. When the job is completed, the screen may be lifted from the tray, thus removing the cuttings and permitting the use of the oil for other jobs. If much work of this kind is handled, the saving of the cuttings may be a worth-while item.

Paraffin Automobile Polish

Paraffin oil, diluted with alcohol and used as a spray, is an excellent polish for automobile bodies. The car is rubbed down with clean cheesecloth to a brilliant polish. The paraffin oil thus used will remove dust and mud spots, and is a clean method of polishing.—W. B. Johnson, Los Angeles, California.

A Clothesline Post

A serviceable clothesline post was made out of an old boiler tube and a discarded wagon hub, as shown in the sketch. The boiler tube was cut to a length of 8½ ft. and sunk into the ground so that 6½ ft. was exposed. Sections of gas pipe were placed at right angles through the hub and the latter fitted snugly into the top of the boiler tube. The construction was given several coats of paint and withstood hard wear in the open. By using wooden plugs in the ends of the pipes and boring suitable holes through them, the old boiler tubes may be used to build a substantial railing or fence.

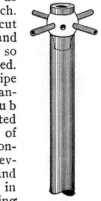

Twisting Wire with a Brace

Having two long single strands of electric-lamp cord, which it was desired to twist together, I fastened two of the ends to a hook and put the other two ends in the chuck of a brace. By turning the brace I was able to twist the wires together quickly and neatly.—Joseph Purdy, Chicago, Ill.

Quickly Made Locknut

A device that locks machine nuts securely without the use of a jam nut is shown in the sketch. A slot is sawed at the edge of the threaded hole in the nut and after the latter is fixed into place a taper pin is driven into it. The end is bent over to insure that the

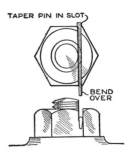

TAPER PIN IN SLOT

BEND OVER

wedge remains in place. This method permits of removing the nut when necessary, yet insures a positive grip.

An Indicator and Tool Holder

The illustration shows two devices which may be made by the machinist

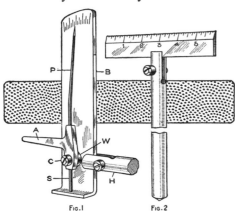

Fig. 1   Fig. 2

The Indicator and Tool Holder Are Simple in Construction and Have a Variety of Uses in the Machine Shop

or tool maker, and which will appeal to mechanics by reason of their simplicity and usefulness. At the left is shown an indicator with a holder to be set in the tool post of a lathe, and at the right is a similar holder attached temporarily to a scale, for use in places where the hand cannot conveniently reach.

The indicator consists of a steel plate, B, bent into the form of a bracket. The contact leg A is a piece of hardened steel, hinged on a shoulder screw, C, and the end of its long arm is the part used in contact with the work when indicated. A washer, W, is placed between the bracket and the contact leg. Since the shoulder screw is below the center line of the contact leg, a slight deflection will give the indicating needle P a considerable movement. A piece of spring wire, S, is sweated into the lower end of the contact leg and fixed to the lower end of the bracket. It returns the needle to the zero point when the contact leg is freed.

The clamp arm H is used to hold the indicator in the tool post, and in Fig. 2 it is shown attached to a scale. The holder consists of a slotted arm clamped at the end with a cap screw. —W. Burr Bennett, Bridgeport, Conn.

Auxiliary Grip for Valve Handle

It is sometimes extremely difficult to open a small-wheel valve, especially when the handle is oily or greasy. An aid in getting a good grip is to thread a piece of covered copper wire through the spokes and around the rim of the wheel. This enables one to grasp the wheel firmly regardless of grease on the wheel or the hands.

Automatic Gasoline-Supply Indicator

The depth of gasoline in an automobile tank or other container of liquid is indicated by the use of the device shown in the illustration. It consists of a hollow metal float fixed to an arm which actuates a lever, one end of which is marked with indications. The latter appear through a slot, as shown, and may be read conveniently.

The device is fixed to the tank at a place where the indicator may be examined, and is supported on a brass plate, A. Attached to the plate are two braces, B, which carry the indicating lever, and the bearing pins C. The diagram at the right shows the shape and arrangement of the lever. The brass plate should be large enough so that the float may be inserted through

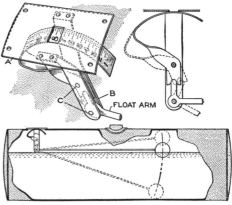

The Device Automatically Indicates the Amount of Gasoline or Other Liquid in the Tank

the opening, and a gasket, or packing, should be placed around its edge, to form a tight joint. The indications on the dial strip may be marked by pour-

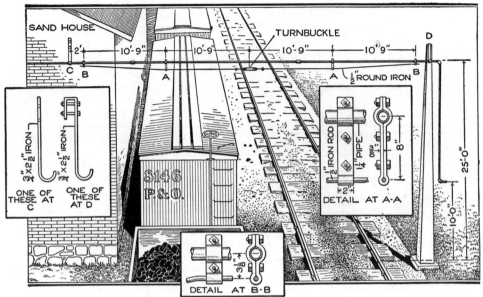

The Strut Fixed to the Pipe Resting on the Supporting Pole Forms a Truss

ing known quantities of liquid into the tank and making marks on the strip at the proper points.

Forge Fire Adapted for Heating Soldering Iron

A forge fire of considerable size is not well suited to the proper heating of a soldering iron, or other small pieces of metal. By placing a piece of pipe in the center of the fire and banking the coals around it, a convenient place, into which  the soldering iron may be inserted, is provided. This also prevents unnecessary wear by the burning of the iron in contact with the fire. For heating small pieces of steel, to be tempered, this kink is also useful.—J. Harger, Honolulu, H. I.

❡When filing thin spindles in a lathe, hold two fine files to the surface, one above and one below the spindle, thus bracing it.

Truss for Long Span of Pipe

Supporting long spans of pipe, particularly at considerable heights, is often difficult. The method shown in the sketch proved effective under severe conditions and may be applied in a large variety of situations.

The arrangement was designed to give a clear way 25 ft. above the outbound railroad tracks adjoining a shop. It was unsafe to place a support between the tracks, hence it was built as shown at the right and a strut fixed to the pipe, which carried steam. The fixtures shown in the detail sketches give a positive grip on the pipe and strut rod. They may be constructed readily of band iron, drilled and bolted together.—S. O. Benjamin, Washington, Ind.

Gasoline Fuel Strainer and Economizer

A fuel strainer and gasoline saver is an unusual combination; the sketch shows a simple, practical device combining these features. It consists of a piece of cast iron or steel fitted to the exhaust pipe with a split cap and machine screws. The gasoline pipe from the supply tank is connected to the metal block at the shut-off valve A and the gasoline passes up through the cone-shaped screen and out at B to the carburetor. The accumulated dirt and

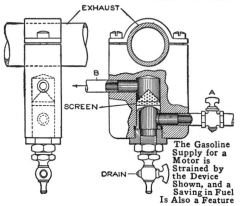

The Gasoline Supply for a Motor is Strained by the Device Shown, and a Saving in Fuel Is Also a Feature

water screened from the gasoline is drained off at the stopcock.

Since the block is clamped tightly to the exhaust pipe, it absorbs heat from it and the temperature of the gasoline is thus raised in passing through. For this reason the fuel will vaporize more readily in the carburetor and a weaker mixture will serve the motor. Less gasoline will thus be used. The block should be in contact with the exhaust pipe for a distance of not more than 2 in., if it is made wider in the lower portion than at the cap.

Snap Gauges

In the manufacture of duplicate machine parts, snap gauges are used to

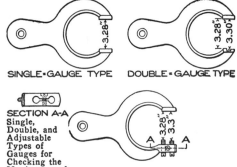

Single, Double, and Adjustable Types of Gauges for Checking the Maximum and Minimum Sizes

check the maximum and minimum sizes. In most factories two gauges are used, a maximum and a minimum,

each a separate gauge. There is now made a gauge that is a combination of the two, having the rear gauge the minimum, and the maximum at the front. These gauges are subject to wear, and if hardened, they must be annealed to take up the wear by drawing the ends together. I designed a gauge, as shown, which is adjustable, having only one jaw hardened and two hardened setscrews. These may be set at any time to take up the wear.—Joe V. Romig, Allentown, Pa.

Leaded Socket for Cable Fastening

Loop ends of cable must be securely fastened to insure safety, and the device shown in the sketch will provide such a fastening. A section of pipe was flattened at one end and the cable inserted as shown. Molten lead was poured into the pipe, fixing the loop firmly. The socket was arranged so that the larger end of the pipe is farthest from the loop. The pull on the loop thus tends to force the wedge-shaped lead filling more firmly into its casing.

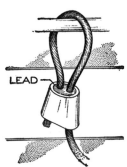

Improving a Razor Strop

To improve the sharpening qualities of a razor strop obtain a strip of soft, smooth lead. Apply a good lather to the strop, both on the canvas and leather sides. Rub the lead over the strop as in stropping a razor until the lather has disappeared. The lead acts as a lubricant and in fine particles gives an excellent honing surface.—L. E. Fetter, Portsmouth, N. H.

⁋In distributing hand-set type after use, printers moisten the batch to be "thrown in," so that the "take," or quantity of type taken in the hand at one time, will cling together.

Shop Notes

Windlass for Raising Wagon Boxes

By A. S. THOMAS

REMOVING boxes or racks from the trucks of a wagon is difficult for one person unaided, and even though he may have assistance in the operation, the unused box or rack is cumbersome to store or replace on the trucks. The lifting rigging shown in the sketch was built to make the lifting by one man convenient, and it also provides a good storage, as well as an easy means of replacing the box on the vehicle. The device has saved me much time on the farm and has prevented damage to wagon boxes, which frequently results from removing and replacing them. The device shown is fitted into a wagon shed, but it may be adapted to outdoor use, and the shaft,

which carries the chains, may even be built to extend inside as well as outside. of a roofed-over area.

The operation of the windlass is simple. The chain shaft is supported on posts, well braced at the ground. Chains are hooked to the sides of the wagon box, and by means of the cross arms the box is raised and its rear end supported on the adjustable bar. To hold the chain shaft from revolving when the operator releases the cross arms under load, the short chain on the shaft support is hooked around one of the arms. The truck is drawn out of the shed and the front end of the box is supported by a horse, as shown at the right in the sketch. When it is de-

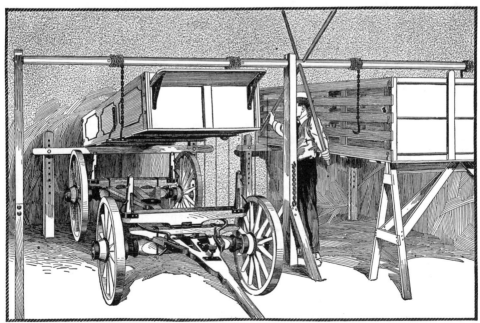

This Device Makes It Convenient for One Man to Remove or Replace the Boxes or Bodies of Vehicles, the Trucks of Which are Used Interchangeably

sired to replace the box upon the truck, the former is again raised, the horse at the front end is removed, and the box is lowered into place.

In wagon sheds or barns that are strongly built, the chain shaft may be suspended from the framing, but it is best to make certain that the load may be carried safely, additional braces being inserted as a precaution. The device may be made of a length suitable to various storage places for vehicles, and may be adapted to automobiles, trucks, or other vehicles on which the trucks and running gear are used interchangeably with several bodies.

Garden-Hose Reel Inclosed in Wall Cupboard

The sketch shows a garden-hose reel which I fitted into my bungalow and which has given much satisfaction as a

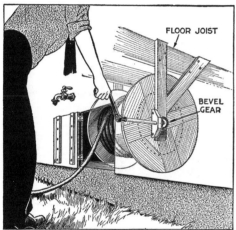

The Garden-Hose Reel Inclosed in the Basement of the House Is Practical and may be Installed Easily

practical means of caring for the hose. When I wish to use it I merely open the small door in the side of the house and draw out the hose. Replacing the hose on the reel is accomplished by applying the crank to the shaft in the wall, and, when out of the way, the small door is padlocked. This is much better than leaving the hose unreeled or rolling it on a reel of the portable type.

The construction of the reel device and fittings is simple. The reel proper

was built up of 4-in. strips for the core, and the round ends were made of ⅞-in. stock, the pieces being nailed crosswise, to reinforce each other. A bevel gear was fitted to the center shaft of the reel, and this engages another bevel gear, the shaft of which extends outside of the basement wall as shown. Its outer end is squared to fit the crank. The reel is supported from the floor joists of the first floor by two brackets, built up of 2 by 4-in. stock and spiked to the joists. The door was cut in the side of the house, and the piece cut out reinforced with cleats. This made it unnecessary to attempt matching paint on the door with that on the house, and made the reel opening quite inconspicuous. The opening was conveniently placed close to the water connection, making it unnecessary to drag the hose considerable distances on the lawn.—S. O. Safholm, Sacramento, California.

Inexpensive Lantern Slides for Advertising

Slides for projecting advertising upon motion-picture screens, or from projection lanterns, may be made with a clean-cut type face as follows: The advertisement is set up on the linotype machine, or by hand, centering the lines on the linotype slug, if that form is used. A proof of the matter is taken on tissue or onion-skin paper and the ink is applied rather heavily. Clean the glass slide on which the copy is to be mounted, and as soon as the proof is made, place the paper, printed side down, on the slide, holding it firmly so that it will not slip. Rub the paper with the fingers gently to transfer the ink. With a knife blade, or piece of heavy paper, curved in the shape of a scoop, cover the surface of the glass with pulverized dragon's blood. This may be purchased at the drug store, and 25 cents' worth will provide for a large number of slides. Remove the excess powder from the glass by tapping it gently, permitting the dragon's blood to drop into its container.

The letters transferred to the glass

will be sharply outlined by the powder adhering to the printer's ink. Pass the glass, printed side down, over a heated stove until the powder adhering to the letters turns a dark red, or black. When the imprint is dry the slide is ready for use.

Where many slides are to be made, this method will be found quite convenient. If it is difficult to have the matter set up in type, it may be worth while to purchase a set of rubber type which may be used in the same manner as the metal type. By the use of ground glass, with the printing on the ground side, an effective slide may be made. The edges of the letters will appear ragged and when thrown on the screen this gives the effect of being in relief.—Frank Kavanaugh, Atchison, Kansas.

Watch Fitted to Automobile Steering Post

To fill the need for an automobile timepiece, the method of attaching an inexpensive watch to the top of the steering post, as shown in the sketch, was devised. The back plate of the watch was removed and a hole drilled through its center. A pin to fit the hole was riveted into the nut A, which held the steering wheel in place. The back was riveted on top of the nut and the watch was screwed to the back. This simple method of fastening

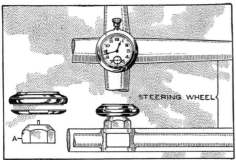

The Back of the Watch was Riveted to the Steering Post and the Watch Screwed into Place

proved satisfactory, and since the watch was a cheap one, it was not likely to be stolen.—Richard H. Jehlicka, Worcester, Mass.

Solid Foundation for a Portable Engine

Varied service demanded of a gasoline engine required that it be mounted upon a truck so that it could be readily transported. This arrangement did

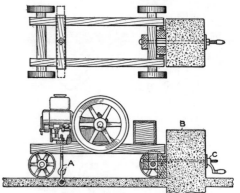

The Portable Engine is Clamped Securely to the Concrete Foundation and Is Stable under Heavy Strain

not, however, render the engine stable enough for very heavy duty in a shop, and the concrete foundation and clamping device shown was arranged to secure the truck. The truck is drawn against the block B, and clamped in the hook and eye at A. The eye is fixed in the floor and swings on a rod imbedded in the concrete. The hook A is fastened by means of a nut at its upper end. The axle of the truck nearest the block B is clamped behind a pivoted wooden block, which is drawn up securely by the threaded bolt and crank C. If properly adjusted, this arrangement holds the engine firmly enough for heavy duty and long belt connection to the driving pulley.—B. Hanson, Martin, Ohio.

Trouble Lamp Operated by Dry Batteries

Dry batteries, testing eight amperes, or less, will operate small electric-light bulbs and doorbells satisfactorily. Four cells wired in series to any desired length of cotton drop cord terminating in a miniature pull socket, that is equipped with a six-volt lamp, will provide a good trouble light for a considerable period.

Rigging for Surface-Grinding Taper Cylinders

Several barrels of malleable-iron castings were returned to a foundry by a customer because they were not

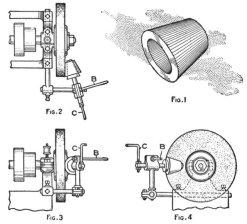

Grinding Malleable Castings to a Smooth Finish was Resorted to with Success After a Large Number were Spoiled in Attempting to Finish Them by a Rolling Process. The Device Viewed from Above is Shown in Fig. 2; from the Front, in Fig. 3, and from the Side, in Fig. 4

as smooth on the outer surface as desired. A detail of the castings is shown in Fig. 1. The foundry's repair shop was not equipped with surface grinders to finish castings, and could not handle the work. Rolling down the roughness on a lathe was attempted, by turning and threading a piece of stock to screw on the spindle in place of a chuck, with a mandrel projecting to take the castings. A roll was fixed in the tool post and fed against the casting on the mandrel, while rotating. The castings were spoiled, rejected by the customer, and new ones made.

Grinding off the roughness on an ordinary grinder, rigged as shown by the sketch, proved successful and economical. Three rest arms, two bolts, three collars, a piece of cold-rolled steel, with a sleeve driven on one end, were assembled and the castings fastened on the sleeve by a slight pressure. They were then swung against the emery wheel by means of the handle, B, with the right hand, and two turns of handle C, with the left hand,

were sufficient to give the desired finish and smoothness. The first method required 25 hours for installation and the second three hours. The castings were stretched and ruined by the rolling method, and were unharmed by the second method. Time was saved in the grinding process, and it was adapted with success for other work of this type.—Stephen Bona, Union City, Conn.

Counteracting Static Electricity in Belts

Much difficulty was experienced in overcoming static electricity in belts and machinery in a large manufacturing plant. Grounding in the ordinary way proved useless and after numerous experiments the device shown in the sketch was installed and overcame the trouble completely. Two pieces of No. 6 copper wire, 14 in. long, were soldered to 12 prongs of No. 24 copper wire, 3 in. long and 1 in. apart. The resulting device appears like a comb, as shown in the illustration. One of the "combs" was fastened above the belt, as indicated, and the other was placed beneath a water pipe, or other grounded metal, so that the prongs came within $\frac{1}{16}$ in. of the pipe or metal. Care must be taken that the combs do not touch the pipe or metal, or belt. The two combs were connected with a No. 24 wire, supported on a piece of wood, about 1 in. square and of proper length.

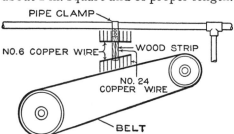

Static Electricity in Belts was Overcome by the Use of the Wire Combs Shown in the Sketch

The device may be used on various types of belts, providing a metal pipe or other medium for grounding the static electricity properly is available.—Samuel Baker, Toronto, Ont.

Mountain-Stream Electric Plant

By John Bunyan

[The author of this article is a banker, who makes electrical work and mechanics his avocation. He wired up his mountain cottage for electric lights, designed a hydroelectric plant to provide energy, and built it with the aid of a mechanic.—Editor.]

CURRENT developed by a small hydroelectric plant, installed on Big Thompson Creek, nine miles below Estes Park, Col., is used to light a mountain cottage, one of a group at a delightful spot called "Sylvania." The water wheel, connecting rigging, and a dynamo are supported on a wooden frame suspended under a private bridge across the stream from the cottagers' camp to the Estes Park road. The illustration shows the general arrangement of the various parts, as well as details of the construction. Cables conducted to the cottage permit easy control of the plant without going out of doors. Old material, gathered in machine shops, was largely used in the construction, and the cost was thus kept down to about $100. The plant is in use its second season, and has given complete satisfaction. When the cottage is unoccupied, the driving belt is removed from the dynamo, the frame is padlocked up to the bridge, and the dynamo house is locked, little opportunity for molestation being afforded. As the plant is on the main road to the Rocky Mountain National Park—Estes Park—it attracts considerable attention from tourists passing by.

The swiftly running mountain stream, operating directly on a water wheel, without a dam, flume, or headgate, furnishes the power. The device adjusts itself throughout the season to the varying height of the water and to the changes in the velocity of the stream. When the device is not in operation it is drawn up under the bridge by means of the cables, which are conducted to the cabin by a series of pulleys, as shown in the illustration, and wound on a windlass shaft, which projects from the side of the house and is operated by a crank on the inside. The crank and its pawl wheel are shown in the photograph reproduced at the left, in the illustration. When light is desired, the cable is wound from the windlass, releasing the supporting frame and permitting it to pivot downward on the eyebolts supporting it. The water wheel comes into contact with the stream and is lowered until the proper flow of current is generated. This is determined by the voltmeter installed above the windlass in the cottage, as indicated in the illustration. The proper height is maintained by setting the pawl wheel on the windlass, when the voltmeter registers a current of 110 volts. A rheostat was installed, but it was found that it was not needed to control the current flow, for, when the water is high and swift, the water wheel is let down in the stream only slightly.

The lights flickered when the plant was first put into use, but this defect was overcome entirely by installing a flywheel, taken from an old ice-cream freezer. It was carefully balanced and fixed on the shaft of the dynamo. Loose-rock jetties were thrown into the stream, above the bridge, to divert a strong current against the wheel in low-water periods. At higher stages these low rock dams permit the water to pass over them and the wheel still has a strong current to turn it.

The mechanical details are shown clearly in the sectional view, Fig. 3, at the bottom of the illustration. A wooden frame forms the main support of the mechanism, and is built up of 2 by 12-in. planks; it is about 17 ft. long and 6 ft. wide. Two eyebolts, fixed through the upstream stringer of the bridge, furnish the support for the frame, which is connected to them by means of iron straps. The frame pivots on the eyebolt joint, permitting the water wheel to be raised and lowered easily, by the change in the water level or by means of the cable and windlass. The water wheel is hung in the downstream end of the frame, while the upper end carries a small house, about as large as a dog kennel, which contains the dynamo, gears, and connecting belt. The top, sides, and bottom of the dynamo house are constructed of tongue-and-groove flooring, and the roof is further protected by a sheet of composition roofing. The lower end of the frame is turned up at an angle so that the water wheel will have a good clearance when the frame is drawn up against the bridge.

The water wheel is built of two iron wheels, from a discarded hay rake, 4 ft. 8 in. in diameter, each wheel containing 20 spokes. These rake wheels are fastened to a steel shaft, 4½ ft. apart, with the corresponding spokes opposite, and paddles are bolted to every other spoke around the wheels, making 10 paddles in all. Each paddle is 5 ft. long, and consists of two 1 by 6-in. boards, joined at an angle of 150°. The boards are held in this position by ¼-in. iron straps, bent to that angle, and the ends are partly inclosed by heavy galvanized-iron braces, shaped to fit the angle.

At the end of the wheel shaft is attached a 16-in. sprocket wheel having 31 teeth. A No. 55 steel sprocket chain, held in position and steadied by four idlers, transmits the power of the wheel along the side of the frame to a 10-tooth sprocket wheel at the outside end of the shaft, nearest the water wheel, in the dynamo house. Inside the dynamo house, a 20-in. cogwheel, with 120 teeth, is fixed to this shaft and meshes with a small pinion having 20 teeth, and set on a countershaft, giving a gear ratio of 6 to 1. At one end of the countershaft is fastened a 16-in. drive pulley, which drives the dynamo by means of a 2-in. flat belt.

The support for the dynamo consists of a piece of 2 by 12-in. plank, 20 in. long, fastened at one end to the upstream side of the dynamo house by heavy strap hinges, secured by bolts. A heavy piece of flat iron, with a ¾-in. hole near the end, projects from the under side of the plank at the other end. A ⅝-in. bolt, hung to a stout hook in the roof by means of an eye, is threaded at the lower end and projects through the hole in the iron fixture at the end of the dynamo platform. A lever nut, at the lower end of the bolt, supports the end of the dynamo platform, and provides a convenient means to tighten the belt. The dynamo is bolted to the platform.

The dynamo has a capacity of about 200 watts and generates direct current at 110 volts. It carries a small pulley, a little less than 2 in. in diameter, and the water wheel, with a working speed of about 11 revolutions per minute, drives the dynamo, through the intermediate gears, about 1,800 R.P.M.

Two eyebolts, one in each side of the frame near the water wheel, are placed nearly in line with the downstream edge of the bridge. Two steel cables are fastened to them and pass up over two grooved wheels, directly above, on top of the bridge planking and lined up with the edge of the bridge. These cables are spliced together, as shown in Fig. 2, and one cable, about 90 ft. long, runs over three pulleys to a windlass, which is installed in the cabin. Another cable, spliced to this cable and pulling in line with it, passes over a pulley at the end of the bridge and supports a heavy rock, which is used as a counterweight,

Fig.1
CABIN WALL
INSIDE OF CABIN
RATCHET
CABLE TO WATERWHEEL

Fig.2
CABLE TO CABIN
STONE
COUNTERBALANCE
WATER LINE
4'-6"
5'-0"

In the Cottage Are the Voltmeter, Rheostat, and Windlass Crank

When Not in Use the Water Wheel is Drawn Up under the Bridge

DYNAMO
HINGES
HINGES
BELT TIGHTENER
DOOR
BRIDGE FLOOR
COUNTERBALANCE CABLE
4'-8"
16" SPROCKET-31 TEETH
150°
10 TOOTH SPROCKET
IDLER WHEELS
20" COGWHEEL-120 TEETH
COGWHEEL-20 TEETH
16" DRIVE PULLEY
NO.55 STEEL SPROCKET CHAIN
IDLER WHEELS
WATER LINE
FIG.3

This Small Hydroelectric Plant, Built on a Mountain Stream from Materials Costing $100, Provides Electricity for the Lighting of a Cottage. The Swift Current is Always Available, and the Water Wheel is Lowered Only When Energy is Desired

The weight of the dynamo house and its machinery partly balances the weight of the water wheel at the other end of the frame. The counterweight further balances the weight of the water wheel, but is not intended to overcome it entirely, as this would raise the wheel in use. The crank of the windlass is inside the cabin, in the living room, as shown in the photograph reproduced at the left, but the shaft projects outside the cabin, and carries an iron spool, about 2½ in. in diameter, on which the control cable is wound.

Two line wires, and an additional wire for the rheostat, are run from the dynamo to the cabin. A voltmeter, a rheostat (the latter a simple resistance coil with a sliding contact) and a combined three-pole knife switch and fuse block are installed in the living room near the windlass. Three 25-watt tungsten lamps light the living room, one 25-watt tungsten lamp is used in the kitchen, and three 15-watt lamps are installed, one each in the bedroom, screened front porch, and the garage, which is attached to the cabin.

How to Judge a Secondhand Automobile

BY P. D. NOREM

Over one-half of the automobiles manufactured in the United States during the past few years have been purchased by individuals who were buying their first car, and who had practically no experience in operating an automobile. It is difficult for the inexperienced person to select an automobile that will give thorough satisfaction, as the number of cars and styles he has to choose from is large. He may examine a number of cars, and often becomes confused with the numerous details; finally he buys one. After the experience of the first season, he feels he can make a better selection and either sells his car or trades it in on a new one. This results in a large number of secondhand cars being sold each year, and the purchasers of such cars should make a thorough investigation of them. Unless such a car has been completely overhauled by a reliable concern, this precaution is necessary, before buying it at any price, no matter how cheap it may appear to be. Otherwise it may prove to be an expensive purchase in the end.

A few of the more important points to be considered in the selection of a secondhand car are the following: Find out the age, make, and type of car, in order to investigate the factory, or company, making the car, to see if it is still in business, financially responsible, can give good service in reference to repair parts for this particular model, or if they can be obtained elsewhere at a reasonable cost. Also determine if possible whether or not this particular model, and other cars manufactured by the same company, have in general proved satisfactory.

The material used in the construction of an automobile is of paramount importance. One should give this feature more consideration than the general appearance of the car, for, if the proper material has not been used, the car will not stand up, or give satisfaction. Do not, however, buy an ugly or very antiquated-looking car even if it has good material. When it is desired to sell the car, the appearance adds much to the value of the car with many persons.

Inspect the engine for compression, by turning it over with the starting crank; start it up and see how it responds to the throttle and if it will run very slowly without missing, knocking, or rattling. Investigate the oiling system, and make certain as to its proper operation. Inspect the radiator and its connections, to see that there are no leaks, and that the cooling water is circulating. Jack up the rear wheels and run them by means of the engine, to see if they run true. Observe whether or not the differential operates quietly. Try the various speeds and inspect the transmission, to see what condition the gear wheels are in, as any wear on these gears will show how much service the car has had. See if the front wheels are in line, if they run true, if the steering gear works properly. Inspect the tires on the car as well as extra ones, and make sure the size and kind can be obtained easily, as some sizes and kinds are obsolete. Inspect the wiring of the ignition, starting, and lighting systems, and ascertain whether or not they are in good condition, and function properly. Determine the condition of the storage battery, if there is one on the car. Inspect the oil, electric, or other lamps.

Make a thorough inspection of the frame, springs, doors, upholstering, top, curtains, and extra equipment. For a final test, run the car with a load, for 15 or 20 miles, trying out the various speeds and observing how the clutch takes hold. Pay particular attention to the engine under load, and, if possible, try pulling a full load up a five to ten-per-cent hill, as a car is practically useless if it will not pull up such an incline. Listen for pounding in the engine, and see if the water in the radiator "steams" quickly, which is a bad sign. Examine the bearings after the run, to see if any are unduly hot. Be sure to watch for cracked water jackets around the cylinders. The exterior finish should be one of the last considerations, although a neat appearance may be an attractive feature. Particular care must be given to the discovery of defects which may be hidden by the surface paint or finish.

Lifting Rig for Heavy Wheels or Pulleys

Difficulty was experienced in handling a large number of heavy, flanged tires for locomotive wheels, and the rigging shown in the sketch was devised as a result. It proved effective and has been adapted for use in handling other objects of irregular shape, by making special grips to fit the upper ring. The rig is attached to the hook of a crane, or other device for transporting the heavy object, and may be used under a variety of conditions.

The grips are fixed to a disk of steel plate, 12 in. in diameter and 1¼ in.

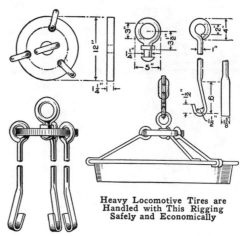

Heavy Locomotive Tires are Handled with This Rigging Safely and Economically

thick. They are made of 1-in. steel rods, forged at the lower ends to the shape shown in the detailed sketches. It will be noted that the construction results in carrying the weight in balance and that there is little likelihood of the tire slipping from the grips because the downward pressure tends to increase the hold.

Silencing Rattle in Wood Turning

When turning the inside of thin-walled wooden objects, the operation is frequently accompanied by a disagreeable, shrill noise, and the turned surface becomes irregular instead of smooth. These conditions are the result of vibration in the unsupported thin walls, and the resistance to the turning tool causes small waves to appear on the surface of the work. The winding of a number of turns of thick soft string around the thin portion of the piece being turned will overcome these difficulties. Care must be taken to wind the string in a direction opposite to the rotation of the work, and the ends must be tied in securely, so that they will not become loosened and cause injury either to the operator or the object.—Charles F. Merrill, Hopedale, Mass.

Bearing Wheel for Gate

Fitting a wheel to the lower edge of a gate so that the weight is carried on

the g r o u n d instead of on t h e hinges, as shown in the s k e t c h, will prevent the breaking of t h e hinges as well as jarring the s u p- p o r t s out of plumb. The gate was fitted i n t o place in the ordinary m a n n e r, and t h e ground in f r o n t of it w a s smoothed and leveled to give a good bearing surface for the wheel, which was taken from an old wheelbarrow. It was fixed to the lower corner of the gate with sheet-metal straps, bolted through the boards.—Arthur Anderson, Batavia, Ill.

Vent Cover for Automobile Gasoline Tank

A small hole is usually provided in the filling cap of a gasoline tank to overcome the partial vacuum caused by the engine taking up the fuel. This hole must be kept open while the engine is in operation, but when not run-

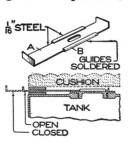

ning the gasoline evaporates, and the gas passes out through the hole. To eliminate this, one automobile owner added a device to the tank cap by means of which the hole could be covered when the car was idle.

The device consists of a shutter, A, which operates between two slides, B, which are soldered to the top of the cap, as shown. The shutter is provided with a hole for the vent. To uncover the hole the shutter is pushed in, and to cover it, the reverse.

Maintenance of Dry-Battery Sets

In dry-battery sets, if two cases are wet and come into contact, if two binding-post nuts, zinc linings, or the metal of any connections, touch, the battery will soon go out of commission because of the exhaustion of one or more cells. Batteries should be separated by wads of paper or pieces of wood, and wet cases dried immediately. A dry-battery tester is inexpensive, and will indicate the condition of each battery. Carry reserves for batteries testing 10 amperes or less. New batteries should test at least 20 amperes. The voltage of dry batteries remains nearly constant at 1½, while the amperage decreases with use and age.

Bending and Polishing Brass Tubing

Brass tubes, 2 or 3 in. in diameter, and of considerable length, are bent into various forms for use as bar, bank,

church-altar, and stairway railing by first subjecting the portion to be bent to the flame of a strong blowtorch, to anneal it. Without doing this, the tube will not bend satisfactorily, but will wrinkle and bulge at the point of bending in spite of a solid filling of rosin. After annealing, which has brought the tube to a dull red heat, it is allowed to cool slowly. It is then taken to the polishing department where it is greased off on a 100-grade emery wheel with plenty of grease, the tube being continually rolled on the revolving wheel. The cutting-down process follows on a sewed-cloth wheel, revolving at 2,800 revolutions a minute, using plenty of tripoli as the cutting agent.

The tube is plugged at one end and filled with melted rosin. Rosin as a bending foundation in tubes is superior to sand in that it solidifies firmly, which sand cannot do. It is often left in the tube, thus increasing its strength, which is impractical with sand. If it is desired to remove the rosin, the tube is drawn back and forth over a gentle gas flame, when the rosin will be forced out in the form of a long core. In bending, care is taken not to mar or scratch the tube, as in the bent state it is difficult for the polisher to handle, when refinishing it. An iron rod, bent by measurement to correspond exactly with the form desired, is used to gauge the bending. On a bench, fastened solidly to the floor and with plenty of space around it, as shown in the sketch, two circular iron castings are bolted, 6 to 8 in. apart, the larger about 2½ ft. in diameter, the smaller about 1 ft. in diameter, and each about 4 in. thick. A wooden block—or two, if necessary, when bending tubes of small diameter—is laid against the smaller iron disk; a piece of leather is held against the side of the other disk, to prevent marring of the tube. The tube is then inserted between the disks and the bending usually done by three workmen. One attends to the gauging and the other two apply the pressure by leverage on the longer end. It must be bent upon the large iron disk, and care must be taken to shift the tube in the forms to produce the desired angle gradually. Once bent, the tube is again cut down and buffed by the polisher to a bright finish. Flanged supports receive the rail; caps are screwed on the ends of the tube, and it is ready for installation. The rail is seldom lacquered, as this would soon wear off in spots. Generally it is kept polished by regular use of a polishing compound. Often it is allowed to tarnish with the atmosphere, when it takes on a beautiful brown color, which is lustrous and lasting, as it cannot be rubbed off by handling.—Ralph W. Tillotson, Erie, Pennsylvania.

⁋In brazing metal objects in a forge it is necessary to keep them on top of the fire so that the result may be readily seen. When the brass used begins to melt it may be known by the appearance of a blue flame.

Sprinkler for Narrow Strips of Lawn

The sprinkler shown in the illustration was made particularly to care for a narrow strip of lawn along a park-

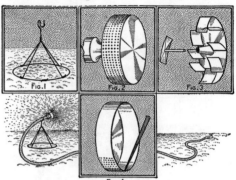

FIG. 4

This Sprinkler was Designed to Care for a Narrow Strip of Parking and was Made of Materials Gathered in the Home

way. It will sprinkle a 3 by 40-ft. area, under 100 lb. pressure, and may be carried easily while in operation without danger to the person moving it. The materials used in its construction were "picked up" about the home and were the following: an oilcan, a hose connection, and 8 ft. of heavy wire. The latter was used to make the stand, shown in Fig. 1, which supports the sprinkler. The upper side of the device is shown in Fig. 2, and the method of punching the holes into the edge of the oilcan is shown in Fig. 4. In order to break up the spray, a wheel to revolve with the water was fitted into the can, and is shown in Fig. 3. A stationary axle was soldered into the can, and the wheel with its conical bearing and curved blades was placed within. Washers prevent it from touching the bottom of the can.—Edward R. Smith, Walla Walla, Wash.

Cover for Washing Machine

Keeping a washing machine clean, thus prolonging its period of usefulness, and having it ready for immediate use, is an economy that may be easily realized by the householder in providing a cover, as shown in the illustration. The use of casters on the legs of the machine is also a good kink, since transporting it thus becomes more convenient. The diagrams below show the patterns for the cover, and may be adapted to various kinds of washers.

The cover may be made of canvas or

The Washing-Machine Cover Is Useful in Protecting It from Dirt, and may be Made Easily

strong cloth, but even an old piece of carpet may be used. To obtain the proper shape of material for the cover it is best to fit a paper pattern around the machine and use this as a guide in cutting the cloth. Use three pieces of paper, pinned together, if one large sheet is not available. The excess material is drawn up toward the top of the machine and pinned into folds. When opened, the paper sheet will appear somewhat like the large pattern C. The top of the pattern and the lower edge B should be trimmed off even with the top and bottom of the machine.

A circular piece of cloth, A, is used for the top. The handle F may be sewed directly to the top, or riveted through it into a wooden strip reinforc-

ing the top. The patterns for the portion that covers the machinery must be made carefully. The section E is the pattern for the inner side of the wheel. The pattern for the edges and outer side of the wheel and fittings is shown at D. They are also made by fitting paper to the parts and trimming it off properly. The cover D is sewed to the main part at the seams C. Adjustment must, of course, be made for the shape of the machinery of each particular washing machine. The method described may be applied to the making of covers for various articles in the home and elsewhere, and the use of paper patterns, made by fitting them around an object, also has a wide application.—L. R. Busch, Omaha, Nebr.

Polishing Marble or Granite

Electrical experimenters frequently have need for a slab of polished marble for mounting instruments, as switch bases and the like. The marble can usually be obtained, but it is not always polished, at least not on the edges and corners. A satisfactory method of polishing marble, or granite, is as follows: Rub the slab to be polished with a piece of sandstone, or emery, until it is perfectly flat. Then rub it with a piece of coarse-grit stone until all the emery scratches are gone. Next rub the surface with a piece of fine-grit stone until the coarse-grit scratches are removed, and then rub with a piece of pumice stone until no grit scratches remain. This done, rub with a piece of barber's hone until not a scratch is visible. Upon this depends to a great extent success in producing a polish.

When all the scratches are effaced, proceed as follows: Take a soft flannel cloth and fasten it around a small block; moisten the cloth slightly, place a few crystals of oxalic acid on the marble and crush them with the rag-wrapped block; then rub the marble until a polish appears. The longer the rubbing is continued the better the polish that results. Take care not to let the rag rest on one place too long, as the acid will eat into the stone. Use the acid sparingly. The acid simply softens the stone while the rubbing brings out the polish. Oxalic acid is poisonous, and care should be taken in handling it, so as not to get any of it into cuts or wounds. Use plenty of water for the rubbing, but use only a moist cloth for the polishing. Rub until all the scratches are apparently gone, and then rub more to insure a good polish. The necessary stones for rubbing can be obtained from almost any marble or granite dealer for a small sum.—F. Sahlmann, Salina, Kan.

Oiling Gang Machine Cutters

Selective distribution of oil to milling cutters arranged in gangs is provided for by the method shown in the sketch. This device is simple and effective. It may be controlled easily, and supplies oil to the cutters as desired. The horizontal supply pipe, shown in the sketch at the right, feeds the oil from small holes, A, B, C, and D, bored at intervals in its under side. These holes are covered by spring-steel clips, as shown at E, when the flow of oil is to be shut off. The device is adaptable to a wide range of uses, and

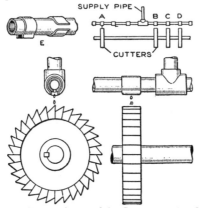

Machine Cutters Arranged in Gangs may be Oiled Economically by the Use of This Homemade Device

the supply pipe may be drilled with as many holes as required.—W. Burr Bennett, Bridgeport, Conn.

❡Joints subjected to heat should be packed with asbestos packing and never with rubber.

Display Board for Gas Brackets

A display board for gas brackets used by a gas company is shown in the

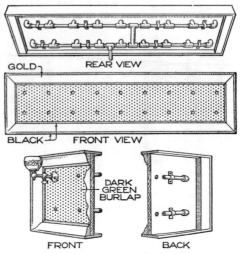

An Effective Display of Gas Brackets

illustration. The board was made with a frame extending around it, giving the appearance of a large picture frame. The parts of the frame were covered with gilt or painted black, as indicated. The gas brackets were screwed into the tees and elbows from the front of the board. The flat surface of the front of the board was covered with dark-green burlap. The device gives a very effective display of the company's wares.

Staining Streaked Wood Uniformly

When a piece of wood which is being stained runs from a dark shade to a very light one, it will be found that the darker portion is sapwood, and being softer, takes up more stain. If several pieces are joined together this may also occur. By cutting an ordinary flat brush diagonally across the hair, so that the bristles will be short on one side and full length on the other, and using it with the longest bristles on the hard wood, the surface may be stained uniformly. The bristles should, of course, be cut to a chisel edge after trimming them off on the diagonal.

Automatic Air Supply for Blowpipe

When no air supply under pressure **is** provided for a blowpipe in the shop or l a b o r a t o r y, the arrangement s h o w n i n t h e sketch m a y be m a d e quickly, and will g i v e a constant supply of air for f r o m 20 to 30 minutes. A wooden frame, or box, is constructed to c o n-tain a large glass b o t t l e or a 10-

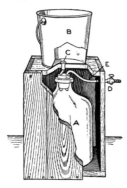

gal. carboy, A. It is provided with a two-hole stopper and rubber tubes, connected through them, to the interior of the bottle. One of the tubes, E, is connected to a stopcock, D; the other is fitted through the bottom of an ordinary water pail, B, as shown at C. A metal, cork, or rubber fitting is provided at C, which may be plugged so that the pail is water-tight. The pail is then filled with water and connected to the bottle as shown. When the water is permitted to drain from the pail into the bottle, the air is forced out of the latter and may be conveyed to the blowpipe from the stopcock D.—Reginald R. Wayt, Pittsburgh, Pa.

Repairing Slide on Brass Horn

In attempting to remove the broken slides from a horn, it was discovered

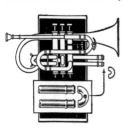

that t h e y h a d corroded and become fixed into place. When an a t t e m p t was made to w i t h-draw t h e m by force, the end of one of the slides b r o k e off, as shown in the detailed sketch. The two portions of the slide which remained in the tubes were exposed very slightly, and apparently could not be removed without damaging the instrument. The following method was devised by which they were removed successfully: An iron plug was fitted snugly into the portion of the slide remaining in the tube. A hand vise was clamped over the small end of the slide exposed and gripped firmly against the plug. With this solid hold the broken-off portions were withdrawn without injuring them or the adjacent parts. The broken joints were soldered and the slide was fitted into its place after a thorough cleaning.—W. C. Loy, Rochester, Ind.

Concrete Foundation Fitted to Machine Base

If the soil in which the foundation for a machine is to be placed is firm

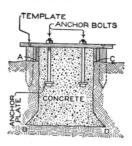

e n o u g h to be self - sustaining, no f o r m s a r e necessary to hold the moist aggregate. An excavation m a y be dug, as shown in the sketch, and to p r o v i d e a l a r g e r bearing area at the base, the sides of the hole may be undercut, as indicated at B and D. If the foundation is to extend above the surface a frame of proper height may be built around it, as shown at A and C. The anchor bolts, which are to hold the machine in place, must be fitted carefully. A template, built up of strips and held in place temporarily by stakes, provides a good means of setting the bolts properly. Bore holes through the strips the proper distances apart and insert the bolts, with anchor plates at their heads, as shown. Fix the templates into place accurately and pour the concrete around them. When the foundation is dry, which requires several days, the templates and forms may be removed.

⁋Use sandpaper sparingly in brightening an armature or commutator, and never use emery cloth, as emery is an electrical conductor.

Average Table for School Grades

By W. A. GOODMAN

Recording and averaging school grades, particularly when extensive daily records are kept, consumes much of a teacher's time, and that usually at a period of the school year when other work is most pressing. The average table shown in the illustration was devised to economize time in keeping and averaging grades. It may be used by teachers as a private record system of grades, or pupils may be made familiar with the system so that they can quickly determine their averages and final grades. The table applies to monthly as well as term averages.

The daily records are to be entered in the daily grade book according to the following code, the grades being represented by numbers corresponding to the percentage grades indicated: 0 for 100, 1 for 90, 2 for 80, 3 for 70, 4 for 60, 5 for 50, 6 for 40, 7 for 30, 8 for 20, 9 for 10, and 10 for 0 per cent.

To find the average, first find the sum of all the grades entered for a particular pupil for the month or term; then find the number of grades entered. Turn to the table and locate, in the exterior column at the left edge, the number that corresponds to the sum of the grades, and, in the horizontal row of exterior figures at the upper edge, locate the figure that corresponds to the number of grades. Trace the finger tip, or other suitable indicator, horizontally along the column from the number located at the left edge, to its intersection with the vertical column under the figure located at the upper edge. The intersecting space contains the average sought.

Suppose, for example, that a pupil is given the following grades: 60, 90, 80, 100, 100, 50, 90, 80, 60, 100, 100, 100, 90. In the record book these would appear as 4, 1, 2, 0, 0, 5, 1, 2, 4, 0, 0, 0, 1. Following the method outlined, it is found that the sum of these grades is 20, and that the number of grades is 13. Turning to the table, locate 20 in the exterior column at the left, and then locate 13 in the horizontal exterior column at the upper edge of the table. Trace the horizontal column opposite 20, at the left, to the space in which it intersects with the vertical column under the figure 13, above, and it will be found that the number in this space is

	1	2	3	4	5	6	7	8	9	10	11	12	13	14	15	16	17	18	19	20
0	100	100	100	100	100	100	100	100	100	100	100	100	100	100	100	100	100	100	100	100
1	90	95	97	98	98	98	99	99	99	99	99	99	99	99	99	99	99	99	99	100
2	80	90	93	95	96	97	97	98	98	98	98	98	98	99	99	99	99	99	99	99
3	70	85	90	93	94	95	96	96	97	97	97	98	98	98	98	98	98	98	98	99
4	60	80	87	90	92	93	94	95	96	96	96	97	97	97	97	98	98	98	98	98
5	50	75	83	88	90	92	93	94	94	95	95	96	96	96	97	97	97	97	97	98
6	40	70	80	85	88	90	91	93	93	94	95	95	95	96	96	96	96	97	97	97
7	30	65	77	83	86	88	90	91	92	93	94	94	95	95	95	96	96	96	96	97
8	20	60	73	80	84	87	89	90	91	92	93	93	94	94	95	95	95	96	96	96
9	10	55	70	78	82	85	87	89	90	91	92	93	93	94	94	94	95	95	95	96
10	0	50	67	75	80	83	86	88	89	90	91	92	92	93	93	94	94	94	95	95
11		45	63	73	78	82	84	86	88	89	90	91	92	92	93	93	94	94	94	95
12		40	60	70	76	80	83	85	87	88	89	90	91	91	92	93	93	93	94	94
13		35	57	68	74	78	81	84	86	87	88	89	90	91	91	92	92	93	93	94
14		30	53	65	72	77	80	83	84	86	87	88	89	90	91	91	92	92	93	93
15		25	50	63	70	75	79	81	83	85	86	88	88	89	90	91	91	92	92	93
16		20	47	60	68	73	77	80	82	84	85	87	88	89	89	90	91	91	92	92
17		15	43	58	66	72	76	79	81	83	85	86	87	88	89	89	90	91	91	92
18		10	40	55	64	70	74	78	80	82	84	85	86	87	88	89	89	90	91	91
19		5	37	53	62	68	73	76	79	81	83	84	85	86	87	88	89	89	90	91
20		0	33	50	60	67	71	75	78	80	82	83	85	86	87	88	88	89	89	90
21			30	48	58	65	70	74	77	79	81	83	84	85	86	87	88	88	89	90
22			27	45	56	63	69	73	76	78	80	82	83	84	85	86	87	88	88	89
23			23	43	54	62	67	71	74	77	79	81	82	84	85	86	86	87	88	89
24			20	40	52	60	66	70	73	76	78	80	82	83	84	85	86	87	87	88
25			17	38	50	58	64	69	72	75	77	79	81	82	83	84	85	86	87	88
26			13	35	48	57	63	68	71	74	76	78	80	81	83	84	85	86	86	87
27			10	33	46	55	61	66	70	73	75	78	79	81	82	83	84	85	86	87
28			7	30	44	53	60	65	69	72	75	77	78	80	81	83	84	84	85	86
29			3	28	42	52	59	64	68	71	74	76	78	79	81	82	83	84	85	86
30			0	25	40	50	57	63	67	70	73	75	77	79	80	81	82	83	84	85
31				23	38	48	56	61	66	69	72	74	76	78	79	81	82	83	84	85
32				20	36	47	54	60	64	68	71	73	75	77	79	80	81	82	83	84
33				18	34	45	53	59	63	67	70	73	75	76	78	79	81	82	83	84
34				15	32	43	51	58	62	66	69	72	74	76	77	79	80	81	82	83
35				13	30	42	50	56	61	65	68	71	73	75	77	78	79	81	82	83
36				10	28	40	49	55	60	64	67	70	72	74	76	78	79	80	81	82
37				8	26	38	47	54	59	63	66	69	72	74	75	77	78	79	81	82
38				5	24	37	46	53	58	62	65	68	71	73	75	76	78	79	80	81
39				3	22	35	44	51	57	61	65	68	70	72	74	76	77	78	79	81
40				0	20	33	43	50	56	60	64	67	69	71	73	75	76	78	79	80
41					18	32	41	49	54	59	63	66	68	71	73	74	76	77	78	80
42					16	30	40	48	53	58	62	65	68	70	72	74	75	77	78	79
43					14	28	39	46	52	57	61	64	67	69	71	73	75	76	77	79
44					12	27	37	45	51	56	60	63	66	69	71	73	74	76	77	78
45					10	25	36	44	50	55	59	63	65	68	70	72	74	75	76	78
46					8	23	34	43	49	54	58	62	65	67	69	71	73	74	76	77
47					6	22	33	41	48	53	57	61	64	66	69	71	72	74	75	77
48					4	20	31	40	47	52	56	60	63	66	68	70	72	73	75	76
49					2	18	30	39	46	51	55	59	62	65	67	69	71	73	74	76
50					0	17	29	38	44	50	55	58	62	64	67	69	71	72	74	75

School-Grade Averages may be Determined Quickly by the Use of the Table, Economizing Time at Especially Busy Periods in the School Year

85. This is the pupil's average. In the table, fractions of less than one-half are dropped, and fractions of more than one-half are counted as one, in the percentage columns.

❧In turning down nails the best method is to strike a slight blow on the point of the nail so as to curve it and then drive the curved point into the wood, thus preventing injury by contact.

Compass Adapted for Making Lettering Guide Lines

Making lettering lines of uniform width for numerous small notes on

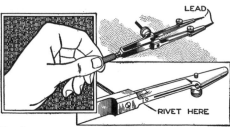

The Compass was Adapted for Making Lettering Guide Lines Quickly and Accurately by Replacing the Needle with a Pencil Leg

drawings consumes not a little time, and must be done carefully to give good results. In order to save time and insure uniformity I devised the double-lead compass shown in the sketch. It may be adjusted for any width of lettering lines up to an inch, and is used along a straightedge like a pencil or ruling pen. The needle leg of the compass was cut off and replaced by a pencil leg, as shown. The joint was shouldered and riveted, or may be welded. By marking an indication on the thumb wheel various standard heights for lettering may be obtained quickly and accurately.—M. A. Wise, Parsons, Kan.

Bar-Lead Molds

Lead, or solder, may be cast into bars of convenient size by pouring the molten metal into an old, straight-bar stove grate, as shown in the sketch. The grate is imbedded in a layer of

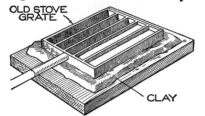

Identification Marks are Made in the Fire Clay as a Part of the Mold

fire clay into which identification marks are scratched so that they may be cast with the bars.

A Mosaic Finish with Paint and Varnish

A simple method of making an effective mosaic finish for furniture is as follows: Determine upon a design to be placed upon the surface, either to cover it completely or to decorate it at certain points. Apply a good quality of paint to form the design in various colors, as desired. The paint must be applied in several coats and allowed to dry between applications. Sandpapering between coats will aid in producing a smooth finish. After the paint has dried hard, sand the entire surface carefully with fine sandpaper and apply a coat of shellac followed by two coats of varnish, sanding carefully between coats. A rubbed finish may be produced by using powdered pumice stone and water, and polishing with oil.

Soot Scraper Aids Water Heating in Kitchen Stove

Soot and ashes which accumulate on the pipes of a water-heating front in a kitchen stove form almost as good a heat insulator as an asbestos covering. When the accumulations are removed better results may be obtained in heating water for the hot-water tank. A convenient tool for removing this soot may be made by filing a half-round portion out of the end of a strip of sheet metal and bending the end to a right angle. The curve at the end should be cut to fit the pipes, and the tool is used in scraping the pipes carefully until all accumulations are removed.

Blueprints That will Not Fade

To keep blueprints from fading when exposed to strong light, wash them in clear water until all the emulsion is removed; then place the wet print, right side up, on a smooth surface. With a paintbrush cover it with peroxide of hydrogen. This intensifies the blue background and brings out the white lines distinctly, making a print that will not fade under hard usage.

Spindle · Turning Device Effects Large Saving

A Lathe Fixture with Which a Sash-and-Door Mill Met an Emergency

By EARL E. HOPKINS

MEANS for utilizing waste from woodworking plants are becoming of much importance, particularly in view of the general shortage of lumber. As an example of how great economy may be made on an apparently insignificant item, by using waste wood in connection with a simple, specially constructed device, an actual experience is in point. The device described was designed and used to meet the special need, but has a wide application in the making of a variety of turned spindles. The illustration shows a specimen spindle, the device in operation, and detailed sketches of its construction. A saving of $21,000 was made by its use, in the filling of a rush contract for 1,000,000 screen doors.

Before closing the contract it was necessary to go into the lumber market to secure prices and deliveries upon the particular kinds of materials specified for the doors. It was necessary also to rearrange the mill so that the lumber would pass directly from the car, through the mill, and the finished doors would go directly into an outbound car. This was necessary, because the mill was not a large one, and the expense of piling the lumber and storing the doors had to be avoided in order to keep within the contract price.

This problem absorbed so much time and energy that it was decided to close the contract and figure out some of the smaller details a little later. This article deals chiefly with one of these details, the making of small ornamental spindles for about 100,000 of the doors. They were to be of a variety of shapes and sizes, and could be bought cheaply in the market, at 1½ to 2½ cents each in large quantities. An average of sixteen spindles to the door, for 100,000 doors, required 1,600,000 of them, which, at 1½ cents each, the price of the smallest, would be $24,000. Thus a small detail became important; and one of the mechanics in the mill was employed to devise a means to get out

the spindles at less than 1½ cents each. He designed an attachment to a shop wood-turning lathe, which is shown in the illustration. The original was made of hard wood, and the knives, shaped to produce the spindles correctly, were mounted upon it. Old machine knives were used for the purpose; a roughing and a finishing knife for one size and shape were made.

A test showed that an operator could make from six to eight spindles a minute, of the 4 by ¾-in. size. It was evident that money and time could be saved on the job, for, at this rate, 2,000 to 3,000 spindles a day, depending upon the size and shape, could easily be turned out.

The material for the spindles was taken from the waste that would have gone to the kindling pile. It was ripped to the proper square size, and cut off to the various lengths to make the assortment required. Thus the material cost practically nothing, beyond the labor to sort it out and cut it up, which was done rapidly, and by the cheaper labor in the shop. The total cost was less than two mills each, and it was figured that power and maintenance would bring the entire cost of the spindles up to 1.9 mills ($0.0019) each—or about $3,000, as an outside figure. The difference between the cost of buying the spindles at about $24,000, and $3,000, actual cost, was a saving of $21,000. This figure is conservative, because the 1½-cent price was for the smallest and cheapest size.

This device, with all the knives, cost about $75 and it required no floor space. The saws for getting out the material were in the regular equipment of the mill, hence no other expense was incurred on account of the spindle job.

Not all sash-and-door mills are working upon screen-door contracts, but it is certain that thought and ingenuity could save considerable money by turning the small, sound scrap into handles, spindles, or grill ornaments, for which there is a demand. In few instances, perhaps, would a saving of $21,000 in a year result, but a saving sufficient to give a handsome return upon a $75 investment could be made easily.

The illustration shows the device fitted in the lathe and in operation. The general arrangement of the various parts is shown clearly in the large sketch, there being no stock between the centers. The base, upon which the sliding carriage rests, is clamped to the lathe bed on blocks, and its right section is milled to form a tongue-and-groove slide with the carriage. The knives, which may be of a large variety, are clamped to their bases at the back of the carriage, which is provided with a handle at its front end, by which the operator moves the carriage and knives forward against the squared blank, between the centers. Two sets of knives are provided for each job, one for roughing out and the other for finishing. When long, slender baluster spindles are to be made, a steady rest is provided, to support the stock against the knives. The steady rest is shown raised in Figs. 1 and 2, and lowered into position, no stock being in place, however, in the larger sketch. In Fig. 6, it is shown in contact with the piece being turned. The carriage is shown, in Fig. 1, brought forward to the point at which the cut-off knives have severed the stock, and the device is in readiness for the next piece, which is inserted in the centering forks, I, Figs. 4 and 5, at the extreme forward end of the carriage. The squared blank is shown in place in the centering forks, Fig. 2, the centers of the lathe having been forced into the ends of the piece, to hold it during the turning operation. The knives shown in the detailed sketch, Fig. 6, are designed to shape a spindle of the type shown in Fig. 3.

The mechanism and operation of the device may be understood by reference to the detailed sketches, Figs. 4, 5, and 6, and in general to the other illustrations. The square blank is placed in the centering forks I, and the carriage

B is pushed back to the stop J, properly adjusted at the screw K. To fix the blank in position it is then only necessary to bring up the tail, or cup, center E until the blank is held by the points of the live center D, and the cup center E. Then the slide is withdrawn, to permit free revolution of the blank, and the cup center is forced into the blank, driving it firmly against the spurs of the live center, as is necessary for the turning operation.

If the work is long and requires a steady rest, Fig. 6, a knife, L, is provided for cutting a groove around the middle of the blank, forming a circular neck on which the jaw of the steady rest bears, as indicated in the sectional view of the blank, at V, Fig. 6. The steady rest is brought forward, after the carriage has progressed sufficiently to permit the knife L to cut the neck, and is held in position with the hand, as shown in the large sketch, only while the heavy roughing-out cut is made, with the second knife M. The third knife N performs the finishing cut, and if an extra-smooth finish is desired, the spindles may be sandpapered lightly after the third cutting operation. The cut-off knives O are then brought against the work and the spindle is completed, by cutting it to the proper length. When baluster spindles are made, on which only the central portion is turned, the cut-off knives are not used. The lathe is not stopped for spindles that are cut off, but for long work it is safer to stop the machine while taking out and putting in blanks.

In using the steady rest, it is important that the rest does not exert too great a pressure on the work, only enough to steady it being desirable. This is provided for by setting the stop-lug collar R so that the lever T is permitted to come down the proper distance only, preventing "springing" of the work. The stop lugs are arranged so that the lever T may be thrown up and back of the supporting shaft Q; thus it will be held out of the way by its own weight. For a more detailed study of the steady rest the

FIG.1

FIG.3

FIG.2

FIG.4

FIG.5

FIG.6

END VIEW

PLAN

The Spindle-Turning Fixture was Fitted to an Ordinary Wood-Turning Lathe, and Its Use Effected a Large Saving in the Making of Spindles for Screen Doors. By Inserting Special Knives, the Device may be Used for a Variety of Spindle Turning, Including Work Requiring a Steady Rest. The Large Sketch Shows the Device in Position for Light Spindles, the Steady Rest being Lowered

following additional indications on the sketch, Fig. 6, will be of assistance: P, standards; S, plain collar; U, steady jaws; V, blank; W, binding bolts.

The large sketch, as well as Figs. 1 and 2, shows the bed and steady-rest frame supported on wooden blocks. The detail drawings of the working parts, shown in Figs. 4, 5, and 6, show an adjustable device fitted to the bed frame A, with screws, G, operating in a base plate, F. This makes the use of blocks unnecessary. The binding bolt H is used to fix the bed frame firmly to the lathe bed C.

A Toolmaker's Vise

A simple and efficient toolmaker's vise, designed for holding small pieces of irregular shape, is shown in the il-

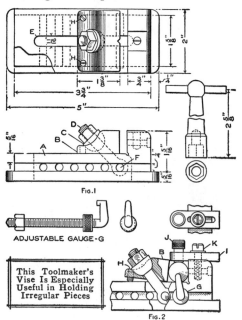

ADJUSTABLE GAUGE-G

This Toolmaker's Vise Is Especially Useful in Holding Irregular Pieces

lustration. The body A, Fig. 1, is made of mild steel finished to the dimensions given, pack-hardened, the edges being ground square and polished on a lap wheel. The movable jaw B is made of mild steel and also pack-hardened, ground, and lapped square on the bottom and face. A hole is drilled through the center of the jaw, at an angle of 45°, and the upper surface of the jaw is cupped out to fit the nut C. The hole through the jaw is relieved on the under side to give ample clearance for the eyebolt D. The latter is fitted in the slot, milled, at E, in the body A, and may be held in various positions in this slot by a tempered steel pin through the holes F, as shown in Fig. 1.

Figure 2 represents the vise holding a piece of round stock while a drilling operation is performed. The movable jaw B is set in an angular position by means of adjusting screws, H. By tightening the movable jaw on the work, the latter is forced down and held securely against the bottom and the fixed jaw of the vise.

The adjustable slide I, which holds the slip bushing J, is made of tool steel, hardened, ground, and lapped to fit into the seat milled into the top of the fixed jaw. It is held in place by the fillister-head screw K.

When a number of pieces are to be machined an equal distance from an end or shoulder, the gauge G is used to locate the work accurately in the vise. It is shown in detail at the left. The slots milled into the side of the body A, are used in clamping the vise to the faceplate of a bench lathe, the table of a milling machine, or any other flat surface where the projections on each end of the vise cannot be used. The holes F are drilled along these milled slots, which are shown in Fig. 1, one of them being exposed at the left corner of the upper view. A socket wrench for adjusting the vise is also shown.—E. P. Fickes, Dayton, Ohio.

Cutting Wide Slots with a Hacksaw

Mechanics frequently find it necessary to cut slots in metal with a hacksaw. When wide slots are required, so that a single cut from a blade will not make them, two or more blades may be placed together and a wider cut made. If the pins, over which the blades are hooked, are straightened slightly they will hold several blades with a uniform tension.—Louis M. Drake, Daytona, Fla.

Shop Notes

Barnyard Crane and Trolley for Silage Feeding

By F. H. SWEET

THE rapid and economical handling of silage with a minimum of manual labor often presents a serious problem where a considerable number of cattle are to be fed. The crane and trolley carrier shown in the illustration was installed to overcome these difficulties, and has been found satisfactory. The boom is guyed to the silo, which is reinforced to care for the additional strain, and has a radius of 20 ft. It is not advisable to attach this device to a silo of light construction, or to an old one which may not be stable in a strong wind. It is best suited to a structure of concrete, or concrete blocks, or to a strongly built wooden silo, properly braced to counteract the strain. In any case, the support for the boom must be anchored to a band of metal, or planking frame, and the guy wires must be fixed to a hook or ring, anchored to a rod through the silo, or to a band around it.

The boom is of wood, tapered from 6 in. at the hinged end to 4 in. at the tip. The hinged end is provided with metal fittings to permit free action in moving horizontally, and bolted so that the boom may be removed readily, when desired. A trolley way of band iron is supported from the lower side of the boom by metal braces. A carrier, having a drop bottom and an adjustable chain hoist, rides on the

Silage is Handled Rapidly and Economically with a Minimum of Manual Labor by the Use of the Crane and Trolley Arrangement

trolley way, and conveys the silage from the chute to the cattle troughs. The latter are arranged in a double semicircle, so as to be readily supplied from the crane and carrier. The cattle feed from only one side of each trough, and are disposed radially in relation to the boom. The silage is thrown down the chutes to a concrete floor, from which it may be pitched into the carrier readily. The device may be rigged to be operated by one man, if the carrier is provided with an automatic trip operated by a rope from the chute. The cattle should not be admitted to the feeding lot until the troughs are filled, if convenient. It would be desirable, also, to provide a good footing for the cattle around the troughs, and if the continued use of the troughs warranted it, concrete areas might be provided.

Fruit Picker's Bag Minimizes Damage to Product

Fruit is often damaged by carelessness in picking, or by the use of re-

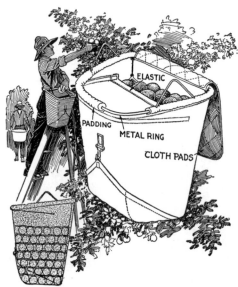

The Fruit is Packed into the Bag with Slight Chance of Damage, and is Conveniently Removed at the Bottom

ceptacles not suited for this purpose. Where the product must be shipped a considerable distance to market, much loss is caused by what appears as only slight damage when the fruit is picked. The bag shown in the sketch provides a convenient container for the fruit as it is picked, and overcomes the possibility of serious damage.

The bag is made of canvas, and has a metal ring at the top to support it. V-shaped loops are attached to the ring and from these the bag is suspended, on the shoulder of the fruit picker, by straps. The fruit is dropped into the bag and upon a guard of canvas having an elastic band at its inner edge. This breaks the fall of the fruit when dropped into the bag. At the back of the wire frame is a series of cloth pads which slide on the wire corner supports at the back. As each layer is placed in the bag, one of these cloths is placed over it as a protection. The bag is emptied at the bottom by opening the flap, which is fastened by a snap buckle.—H. F. Rundell, Chicago, Ill.

Improving Commutator Contact at Brushes

Commutators on motors, or small generators, particularly automobile generators, wear down, leaving the mica insulation strips exposed. The brushes will not make good contact, decreasing the efficiency of the motor, or in the case of the generator, will not permit it to operate properly. A tool convenient in remedying this trouble is shown in the sketch. It was made from an old hacksaw blade, about 8 in. long. One of the ends was ground to a

This Tool was Made from an Old Hacksaw Blade and Is Useful in Reducing Mica on Commutators

point, as shown, and the other was shaped to form a hook. Both ends have chisel edges. The middle of the blade was wrapped with a piece of thin sheet metal and electric tape. The mica is removed by the use of the sharp end of the blade, which produces a V-shaped groove in the mica. The hook end is used to finish the scraping. A small magnifying glass is useful in examining the commutator to make sure that the mica has been cut down properly.—J. C. Grindell, St. Louis, Mo.

Kinks in the Use of Tire Patches

"Hook-on" tire patches hold rim-cut blow-outs well. They fit outside the shoe, and hook with metal fingers under the rim on both sides, except on straight-side tires. An ordinary inside blow-out patch will hold tread blow-outs, but is not satisfactory for rim cuts. Self-vulcanizing inner-tube patches are effective only when carefully applied. Follow the maker's directions closely. Gasoline should be "dribbled" on the patch from 30 seconds to two minutes before application; if any portion of the patch then fails to stick, lift the edge at that point and brush lightly with a gasoline-dampened rag; then knead into place. The necessity of kneading and pounding the patch into perfect contact must not be overlooked. Properly applied, these patches often outlast the tube.

Hastening the Settling of a Ground Fill

When ditches, or similar excavations, are filled the surface of the ground is often made irregular, because the earth does not settle properly; or if filled level, a trench may result when the earth settles. In lawns, or other places where it is desired to cover the surface quickly with sod, this is particularly objectionable. If the fill is built up to form a slight ridge, and the crest of it hollowed into a shallow trench, the rain water will remain in it, causing the fill to settle quickly and evenly. Lawn, a pavement or walk built over it will thus be more secure, and not liable to the danger of settling.—John V. Loeffler, Evansville, Ind.

Block-and-Tackle Hoist for Cellar

Removal of ashes, or other heavy material, from a cellar is often difficult; the device shown in the sketch

Ashes or Other Material may be Removed from a Cellar Conveniently with the Device Shown

was installed to facilitate such work. A davit, or curved standard, to support the block and tackle used, was fitted into the stairs, with the upper portion projecting out of the cellar door. The support is made of a 2-in. pipe, fitted at its upper end with a clevis to which the pulley is attached. At its lower end it is set into a larger pipe, which is bolted to the stairs. This arrangement enables the operator to load the bucket in the cellar, raise it by means of the block and tackle, and revolve the load on the standard for convenient dumping into a wheelbarrow.

The standard may be arranged so that its upper portion slides down into the supporting pipe, when not in use. It may thus be inclosed in the cellar, making it unnecessary to remove the tackle.—Stephen Bona, Union City, Connecticut.

Drafting Table for Full-Size Detailing and Large Drawings

A drafting table, simple in construction and which affords the draftsman

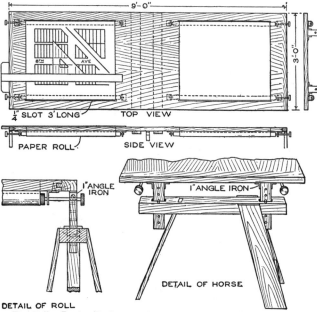

DETAIL OF ROLL

The Roller Device Enables the Draftsman to Make Large Drawings, on a Board of Small Size, without Injuring Them in Process

a practical means of making large drawings, without soiling or injuring them in process, is shown in the illustration. It is designed for use by two draftsmen working on opposite sides of the board, and may be used by one man, who may have occasion to make two related drawings that can be handled more conveniently in this way. The paper is fed from a roll under the table top, and is rolled up on the opposite roller as the drawing progresses. The top is braced with angle iron and rests upon three adjustable supports. The dimensions given are suggestive only. The slots through which the paper passes may be made of any convenient length, and 3 ft. will be found satisfactory as a maximum. Their edges are rounded to protect the paper.

The rollers are supported on iron rods, on the ends of which are thumb wheels to make adjustment convenient. A satisfactory tension on the paper may be obtained by the use of plain

rollers fitted carefully, and kept snugly rolled up. Rollers having pawl devices, like those on ordinary curtain rollers, may be used if proper allowance is made for winding off the paper when it is desired to remove the drawings. The horses which support the top are made with three legs, spread considerably so as to give stability on an uneven floor. The height of the table may be adjusted to suit the individual users by setting the pins in the vertical end pieces provided with holes. Sufficient play is permitted in these parts so that one person using the double table may tilt the top. The same general construction may be applied to a single table and in that case the tilting feature may be made more pronounced. When it is desired to make full-size details, or other very large drawings, in which a greater area of paper must be exposed at one time, the roller device may be fitted to the ends of the drafting table. It would be better in such cases to add a strip at the ends to provide for the slot, through which the paper is drawn, rather than cut a slot through the top of the table.—J. E. Cahill, New York, N. Y.

Sound Deadener for Fan Ducts

Small fans running at high speeds often vibrate considerably, and the vibrations are conducted to the ducts, causing a disagreeable roaring throughout the ventilating system. If the connection of the fan to the duct is made with a cloth sleeve, so that there is no direct contact of the metal parts, the noise will be eliminated. Canvas is suitable and may be made air-tight by painting it.

Gilding Old Frames

The fault with much of the gilding of old picture or mirror frames done at home is that the surface tarnishes rapidly. Two coats of gilt should be applied, each coat being permitted to dry thoroughly. Placing the frame in a warm place aids in the drying. Apply two coats of a good quality of varnish to the gilded surface, each coat being dried carefully, using a light stroke without laps.—Ralph W. Tillotson, Erie, Pa.

Winding Small Compression Springs

Having to make a number of open-coil compression springs of small music wire, a plain speed lathe being the only machine available, the problem was to wind the wire on an arbor uniformly, and with the desired space between the coils. After several tests, the device shown in the sketch was made in a few minutes, from scrap material. It proved satisfactory, the work being uniform and of even tension. The springs were wound several inches in length, and cut off as desired.

A round rod was used for the arbor, and was clamped in the lathe chuck. A steel tool, having a notched end and fitted with three steel pins, was made to fit the wire and the arbor. One end of the wire was fastened to the chuck and the other fed through the hole in the guide and over the pins, as the arbor was revolved in the lathe. The

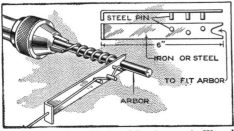

Springs of Uniform Pitch and Tension may be Wound Quickly in a Lathe with This Device

small pins give the wire the necessary tension, and must be located according to the thickness of the wire.—Charles F. Merrill, Hopedale, Mass.

Safety Throttle for Air Motors

Several accidents occurred in a shop from the unintentional starting of air motors, by jarring them or brushing

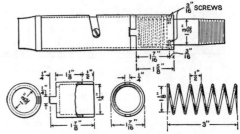

This Safety Throttle Prevents the Accidental Starting of Air Motors, by Securing the Throttle

them aside with the foot. The safety throttle shown in the sketch was devised to prevent such accidents. The throttle is opened ordinarily by turning the sleeve. The bushing, 1⅝ in. long, has a projection in which a number of small teeth are filed, to engage similar ones in the end of the sleeve. A spring, made of No. 16 wire, forces the bushing into contact with the sleeve at the teeth. In this engaged position the motor is shut off. To start it the operator must move the bushing to disengage the teeth, after which the throttle sleeve may be moved freely. In shutting it off the teeth are again engaged. The bushing is fastened by two ³⁄₁₆-in. screws, fitted in slots, so that it may be moved without releasing it completely. A ring is fitted between the spring and the screws, as indicated at the right end of the spring in the upper sketch.

Testing through Insulation on Wires

It is sometimes necessary to test for open or short circuits, and, especially in armature or field testing, it is essential that the insulation remain perfect. A satisfactory method of testing without breaking the insulation is as follows: Solder a needle to each end of the testing wires and force the needles through the insulation until a contact is made. The test may then be carried on in the usual manner.

Metal Points for Fence Posts

Posts, fitted with metal points like that shown in the sketch, may be driven into the ground more readily, and will last longer than those not so guarded. The guard may be made of ordinary tinned sheet metal, or galvanized iron, cut to the shape of a maltese cross, as shown at the right in the sketch. Small holes are punched at its extreme edges, and the piece is folded to fit the end of the post and nailed into place. Similar pieces may be fitted to the tops of posts as a weather protection.—George H. Holden, Chesterfield, England.

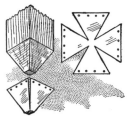

Silencing a Noisy Gas Burner

The type of gas burner that consists merely of a small pipe entering a larger one where the air is mixed, often gives out a roaring noise when turned on strongly. To stop this noise; drill a small hole through both sides of the larger pipe near the flame end and insert a nail. This simple expedient effectually quiets the burner.

Hinge for Light Box

Hinges to be fixed into place with screws are often unsatisfactory for applying to light boxes. The hinge shown in the sketch was designed for use in such cases, and is inexpensive and can be quickly applied. No screws are required and the leaves of the hinge B are perforated with triangular holes. The portions cut out,

as at A, are bent back and driven into the wood. They are set so that when driven in they tend to clamp against the strip of wood between them, making a secure fastening.—Charles Homewood, New Brunswick, N. J.

Milling Small Slots with Combination Center Drill

Elongated small slots must frequently be machined into constructions in the machine shop. A usual method of making them is to drill two holes, one at each end of the proposed slot, and then mill the intervening stock out by the use of a small milling cutter. A method which has been found more rapid and convenient is to use a combination center drill and countersink as a milling cutter. Drill holes, as shown in the sketch, at each end of the slot. Then set the countersink to a slight depth and mill a groove the length of the slot. Repeat this in gradual cuts until the slot is of the required depth. The work is held in the milling-machine vise, and the drill in the vertical milling attachment.—George P. Breitschmid, Arlington, R. I.

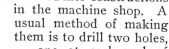

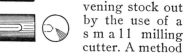

End Guards for Plug Gauge

Plug gauges, like that shown in the illustration, are usually made to very close dimensions and nicking or otherwise injuring the ends makes the gauge useless. In order to protect such a gauge while being used on the workbench or stored with other tools, end guards were made, and fitted into the ends as shown. The guards permit the gauge to rest on their edges so that the surface of the gauge does not come into contact with the bench or other resting place. They may be removed quickly when necessary.

Soldering Drilled Lug on Sheet Brass

In electrical work, and other mechanical fields, it is sometimes necessary to thread a thin piece of brass, or copper, and in order to have sufficient stock so that the thread will not strip, a nut must be soldered on as a reinforcement. After soldering on the nut the hole must be drilled in the sheet metal before the threads can be tapped. Time may be saved by providing a piece of sheet aluminum with an aluminum plug projecting from it. The latter may be made by cutting cross slots in the metal and bending up the resulting points. The aluminum plug, or stop, is fitted to the hole bored in the sheet metal. A flux is applied to the brass around the stop, and the nut is placed over it. The portion around the hole is then heated, and solder is applied. The nut will be soldered firmly and accurately over the hole, and the aluminum piece will not bind, as it cannot be soldered fast under the conditions.—W. T. Derr, Rochester, Ind.

Safety Block for a Bench Vise

In filing small pieces of material in a bench vise, or in attempting to hold pieces of peculiar shape, time otherwise lost in adjusting the piece may be saved by the use of a safety block,

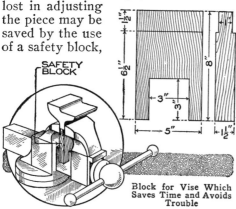

Block for Vise Which Saves Time and Avoids Trouble

shown in the sketch. It should be made of hard wood and the end grain should be at the shorter edge, so that the heavy wear will be taken at that point. Straight-grained stock is best for this purpose.

Eccentric Catch for Sliding Barn Doors

A blacksmith fashioned the door catch shown in the sketch to secure a heavy sliding door on the outside of

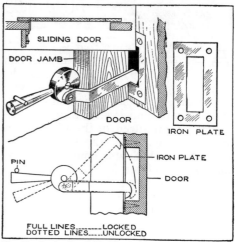

SLIDING DOOR

DOOR JAMB

DOOR

IRON PLATE

PIN

IRON PLATE

DOOR

FULL LINES_____LOCKED
DOTTED LINES____UNLOCKED

The Eccentric Catch Holds the Sliding Door Firmly and Prevents Outward as Well as Sidewise Movement

his shop, without the use of a device requiring a key. An iron plate, with an oblong opening in the middle, was fitted to the door so that the plate would be at the door jamb when closed, as shown in the inset plan. A hook was pivoted near the edge of an iron disk, which was fitted with a handle. To engage the catch in the plate the hook is lowered and the handle is turned down to give the necessary freedom of action. The handle is then raised to the pin, which acts as a stop, and the eccentric action secures the hook. To release it the handle is lowered and the hook raised from the plate as indicated by the dotted lines.

Weights for Drying Large Pieces of Cloth

When a flag, or large piece of cloth, is hung out to dry on a windy day it often becomes entangled about the line. This may be overcome by fastening small weights, or wooden clasps, along the lower edge of the cloth. If wooden clasps are used, small cloth bags filled with sand should be suspended from them.—A. Fleck, Yonkers, N. Y.

A Farm Sale Pavilion

By James A. Herren

A FARM structure that is desirable not only because of its primary use as a sale pavilion, but also by reason of its adaptability to a wide range of other uses, was built by an Iowa farmer, and is shown in the photograph reproduced in the illustration. It was designed for the sale of pure-bred hogs, but its convenient size makes it available for the sale of various kinds of farm animals. It was used as a farrowing pen when not needed for occasional sales, and gave thorough satisfaction. In regions where hog raising is not important enough to require a sale pavilion or a farrowing pen, the building may be used for housing other young farm animals, or for machinery and other storage purposes. It is 30 by 36 ft., with a clear space of 10 ft. from the concrete floor to the rafters. The seats for the spectators are arranged upon stringers, and built in sections. They are hinged on bolts set in the studding, and when the pavilion is not in use for sales purposes, the seats are raised and held at the roof rafters, as shown in the sectional diagram. The construction is light and standard, hence the expense of building such a structure is not great in proportion to the accommodations. A feature not to be overlooked is the better prices obtained for stock, because the pavilion, heated by salamanders, will attract many more buyers than would come to a sale held in the open, especially in cold weather.

The structure is supported upon a concrete foundation and provided with a concrete floor throughout. The latter is especially desirable, since it makes cleaning after use for purposes other than as a sale pavilion, quite convenient. The foundation is built as a unit with the floor, and has a footing ample to carry the load. The footing section of the foundation is 20 in. wide and 9 in. thick, a section of the same thickness supporting the floor and tapering to a width of 7 in. where the studding rests, 1 ft. above the floor, as indicated in the sectional diagram. The foundations for the main supporting posts have a footing of 20 in. and are 12 in. thick. The foundations are poured in wooden forms, and their lower portions may be poured into the excavation, if the ground is suitable and the excavation is carefully done. A mixture of 1 to 3 to 6—one part cement, three parts sand, and six parts crushed stone or gravel—is suitable for the making of the foundations and floor. The concrete work should be permitted to dry three days before removing the forms, and, if moistened occasionally for several days thereafter, will dry more uniformly. Bolts are set into the foundation at intervals so that the plate, on which the studding rests, may be fastened securely to it.

The roof is built with a raised portion along the ridge, provided with several windows to give light and good ventilation. At either end of the central driveway are sliding doors, making it convenient to take stock in and out. The framing is of light timber, built into simple squared frames. The central supports are of 4 by 6-in. stock, 15 ft. long. The studding in the sides is of 2 by 6-in. stock, 9 ft. long above the concrete foundation. The supports are set 12 ft. apart, as shown in the sectional diagram. The roof rafters are of 2 by 4-in. stock, and the horizontal rafters of 2 by 6-in. stuff.

The seats or "bleachers" are supported on stringers, 2 by 12 in., and 12 ft. long. They are built in sections pivoted on bolts through the studding, so that they may be raised to the roof rafters without interfering with the

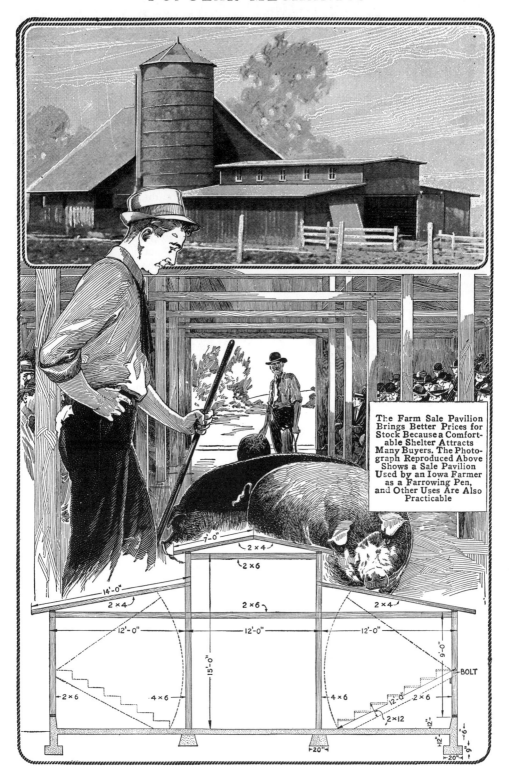

The Farm Sale Pavilion Brings Better Prices for Stock Because a Comfortable Shelter Attracts Many Buyers. The Photograph Reproduced Above Shows a Sale Pavilion Used by an Iowa Farmer as a Farrowing Pen, and Other Uses Are Also Practicable

horizontal rafters. The seat boards are of ⅞-in. stuff, and may be made of strips if thicker material is used.

The roofs are covered with rough boarding and surfaced with a composition roofing material. The sides of the building are finished with matched siding, and the raised section at the top is finished with the same stuff. The windows are of the common four-light type and may be purchased at local lumber yards or mill-supply houses.

Wind Indicator for Greenhouse

Difficulty was experienced by the gardener in a large greenhouse in regulating the ventilators at night, be-

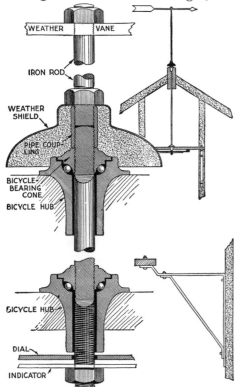

The Wind Indicator was Devised to Enable the Gardener to Note Changes in Wind Promptly and Regulate the Greenhouse Ventilators Accordingly

cause he could not ascertain readily the direction of the wind. The wind indicator shown in the sketch was devised and proved satisfactory, as the direction of the wind is shown on a dial in the greenhouse, so that any

change in the wind may be observed promptly, and the necessary adjustments made. The device was made of an old bicycle hub, as a bearing for the vertical rod and the dial arrangement, strips of iron for the brackets, and a rod for the vane support.

The bicycle hub was cut at the middle, and one section used for the upper bearing and the other for the lower one. A rod was fitted between the bearings, as shown in the sectional view, and extended at its lower end to provide a threaded seat for the indicator in the greenhouse. A pipe coupling was fitted to the upper end of the rod, immediately above the upper bearing, and a similar section of rod screwed into it, to give a support for the weather vane, which is held in place by a nut. The upper bearing is fitted into the ridgepole, through which the vane support projects, and is protected by a weather shield, as shown in the sectional view. The lower bearing is supported in a wooden piece carried on two brackets, shown in the views at the right of the sketch. The dial is supported on the lower side of the wooden piece resting on the brackets.—Nicholas Gerten, Urbana, Ill.

Holding a Small, Irregular Piece in a Vise

Small pieces of material, which are difficult to hold in a vise or other clamp, should be fastened to a small block having its sides parallel, and then clamped into position. If there are no holes through the piece, which may be of wood or metal, the screws may be placed along the edges to act as clamps.

Translucent Window Covering

Repeated coats of raw or boiled linseed oil applied to a finely meshed wire fabric will give a good substitute for window glass. The wire may be used for many purposes, and is especially good where glass might easily be broken. The fabric may be dipped in the oil instead of applying it with a brush.

Obtaining Long Wear Out of Piston Rings

The cylinder in my gas engine became badly worn so that new piston rings would not hold for perfect compression. I observed that my worn-out piston rings were about one-half the thickness of the ring groove, so with a hacksaw I cut a portion out of one ring so that, when it was placed inside of another and squeezed together, the ends would almost meet. I placed a set of these double rings in my engine, and the result was very satisfactory. The rings were used until worn very thin, and gave about three times as much wear as when I used single rings. The openings in the rings should be placed on opposite sides of the cylinder.—W. M. Hohner, Lowgap, Washington.

Sprocket Made of Wooden Disk and Staples

Sprocket wheels for experimental work or other constructions, where strength is not a large factor, may be made by fixing staples around the circumference of a round wooden disk of suitable diameter. Link chain of the ordinary variety as well as the sprocket-wheel type may be operated on such a sprocket if the staples are set properly. In order to determine the points at which they should be placed the chain must be fitted around the circumference of the disk and the staples inserted and driven at the proper points.

Canvas Tool Bag

Electricians, carpenters, automobile-repair men, and other mechanics, will find the tool bag shown in the sketch convenient, although it was designed for use by car inspectors in railway service. The frame is made of $\frac{1}{16}$ by $\frac{3}{4}$-in. brass, or galvanized-iron, strips, covered with 10-oz. canvas, and supported by a 2-in. leather shoulder strap. The frame is reinforced across the ends by similar metal strips, and No. 12 cop-

per rivets are used in fastening the material throughout. The cover is kept in place by a buttoned strap, and

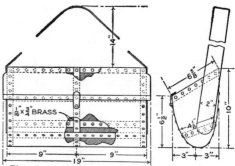

This Canvas Tool Bag Is Strongly Reinforced with Metal Strips and Is Useful for Mechanics Who Carry Small Tools

extends $\frac{1}{2}$ in. beyond the ends of the bag at the portion below the fastenings of the shoulder strap. The shape has been found convenient for the special purpose for which the bag was designed, but this may be readily adapted to the carrying of special tools, or even material.—Joseph K. Long, Renovo, Pennsylvania.

Convenient Show-Card Holder

A holder for show cards, or other purposes where a small stand or easel is required, may be made from a piece of cardboard, cut and folded as shown in the illustration. A section of cardboard of a suitable color is cut to the shape shown at A, and the dotted line indicated upon it. By folding the

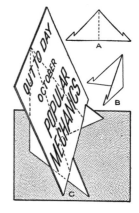

piece on the dotted line, as at B, two supports are provided, and the card or other article may be set in the two small notches at the front of the device, as indicated at C. The holder has the advantages that it may be made quickly and is quite inexpensive.

Babbitting Split Bearings in One Operation

When the bearings of machines become worn so badly that rebabbitting is necessary, the work may be done in one operation, instead of babbitting the

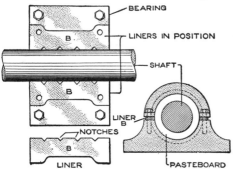

Fit the Liners into Place, Center the Shaft, Put On the End Rings, and Pour the Babbitt into the Bearing

halves separately. No extra labor or equipment is required, and the process is simple. The illustration shows the bearing with the upper section removed, and at the right, an end view of the bearing with the cardboard rings in place for the pouring of the metal. A liner, or packing, of leather, or sheet metal, is also shown. It is placed between the halves of the bearing to provide the necessary space for taking up the wear in the bearing.

First, two liners, B, are cut to fit the bearing and fitted between the halves of it, as shown in the end view. The small notches are necessary so that the metal may flow from one half of the bearing to the other. The shaft around which the babbitt is poured must be centered carefully, and two small pieces of wood or leather are placed in the bottom half of the bearing to hold the shaft in position. Cardboard rings are fitted around the ends of the bearing, as shown in the end view, and, if necessary, clay may be packed around the end of the bearing to prevent leakage. When the metal has been poured and permitted to cool, the halves of the bearing may be separated with a hammer and cold chisel. If the work is carefully done, little dressing will be necessary around the edges.

Trouble Signal for Motor-Starting Rheostat

A pump furnishing water to a small city is situated about one-half mile from the power-plant engine room, and on various occasions, particularly at night, it stopped suddenly. The man on watch was unable to observe promptly that the pump had stopped operation. For this reason the device shown in the sketch was installed, and gave thorough satisfaction, making it unnecessary for the watchman to remain in close proximity to the electrical switch, which controlled the power at the rheostat. Batteries, a relay, and a single-pole knife switch were installed at the watchman's quarters, arranged as shown at the right. The arm of the rheostat is at the position A when under extreme load; at C when the current is shut off, and at intermediate points when the current varies. A wire, with a spring attached, was fixed to the arm at C and conducted over pulleys to the switch B. When the power is started, the arm is brought to A, and the switch B is opened. The switch at quarters is normally closed. When the arm drops to position C the switch B is closed, completing the circuit, and causing the bell to ring. The watchman stops the ringing by draw-

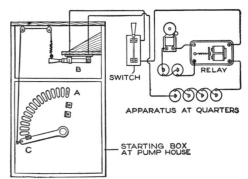

When the Arm of the Rheostat Falls the Bell Circuit is Closed, Warning the Watchman

ing out the switch at quarters and goes to the power room to attend to the rheostat, and to open the switch B for further use.—A. P. Sitton, Fort Stanton, N. M.

The Woman's Home Workshop

By Avis Gordon Vestal

PART I—Designing the Kitchen for Comfort and Convenience

[This is the first of three articles, in which Mrs. Vestal, "domestic engineer," sets forth the mechanics of the kitchen, illustrating fundamental design and details with practical examples. Each installment is complete in itself, but will be more fully appreciated in connection with the others.—Editor.]

PRINCIPLES of mechanical efficiency, applied successfully to the design and equipment of factories, stores, and offices by men, are capable of application to the domestic workshops of their women-folks. Only seven per cent of the families of the United States employ one or more regular domestic helpers. The ninety-odd housekeepers remaining out of every hundred, must do their own work, with only such help as their children or an occasional hired laundress or scrub woman can give. The difficulty of securing servants, even inefficient ones, and the high wages, board, and breakage are urgent factors at present demanding the building of kitchens of the labor-saving type. The many outside demands now made upon the time and energy of wives and mothers also force women to think, as never before, of means to "cut the work out of housework."

Kitchens are changing rapidly from general-utility rooms, as used by our grandmothers for all the industries of the home, to specialized workshops, smaller in size, more compactly arranged, and equipped with modern conveniences. Washing and ironing are usually banished to a basement laundry, and sewing and dining are commonly moved toward the front of the house. The kitchen of many city apartments now provides only for cooking and dishwashing. The suburban, or small-town, house is likely to need some provision for young children.

The farm kitchen frequently must retain dairy work.

We cannot hope, nor do we wish, to standardize kitchens as completely as factories are. They must remain individual in many respects, yet there are certain general principles of design in the room, of choice and grouping of built-in and portable equipment, that all of us can use, modifying details to suit our purses and our personal needs.

A kitchen should be large enough to house necessary furnishings, yet small enough to save miles of needless walking every week. It should be adequately heated in winter but reasonably cool in summer. Ventilation must not be neglected. Floors and walls should be easy to clean. Colors should be cheerful and harmonious. Good artificial lighting for nights and cloudy days must not be forgotten. The climate and the direction of prevailing summer breezes are other determining factors in the design of a woman's workshop.

Inside of the room we should observe this fundamental principle: Things used for a common purpose should be grouped as nearly as possible together. A second rule, formulated by an authority after extensive tests, is that the height of all working surfaces, at which a woman stands, should be in a definite relation to her own height. A woman of average height, 5 ft. 4 in., requires a table, ironing board, or sink bottom 30 in. above the floor. For every inch she is shorter or taller than that, she should subtract or add half an inch.

Doors in a kitchen should be as few as possible, for they consume much usable wall space when closed, and twice that amount when open. They are usually best placed near corners, for doors or windows in the middle of walls tend to separate equipment which should be kept close together. If possible, make the path through the room along one side, not diagonally through it, that other members of the family, passing through, may not interfere with the cook.

Windows are well placed higher in the walls than in other rooms, and for two reasons. The space beneath a high window may be used for placing furniture, as a sink or table. Further, hot air rises to the top of the room, and, if at least one window rises to the top of the room, it can be lowered from the top for ventilation. Alternate arrangements for cooling the room and freeing it of cooking odors are the use of transoms, of hinged casement windows, or the installation of a hood above the range opening into the chimney.

Floors should be smooth, hard, non-absorbent of water and grease, and elastic to the step. If tile, or composition flooring, is used, provide rubber mats to stand upon, in front of the stove and the cabinet. A rounded, or cove, base, and rounded corners are easier to clean thoroughly, with either broom or wet mop.

Several specific kitchens embodying many of the principles of mechanical efficiency will be of interest. They are shown in plan and in detail in the full-page illustration. The kitchen in the home of a member of a college faculty, shown in the upper views, is of medium size, 10 by 13 ft., compactly arranged for cooking and its related industries. Washing and ironing are banished to the laundry. Two north windows light the work counter, beneath and above which are cupboards, drawers, and bins for all the supplies, utensils, and tools,

everything needed for cooking, save foods in the refrigerator, being within arm's reach. Enameled steel gives a smooth, sanitary surface to the table part. Running the width of the room, it provides generous space for food preparation, in efficient contrast to the single small table used in many kitchens. The windows are set high enough to permit use of the wall between them and the counter. The window ledge holds scales and alarm clock. A narrow shelf beneath is devoted to spices in neat, covered containers. Below this are hooks for cooking utensils and small implements, in frequent use. The two cupboards flanking the windows reach from a foot above the counter quite to the ceiling, leaving no top to collect dust. Racks inside the doors hold lids and flat pans. Beneath the counter are tilting flour bins and an unusual double-door compartment, into which the fireless cooker is rolled.

The gas range is at the west wall, just a step from the cook's counter. The special point of merit in its selection is the cabinet form with high oven at one side. This saves stooping. Beyond the range is the radiator under the west window.

Coming next, in our tour around the room, is the south door leading to the basement and out of doors. Built-in storage, of much interest, occupies the rest of the south wall. The narrow door discloses table leaves and cleaning equipment. What appears to be a wide, high cupboard is a refrigerator set with its front flush with the wall, raised to save stooping, and filled from the rear. Barring out the iceman, with his muddy shoes—the welcome block of dripping coolness notwithstanding —saves much cleaning of the floor.

The east wall is given over to food service and dishwashing. First is a cleverly designed serving cupboard, opening into both kitchen and dining room, and invaluable to one serving a course dinner without a maid. The first hot courses can be put through the lower counter; salad and dessert can be prepared in advance and set upon the shelves above. Each course, as re-

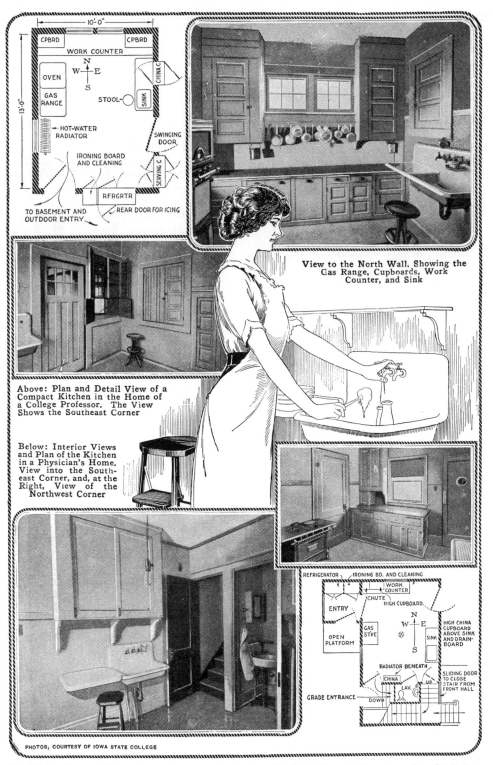

View to the North Wall, Showing the Gas Range, Cupboards, Work Counter, and Sink

Above: Plan and Detail View of a Compact Kitchen in the Home of a College Professor. The View Shows the Southeast Corner

Below: Interior Views and Plan of the Kitchen in a Physician's Home. View into the Southeast Corner, and, at the Right, View of the Northwest Corner

PHOTOS, COURTESY OF IOWA STATE COLLEGE

The Kitchen Layouts Shown in the Plans were Designed to Afford the Greatest Convenience in a Small Area, the Cupboards, and Other Equipment, being So Disposed as to Reduce Necessary Walking to a Minimum

moved, goes back to the waiting cupboard. The dining-room door has a glass panel to avoid awkward collisions, so frequent when persons approach the door from the two sides, each unaware of the other.

The dishwashing group utilizes the remaining space on the east wall, and is closely related to three positions. It has a china closet above, into which dishes are set as cleansed, without moving a step. They are ready then for removal from the dining-room side. The sink is also in close proximity to the work counter, making it easy to draw water for food preparation, and to place soiled mixing dishes to soak. The distance to the stove is also not great.

The upper walls are of rough plaster, the lower being smooth cement plaster, marked into bricks. The woodwork is pine finished in white enamel, easy to wash. The tile floor slopes to a drain under the sink; it can be flushed with water and dried with a rubber window brush, on a long handle.

In a small city in Iowa, I had the pleasure of visiting a delightful kitchen in a doctor's residence, the plan and details of which are shown in the lower part of the full-page illustration. It has the same dimensions and same north-and-west exposure as the first kitchen, but has only one window at the north. The light walls, rough plaster above and plain cement below, and the deep-cream enameled woodwork reflect all the sunshine that enters the room. Many a woman could transform a gloomy workroom by changing its dark-green painted walls, or its brown-papered ones, for some warm color, as cream, yellow, or tan, which reflects light instead of absorbing it. The floor is of varnished hard wood.

The built-in cabinet, under the north window, is of correct height for the doctor's wife, is finished in cream enamel, with glass knobs, and has a tilting bin, cupboards, drawers, and bread boards beneath. Through one corner of the high cupboard runs the clothes chute, with an opening into the kitchen.

On the west, the outer door opens upon an entry, which holds the refrigerator, and a closet for an ironing board, outdoor wraps, and cleaning equipment. A door stop keeps it from striking the gas range when opened. It would be convenient to have a narrow shelf upon the wall above the range, to hold fresh and spent matches, and salt and seasonings of frequent use in cooking.

Along the south wall is shown a door leading to the basement, and to a grade-level outside door; then the radiator, with a china cupboard above; next, a convenient closet beneath the stairs, housing a toilet, lavatory, mirror, and clothes hooks, and finally, a short branch of the one central stairway, the second step being hinged to open up a cubby-hole, providing for the dish drainer and unsightly utensils, not often used.

On the east wall is the sink, with china closets above, closed by sliding doors. A stepladder stool is provided as a seat for working, and for use in reaching high shelves in the cupboards. The electric light is on a drop cord from the center of the ceiling, but a hook over the range holds it when desired. A second light is in the lavatory and there is a wall outlet for the electric iron.

The problems of the isolated country house are somewhat different. Usually cooking must be done for a larger family and more transients. Distance from markets makes more storage place for staple groceries necessary. Lacking city utilities, ready to be piped or wired in, the farmhouse cannot be labor-saving in its kitchen arrangement unless individual installations of water, pump, sewer, and lights are arranged. The third workshop is one I designed for a new farmhouse, and is shown in plan and detail, in the inset illustrations. There are no young children to consider, but there are three in school, and a grown daughter who assists her mother with the work. There are, also, hired men to be boarded during special seasons.

The kitchen will have running hot

and cold soft water for cleansing purposes, and hard water for drinking and cooking, for farmers demand well

house, heat the water, cook the food, and iron the clothes.

This kitchen is large because of its

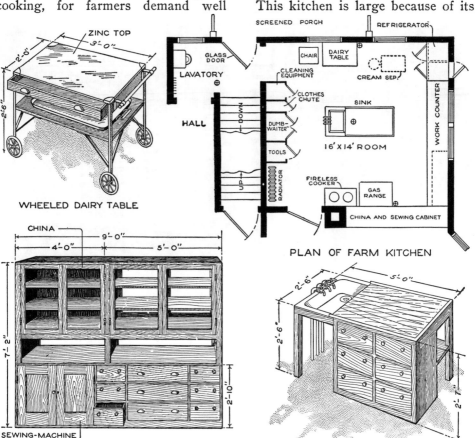

WHEELED DAIRY TABLE

PLAN OF FARM KITCHEN

CHINA AND SEWING CABINET

SINK AND DISH-WASHING TABLE

The Farm Kitchen is Designed to Provide Adequate Space for the Varied Work to be Done, and to Enable Two Persons to Work in It without Hindering Each Other. The Centrally Located Sink Is a Distinctive Feature

water for drinking, no matter how carefully the cistern water is filtered. In winter the water is heated by furnace, in summer by a gas heater in the cemented basement, where the hot-water tank is located. The need of much hot water, all the year round, is very great in the farm home, and the mother and daughter will be saved carrying in tons of water every year, thus being relieved of one of the heaviest burdens of the old-fashioned farmhouse. Several types of gas plants are giving excellent service in rural homes, among them gasoline and acetylene. The gas plant of this farm will "kill several birds with one stone"; it will light the

varied industries, its storage space, and the fact that two women work in it. The mother thought she could not get along without a coal range, for she has always had one. I have told her that coal overheats the kitchen in winter, since she has a furnace. It throws waste heat into the room and "cooks the cook" in summer. The basement gas heater will do away with the need of the coal range to warm water. To please her, however, the chimney is so located that if she pines for the old range she will have a place to put it. The gas range she has ordered is as convenient as any city housewife's, with its four open burners, simmerer, high oven, and broiler. The floor space saved by the narrow stove is given to a two-compartment fireless cooker, frigerator and staple foods in the long cabinet are mixed with utensils close at hand. Next, to the right, is the

The Space beneath the Long Work Counter is Utilized for the Storage of Food Materials and Other Articles Used on the Counter

raised to a convenient height by a cabinet, in which the special utensils are stored, when not in use.

The path through the room is located at one side. One wall is given over to storing staple supplies; a closet for cleaning equipment; a dumb-waiter used to carry potatoes, other vegetables, apples, and canned fruits, up and down; a clothes chute, and the register. The same dumb-waiter brings up the heavy basket of wet clothes, washed in the basement laundry, ready to hang out in the sunshine.

The opposite wall, on the south, where the prevailing summer breezes may be enjoyed, is designed for cooking preparation. It has a long work counter, shown in detail in the sketch, with storage beneath, and a high cupboard at one end. The refrigerator is built into the wall and iced from the rear. The owner of the farm built his own ice house, and cuts ice every winter from a river a mile away, selling enough ice to his neighbors to compensate for his labor. In winter the outside icing door can be left open, and cool air will circulate and keep food nicely. The arrangement permits routing work from left to right in order, as performed. Food in the re-

stove for cooking it. Swinging around on her heel, the cook can place soiled dishes to soak in the sink. The proximity of one end of the counter to the stove makes it handy in serving up a meal, which is placed upon the open serving shelf of the china cupboard, which opens, also, to the dining room. The east side of the room is specialized as the dairy. There is a wheeled dairy table, shown at the left of the plan, and the cream separator. The daughter can attend to this work while her mother is cooking. When the work is finished, she rolls the table beside the sink and washes the buckets, pans, and separator parts.

A great convenience for the men, coming in dusty and sweaty from the fields, is the location of a lavatory, mirror, towels, and coat hooks off the rear entry. After cleaning up, they can go through the hall to the dining room, or reach the bedrooms easily. The use of this entry makes it possible to carry vegetables and fruits to the cellar for storage, without passing through the kitchen, and makes unnecessary the building of a second stair from the cellar to the outside of the house. It is also handy for removing furnace ashes.

The Woman's Home Workshop

By Avis Gordon Vestal

Part II—A Practical Kitchen for the Home with Children

[This is the second of three articles, in which Mrs. Vestal, "domestic engineer," sets forth the mechanics of the kitchen, illustrating fundamental design and details with practical examples. Each installment is complete in itself, but will be more fully appreciated in connection with the others.—Editor.]

REQUIREMENTS and needs typical of thousands of homes form the basis for the kitchen described in this article. The wife believes in children and has three bright "kiddies," ranging in age from six years downward. The husband has an income of $2,000 to $2,500 a year. The family moved from a city apartment to a suburb, to provide a safe play place for the youngsters, a garden for the special recreation of the head of the household, as well as for the other members, and an abundance of light and fresh air, denied them in the city flat. A floor plan of the kitchen and adjoining features is shown in the illustration. Above is a sketch in perspective, showing the pantry, and the children's alcove as viewed from the opposite end of the kitchen. Details of the exterior supply cupboard and refrigerator icing door, the sink and sink cabinet, guard for the screen door, and a curtain arrangement for the special benefit of the youngsters, who must "look out," are also shown.

With the home to pay for and the expenses of the growing children increasing each year, economy is necessary. The housewife wishes to put her kitchen work upon as efficient a basis as possible because she cannot afford to employ a "meat maid." A staff of "mechanical maids," and the weekly assistance of a laundress, is all the aid she can count upon. She has in mind the future as well as the present. Should more prosperous days arrive, she knows that it will be easier to em-ploy and keep a higher-class maid, if the kitchen work is lightened by a conveniently arranged room. The new house has a furnace and all the community conveniences, such as water, sewer, gas, and electric service.

"The children insist upon following me to the kitchen," the mother declares, in stating her needs, "so I must have some suitable place for them there, where they can play happily, without being in the way. Besides, they are yet in that undeveloped age where civilization has not fully 'taken.' Little barbarians will have their differences of opinion which mother must arbitrate. I cannot supervise their training carefully if I shut them out of the kitchen where I must remain to work."

It is around this need to guard young children while attending to household cares that this kitchen is evolved. The mother can keep an eye on the little folks while they play in the house, and her windows are planned to give her a lookout station from which she can watch them in the yard. Though the room has nursery provisions, which will be required for some years, these features are not rigid and unchangeable, but quite adaptable. When the fledglings outgrow the kitchen alcove provided for them, it can be used as a breakfast room or to serve a simple noon lunch when but part of the family is at home.

Should the husband's "ship" come in,

with a servant on board, the alcove can be converted into the maid's dining room. Other possibilities of future development are a sewing room or a rest corner with a couch or rocker, or a kitchen "office" with desk and library of household books and magazines.

The long box seat is to store the precious toys, keeping the living rooms free from the clutter so often found in small houses where the mother is both mistress and maid. It also forms a seat before the table which is used for play and for serving the frequent small meals required by children. Above this table the wall supports a small set of shelves for the dishes used daily for the bread, milk, and cereals.

One who is familiar with children knows that when they are house-bound on stormy days they are continually pulling aside the drapery curtains to look out, a very natural impulse, which causes rumpling and soiling of the curtains. To permit unobstructed view, admit abundant sunlight, yet have some soft framing, these windows are given narrow curtains gathered in snugly at the top and bottom by rods, and the folds pulled back to within 6 in. of the window casing. Gay-flowered cretonne is used, brown and yellow stocks on a cream ground, a split strip at each side. The effect of the alcove is almost like looking into a flower garden, even though snow be in the air without. The windows are casements and are completely screened. The seat permits the juniors to clamber easily up to the flower-framed lookouts. A chair for mother and a high chair for the baby complete the furnishings of the nursery.

The "cook's corner" is the second section of this home workshop. It is a combination of a pantry and a kitchen cabinet. It is, in fact, what might be called a "wide-open" pantry, since its two doors open practically the entire storage space, when in use. The built-in refrigerator is filled from the screened back porch, and has a delivery station above it to receive foods and milk. Every housekeeper knows what a nuisance it is to have the grocery boy open

the door, unannounced by a preliminary knock, and leave a trail of muddy footmarks across a freshly scrubbed floor. If the door is kept locked, the housewife is likely to be called down from the bedrooms or up from the laundry to let him in. Sometimes she is away when deliveries are made and the milk sours in the summer sunshine or the bananas freeze in the cold. Again, few kitchens have a place to receive supplies until they can be checked up and put away, and they are often piled in the middle of the worktable while the biscuits are being rolled out.

With such an array of reasons to back it, I invented this case to care for them. The top of the refrigerator is its floor; the sides and top are of wood, and it has glass doors both at the front and back, either or both of which can be locked. The transparency of the doors is for two purposes: One can glance in to see whether supplies have arrived and also peep through it when the youngsters are playing on the porch.

The east wall has a work counter across it, with storage beneath and above at both sides of the window. The high shelves are for jelly. The large low shelf is for the bread mixer. On the south wall, from counter height upward, are narrow open shelves, hooks for utensils being placed beneath the lower one.

A secondhand office stool, cut to the housewife's needs, and having the four legs shod with sliding metal casters to make moving easy and silent, is used during most of the cooking preparation. Its further merit is a seat broader than is made for many kitchen stools, the larger seat being more comfortable.

"I had enough of dark rooms while we lived in apartments," the housewife explains, recalling the air wells of earlier years, "so I want glass in the upper part of my back door. That will be as good as another window."

This door, with the several windows, makes splendid ventilation on warm days. The dining-room door also has a glass pane to prevent collisions. It is double-acting, can be anchored open

Looking into the Children's Alcove, Showing the Box Seat at the Rear Wall and the Sink Cupboard at Right

View into the Pantry, Showing the Compact Arrangement of the Refrigerator and Receiving Cupboard, at the Left, and Other Equipment

SCREENED PORCH

DELIVERY STATION FOR SUPPLIES

ICING DOOR

CLEANING CLO.

ELEC. LIGHT

GLASS DOORS

4'-6"

BOX SEAT

TOWEL

RGSTR

GLASS DOOR

4'-6"

SHELVES

COUNTER

ELECTRIC LT.

STOOL

REFRIGERATOR

6'-0"

6'-0"

SHELVES

DISH CUPB'D

RGSTR

CHAIR

13'-0"

13'-0"

FIRELESS COOKER

HIGH-OVEN GAS RANGE

12" BOX SEAT

CHILDREN'S ALCOVE

6'-6"

PLAY TABLE

HIGH-CHAIR

DRAIN BOARD

STOOL

SINK

ELEC. LIGHT

SERVING TABLE

SHELVES

DINING ROOM

CURTAIN ARRANGEMENT ON CASEMENT WINDOWS

METAL GUARD

SCREEN DOOR

18"

24"

SINK CABINET

30"

31"

30"

FOR TOWELS AND APRONS

The Iceman and the Grocery Boy Deliver Their Goods without Entering the House. The Door Guard and Curtain Arrangement were Devised with the Children in Mind

This Kitchen was Designed to Lighten the Manifold Duties of the Mother and Housewife. The Alcove and Porch Provide Play Space for the Children, so That the Mother may Be at Ease over Their Safety. The Pantry Provides Ample Storage Space and a Work Counter when serving meals, and has no raised threshold. Through it a wheeled serving table, details of the construction of which will be given in the final article, rolls easily.

Separated from the cabinet corner only by a comfortable path is the wall given over to the cooking processes. It is a general rule of kitchen planning that the more fully all wall space is utilized the less floor space will be required. A smaller room means less cost to build, less labor in cleaning and fewer steps in routing the work. The gas range chosen is of the high-cabinet type, the oven being too high for the fingers of childish curiosity. The side-oven type of cabinet range is equally convenient in use, but takes more floor space.

The small space needed for the stove leaves room by its side for a two-compartment fireless cooker, raised upon a homemade stand, which holds utensils. The use of the cooker cuts down the gas bill and makes a cooler room in summer, for even the best of gas ranges raises the temperature of the room and of the cook, when the oven is used in warm weather. The further merit of the fireless stove for a cook whose mind is much interrupted by childish activities, is that food in it does not require watching lest the roast get dry, the vegetables boil over, or the cereal scorch.

This brings out an important point in household efficiency: the conservation of the housewife's nervous energy. This is quite as important as the saving of time or of steps, as vital to the welfare of the family as the saving of money. Some kitchens waste much nervous power. The safe play places, indoor and out, with the window outlooks for the mother, make child care less exacting in its demands on nerve force. The abundant light and air serve in part the same purpose. The selection of an inlaid linoleum as the floor covering was made primarily because it is elastic and will deaden the noise of pattering feet, though its ease of cleansing also is a factor.

Along with conserving muscular and nervous strength, in the design of a kitchen, the effect of color and line in its decoration may well be considered. It is easier to work in a pretty room than in an ugly, irritating one. A combination of colors, all beautiful, but fighting in combination, is far from restful. Large spaces of red, as in the walls, are irritating to the senses because they overstimulate the nerves of sight. Large figures in a linoleum on the floor seem to rise up and hit the observer, instead of keeping the floor subordinate and in its place. This kitchen has washable painted walls, the lower portion brown as high as little hands can reach, the upper wall and ceiling a warm tan. The linoleum is of the same two colors, in a small-tile pattern. The room is so sunny that it could have been developed nicely in light gray with a blue and gray linoleum, and blue in the pattern of the window draperies.

The arrangement of the dishwashing corner will, doubtless, take much of the drudge out of this task. The use of the serving table, set at right angles to the sink, holding the soiled dishes ready to be washed and routed from right to left, has some mechanical advantage as compared with a table or second drainboard set in the usual line against the wall. The customary arrangement is satisfactory when one stands and walks before the group, but when one sits upon a stool the right-angle arrangement makes things easier to reach without rising.

Setting the sink bed 30 in. high would have been correct in this house had its mistress intended standing at the dishwashing. As she is learning that if everything is studied out and properly arranged, she can work quite as well from a stool, she can use a lower sink to advantage. Her drainboard will be 30 in. high, the table top the same, and the height of the sink bottom and the top of the stool 24 in. A set of drawers beneath the drainboard holds towels and aprons.

When slow cooking is to be watched, as the stirring of jam, the sink stool is moved beside the range. When a meal is being dished up, the wheel table is rolled up to the stove with the serving dishes ready upon it.

The bedrooms and the regular bathroom are all upstairs, so there was a need for a supplementary toilet room on the first floor, as this will save many trips up and down stairs every day. Here the play wraps and rubbers are stored, the first upon low hooks, the latter in a box seat upon which the older children can sit to put on their rubbers. The younger children stand upon it while mother fastens their wraps, saving her some stooping. There is a much-needed comfort station, and a lavatory where smeared baby faces and grimy little hands can be freshened up after play. The screen doors are provided with a metal guard to protect the wire from the destructive hands of the children, as well as to prevent injury to the prying hands. A detail of the guard is shown in the illustration.

The 6-in. shelf, around the southwest corner of the kitchen, beneath which the wheeled table usually rests, "feeds the cooking" by bringing close to the stove the salt, pepper, soda, matches, shortening, and other things used daily in attending to the cooking. Beneath are hooks for implements used in serving up the food, as the potato masher and puree sieve. Nearer the sink itself, as the shelf turns to the south wall, are found cleaning preparations, as steel wool for polishing aluminum utensils, silver polish, sink brush, water softener, knife-scouring cork, and the like. Beneath, on hooks, hang the towels and dishpan.

The hot-air furnace has wall registers in the lavatory and kitchen, that for the latter at the joining of the two alcoves. The path between the two doors of the kitchen is a short one. A closet for broom, dustpan (a long-handled one), chemical mop, wet mop, scrub pail and related cleansing tools, is provided in the entry, just outside of the kitchen door. A bench on the porch holds a sanitary, covered metal garbage can. Plate scrapings and vegetable parings are freed of liquid in a sink strainer and are emptied into the can, which is scalded daily. Beside it is a basket to receive tin cans and broken dishes, which are carried twice a week to the back gate on the days the collector comes.

Dust Cover for Bathtub

The task of keeping the bathroom scrupulously clean is a difficult one at best. While it is desirable to have the

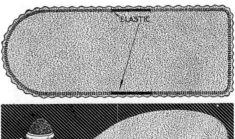

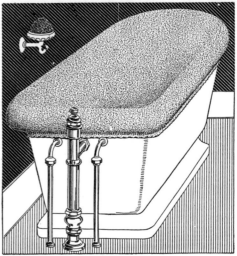

The Cover Protects the Bathtub from Dust and Saves Much Labor in Cleaning

windows of the room opened for airing frequently, the result is often the undoing of much labor, by the blowing in of soot and dirt to mar the clean, white fixtures. By fitting a cover of washable cloth over the tub, as shown in the sketch, particularly while the bathroom is being aired, the enameled surfaces may be protected. The cover, being fitted with a drawstring to fit under the roll edge of the tub, may be removed quickly, and as easily replaced.—L. J. Hough, Toledo, Ohio.

Sounding Board for Large Auditorium

The problem of carrying the voices of speakers to a capacity audience, in

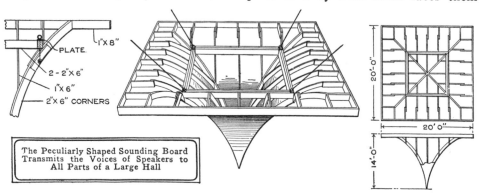

The Peculiarly Shaped Sounding Board Transmits the Voices of Speakers to All Parts of a Large Hall

intermediate ribs are cut to the proper curve from 1-in. material. Lookouts are nailed to their upper ends, and a plate of 1 by 8-in. stock faces them

one of Chicago's largest convention halls, was solved with great success by the installation of a sounding board in the form of an inverted concave pyramid. The construction of the device, as shown in the sketch, is simple, and may be adapted to various other uses, particularly where a sounding board is required for either indoor or outdoor assemblies. The board was supported from the roof girders by means of four guy wires, fixed to a heavy frame, which formed the chief support of the framework. The curved surfaces were covered with composition board, a layer of muslin, and shellacked with several coats, to produce a close but resilient surface. The speaker's position was slightly to the rear of the point, the latter being about 6 ft. above the speaker's head. The curved surfaces receive the sound waves and transmit them to all parts of the auditorium, without echo.

The foundation for the composition board is a typical framed structure. The center sketch shows a general view as seen from above; at the right is a framing diagram, and at the left is a detail of one corner, showing how the supporting frame, of double 2 by 6-in. stock, is bolted to the corner rafters, the latter being reinforced with fishplates. The device as illustrated is 20 ft. square and 14 ft. high. The corner ribs are of 2 by 6-in. stock, and the

around the outer edge. The eyebolts, supporting the guy wires, are fitted through steel plates, over the corner joints in the supporting frame, as shown in the detail at the left.

Fastening Washer upon Wood Without Screws or Nails

In fitting a thin sheet-metal washer, or bearing, to a wooden surface, it is often desirable to fix it into place so that it will not revolve, and still leave the surface unmarred by screws or holes. A satisfactory method is to turn down a small triangle at each corner of a square washer and drive these points into the wood. If round washers are used, small nicks may be cut into the edge and the resulting corners turned down and set into the wood.

Drills Made from Hacksaw Blades

Broken hacksaw blades may be ground into satisfactory drills for boring small holes through thin material or for drilling shallow holes. The steel blade should be broken into short sections and the ends ground to standard sizes not larger than $\frac{3}{16}$ of an inch. The point is ground like a straightfluted drill. The drills may be held securely in a brace having two parallel jaws.

The Woman's Home Workshop

By Avis Gordon Vestal

Part III—Built-In Features and Details Adaptable to Various Kitchens

[This is the final article of the series, in which Mrs. Vestal, "domestic engineer," sets forth the mechanics of the kitchen, illustrating fundamental design and details with practical examples. This installment is complete in itself, but will be more fully appreciated in connection with the others, which appeared in the October and November issues.—Editor.]

BUILDING a kitchen as an integral part of a new home, with every feature carefully planned, is no doubt the ideal method of making the woman's home workshop what it should be. However, lacking this opportunity, the resourceful housewife need not despair of having a practical kitchen, if she will but study the possibilities for improvement. The details of construction and equipment described in this article offer numerous suggestions, and may be included in the design of a new kitchen and allied rooms, or adapted to various other situations. Many of them may be carried out by the woman of the house herself, others may require the aid of the men of the household, and the more extensive ones may be undertaken only by competent workmen. An installation of the latter type is the dumb-waiter and shaft, as shown at the left in the double-page illustration. The receiving shelf and dust and paper chutes, shown in the plan at the right, may be built by a man of fair mechanical skill. The economical arrangement of kitchen tools and supplies, as suggested on the right, is easily within the range of the able housekeeper. A practical refrigerator built under a sink, drawers and storage space provided under a stairs, and a convenient warming oven over a radiator, are shown in the smaller sketches.

The pantry connected to the various floors from the basement to the attic by the shaft and dumb-waiter was designed by experts from a state agricultural college for a modern farm home. It is situated between the kitchen and the dining room, facilitating the serving of meals, and keeping the heat from the cooking range from the dining room. The dishwashing is done here, and china cabinets as well as other storage spaces are close at hand. The sink is provided with ample drain boards, and receives plenty of light from a large window. The sliding door is economical of space, and practically all of the wall space is utilized. By reference to the first floor of the vertical section at the left, the plan of the pantry may be understood readily.

On one side of the flue is a bread-raising cabinet, warmed by a coil of the water pipe, which extends from the reservoir of the kitchen range to the bathroom on the floor above. It is metal-lined and provides space for a large batch of loaves. On the other side of the flue is a storage space for coal and other fuel for the kitchen range. In the adjacent corner is the dumb-waiter shaft, and adjoining it, opening to the pantry, is a cupboard for storing extra table leaves, and other articles of only occasional use. Between this cabinet and the flue is a counter of table height, opening from the pantry to the kitchen.

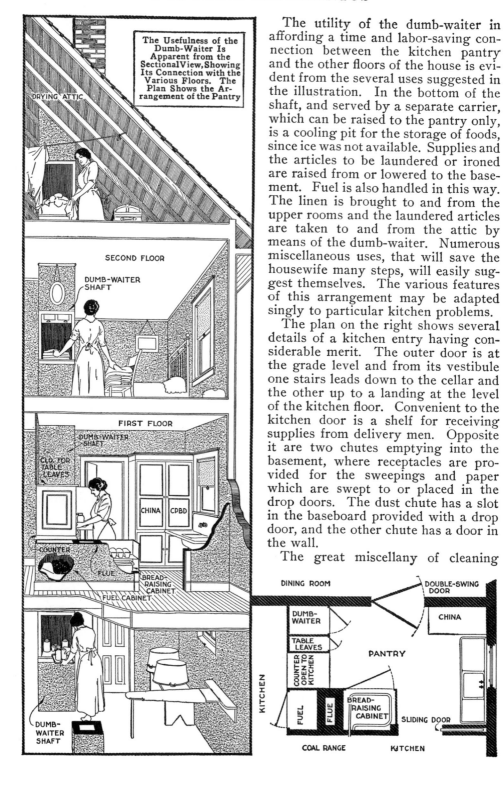

The Usefulness of the Dumb-Waiter Is Apparent from the Sectional View, Showing Its Connection with the Various Floors. The Plan Shows the Arrangement of the Pantry

DRYING ATTIC

SECOND FLOOR

DUMB-WAITER SHAFT

FIRST FLOOR

DUMB-WAITER SHAFT

CLO. FOR TABLE LEAVES

CHINA | CPBD

COUNTER

FLUE

BREAD-RAISING CABINET

FUEL CABINET

DUMB-WAITER SHAFT

DINING ROOM

DOUBLE-SWING DOOR

DUMB-WAITER

CHINA

TABLE LEAVES

COUNTER OPEN TO KITCHEN

PANTRY

KITCHEN

FUEL

FLUE

BREAD-RAISING CABINET

SLIDING DOOR

COAL RANGE

KITCHEN

The utility of the dumb-waiter in affording a time and labor-saving connection between the kitchen pantry and the other floors of the house is evident from the several uses suggested in the illustration. In the bottom of the shaft, and served by a separate carrier, which can be raised to the pantry only, is a cooling pit for the storage of foods, since ice was not available. Supplies and the articles to be laundered or ironed are raised from or lowered to the basement. Fuel is also handled in this way. The linen is brought to and from the upper rooms and the laundered articles are taken to and from the attic by means of the dumb-waiter. Numerous miscellaneous uses, that will save the housewife many steps, will easily suggest themselves. The various features of this arrangement may be adapted singly to particular kitchen problems.

The plan on the right shows several details of a kitchen entry having considerable merit. The outer door is at the grade level and from its vestibule one stairs leads down to the cellar and the other up to a landing at the level of the kitchen floor. Convenient to the kitchen door is a shelf for receiving supplies from delivery men. Opposite it are two chutes emptying into the basement, where receptacles are provided for the sweepings and paper which are swept to or placed in the drop doors. The dust chute has a slot in the baseboard provided with a drop door, and the other chute has a door in the wall.

The great miscellany of cleaning

tools, supplies, and other small kitchen
equipment may easily give the appearance of continual disorder unless specific places are provided for their
proper storage. The items of undue
wear, breakage, and waste are of con-
sequence also. A good plan is to store
these articles according to their classi-
fication and place of use. The cleaning
equipment and supplies may be placed
in a cupboard, as shown in the illustration at the right, and the cupboard
itself again subdivided with care, to
provide a good place for each article.
Several shelves, caring for the lighter
articles above, and the heavier or more
bulky ones below, are desirable.
Brooms, mops, and similar cleaning
tools should be hung on catches, so
that the working parts may not be injured. Opportunity for economical
and compact arrangement of individual
cupboards is almost unlimited, and affords an interesting problem.

The storage of the tools and supplies
needed for the preparation of food, baking, etc., may profitably be given careful study. An arrangement of the tools
and materials most needed, convenient
to the worktable, is shown in the illustration at the right. The smaller tools
are hung on the back of the open portion of the cupboard, with silhouettes
of the various tools marked at their
respective places. Heavier articles,
that are not suitable for hanging in the
cupboard, are placed on the shelf below
the open portion. On another shelf is
a row of cans, labeled, and containing
various food materials. A receptacle

Three Useful Features are Suggested in the Plan of the Kitchen Entry. The Well-Planned Cabinet, Worktable, and Cupboard Aid in Organizing the Work of the Kitchen

SLIDING SHELF

DUST SLOT IN BASE-
BOARD AT FLOOR LEV-
EL EMPTYING INTO
BASEMENT

PAPER CHUTE TO
BASEMENT, WITH DROP-
DOOR IN WALL

CABINET FOR
HOUSE-CLEANING
TOOLS AND
SUPPLIES

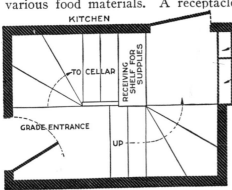

KITCHEN

TO CELLAR

RECEIVING SHELF FOR SUPPLIES

GRADE ENTRANCE

UP

for sugar may be placed handily on a bracket shelf at the end of the work-table or at the side of the cupboard, not too high up. The sliding shelf at the lower edge of the cupboard is con-

A Refrigerator Built under a Sink Drain Board in a Kitchenette Proved Economical and Useful

venient as a temporary rest for various articles. Additional storage space for articles not used so frequently is provided in the closed cupboard above. Doors on all cupboards in the kitchen should be considered carefully, as to available space, and possibility of damage to them, if left open. Sliding doors, particularly those that slide vertically, are economical of space.

The worktable is provided with several drawers, which are graduated in depth from the shallow one at the top to the deepest at the bottom. The upper drawer is subdivided into sections by small strips, and each section is marked with a slip indicating the tool or article which belongs there. The smaller articles are kept in the upper drawers and those more bulky in the lower ones. The stool shown near the worktable has many uses in the kitchen, and will save the housewife much useless drudgery in performing work at which most women stand, once the habit of using it has been formed.

Most of the shelves in cupboards should be narrow, and provide for only one row of articles, or receptacles. The inner side of swinging doors may be fitted with wire racks for the keeping of covers and similar flat objects. Nar-

row shelves, either fixed or hinged to drop out of the way when not in use, are convenient for special uses, such as for a clock, scale, etc. They may be enameled white and made so that they can be lifted out of place and washed easily. If it is desired to provide inexpensive or temporary covering for open shelves, roller curtains may be fitted to them, or denim curtains, to slide on an upper and a lower rod, may be used.

For the cooking cabinets, sliding drawers are preferable to tilting bins for the storage of flour and similar supplies. The bins are usually narrow, and it is necessary to stoop uncomfortably to remove all of the contents. They also are likely to catch the fingers, especially when well filled. Drawers for such purposes should be tin-lined and covered, the back portion being fixed and the front part of the cover hinged to be raised forward when the drawer is opened slightly over half its length. Tin does not absorb odors, is mouse and bug-proof, and is easily cleaned. The drawers may be removed readily and carried out of doors for sunning.

A number of other features making for kitchen efficiency, and which may offer suggestion for adaptation to particular conditions, will be treated briefly, without attempting to relate them systematically to the various kitchen industries. The first of three such items, shown in separate illustrations, is the installation of a refrigerator under the drain board of a sink. It was designed for use in a kitchenette, where space was limited. Another suggestion for a refrigerator, practical but not new, is the fitting of a box to a window, for use in the colder months. A cooling pit for the country home has already been mentioned in connection with the dumb-waiter, shown in the double-page illustration.

An interesting use of space otherwise wasted is the building of drawers into the risers of stairs, and the hinging of a section of several treads at the bottom of a stairs, to form a cupboard beneath them, as shown in the sketch.

These adaptations may, of course, be used separately. A small cupboard, such as is commonly used in bathrooms, was set into the wall of a kitchen, above the sink, and proved useful for the storage of brushes, powders, and other cleaning materials.

Table service is improved, especially in winter, by the use of warmed plates. The warming oven above a radiator, as shown in the illustration, was made for this purpose, and is useful also in preventing the cooling of food to be served.

When ironing must be done in the kitchen, a special cupboard for the supplies and equipment is desirable. This may often be combined with a storage space for cleaning tools. Several places affording the best light for ironing at various hours of the day should be selected and hooks fixed in the walls, or other supports, for the ironing board. A board hinged or hooked to the wall at one end, and supported by a strong brace, affords a free end that is often desirable. If this method is not feasible, a portable board with firm supports, that may be folded into small space, should be provided. A mat of rubber, composition, or other suitable material, should be placed on the floor, beneath the feet of the person ironing, as this saves much strain in ironing with heavy pressure. For many kinds of work not requiring this, it is convenient to sit on the kitchen stool. A

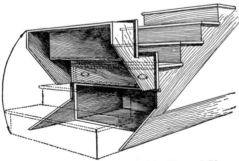

Storage Space may be Provided in Unusual Places, as Suggested by the Drawers Built into the Risers and the Cupboard under the Hinged Section of the Stairs

wheeled table or clotheshorse, both of which may be made in the home workshop, should be convenient to the ironing board.

In the selection of equipment for the kitchen various practical and space-saving articles manufactured commer-

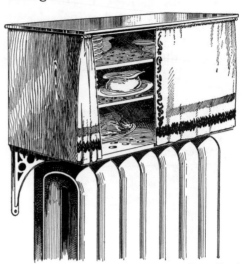

A Warming Oven Built over a Radiator Keeps Food and Dishes Warm in Cold Weather

cially, some of which may be duplicated by the home worker, should be considered. Thus a homemade "hay stove" may serve as a fireless cooker. A combination chair and ladder is useful. Where children are to be cared for, a "one-arm" chair, with a fixed or removable arm, may be used for play as well as lunches. A small table that may be adjusted as a chair, and which has a cupboard for children's toys, is also economical of space. By far the most useful of such items of extra equipment is the familiar tea wagon, adapted for use in the kitchen. It may be used to carry clean dishes and hot food to the dining room, or to the porch in summer, and to return dishes and left-over food to the kitchen. It is a universal side table in the kitchen and allied rooms, and invaluable in the canning season. Such a table should be narrow enough to pass through doors easily, and the top should be covered with zinc. Other useful features are a drawer for silver and a shelf below, for soiled dishes. A detailed sketch of such a wagon was shown in describing the equipment of a farm kitchen in the first article of this series.

Merely rearranging the furniture in a kitchen for convenience often brings about marked improvement. If the cooking and the work directly related to it are concentrated on one side of the room, and the other side is reserved for other industries, a basis for the placing of the equipment is established. The two fundamental principles to be observed are: equipment and materials used together should be placed accordingly; and working surfaces should be suited to the height of the person using them, 30 in. being correct for a woman of average height. By adapting some of the suggestions outlined, and rearranging the equipment, even a kitchen quite out-of-date may be improved.

Novel Window Advertisement

A simple means of providing a novel advertisement for the show window

The Arrangement of Cords from a Window Display to the Door Causes the Former to Move Up and Down, Attracting Attention

of a store is shown in the illustration. A number of pictures, post cards, etc., are arranged on three cords which travel in pulleys at the top of the window sash. The three cords are joined and conducted through three intermediate pulleys; the end of the cord is fixed to the top of the door. Three colored disks are suspended below the window display. Whenever the door is opened, the window display and the disks are moved up and down a distance of about two feet, and attract much attention.—G. F. Thompson, Pittsburgh, Pa.

Templates for Cutting Packing Gaskets

Many forms of packing for machinery, pipe joints, etc., are expensive, and the careful maker of them will economize in material. By making a set of templates cut to the exact size of the various gaskets used on the steam chest, cylinder head, pipe flanges, and other machinery parts, there is not only an economy of material but of time. In some instances such templates may even prevent dangerous accidents, which may result while a gasket is being fitted by the usual method of cut and try. When cutting up packing material it is desirable to cut gaskets of various sizes, using the templates, so that they may be on hand when needed, and this also aids in cutting the stock to the best advantage.—C. Anderson, Worcester, Massachusetts.

Alining Wheels of a Sidecar or Automobile

If the wheels of a vehicle, particularly a sidecar motorcycle, do not run true, the motor is overburdened as if pulling an extra load. If the sidecar wheel has a tendency to run toward the right, then, to make the motorcycle go straight ahead, it is necessary to keep the front wheel turned slightly to the left. Both the motor and the tires receive undue wear. A method of alining the wheels is to measure the distance between them at the points indicated by the dotted lines in the sketch. If they do not measure the same at these points, proper adjustment should be made on the cross rods. In the case of an automobile the test is the same although the adjustment is more difficult, especially if the axles are bent. In that case professional attention is required.—L. E. Turner, Jamaica, N. Y.

Straps to Fit Double-Pipe Runs

In the course of my work I found it necessary to run a considerable length of ¾-in. conduit parallel with and closely adjoining a 1¼-in. pipe. The clamp shown in the illustration was found to be easily made and practical, in use as well as installation. The clamp is made as follows: A strip of ¹⁄₁₆-in. band iron, ¾ in. wide, is bent halfway round the smaller conduit, as shown at A. The successive stages of the forming of the clamp or strap are shown in the sketches B to F. The strap around the small conduit is clamped into a vise, as at B, and the ends are bent at right angles, to make the larger pipe the proper distance above the lower one, as at C. The ends of the strap are then shouldered, as at D, and bent around the larger pipe, as at E. The completed clamp is shown in a sectional view at F. The double run of pipe may now be suspended as a single unit. If desired, the clamps described may be made with

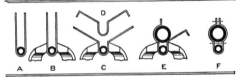

The Strip of Band Iron is Bent to the Proper Shape by Clamping It in a Vise and Forming It around the Conduits

shoulders at their upper ends so that they may be used to suspend the double run.—G. Raymond Flake, Lewistown, Pa.

Sulphate-of-Zinc Paint

A paint which has been found efficient, using coal oil and water as a vehicle, is made as follows: Dissolve 18 oz. of sulphate of zinc in 1 gal. of distilled water, mixing thoroughly. Stir in 1 qt. more of distilled water, mixing carefully, and add ½ pt. of kerosene, or coal oil. Considerable stirring is necessary to effect a good mixture of the water and the paint, although this is aided by the chemical. —L. R. Kelly, Chicago, Ill.

Underground Brace for Gatepost

Gateposts sagged so as to make the gate ineffective are quite common, largely because of poor bracing. The method illustrated of bracing the posts underground is simple and substantial. It leaves the exit clear of surface braces and provides a rigid support for the gate even when the posts are sunk only 15 in. in the ground. A cross brace is housed into the gateposts at the surface, and another binds the posts at their lower ends. The joints

should be spiked together strongly, and the portion underground should be tarred to prevent it from rotting quickly.—Frederick W. Brown, New York, N. Y.

Long Wrench for Automobile Drain Cocks

The necessity of crawling or reaching under automobiles in order to clean drain cocks may be obviated by the use of the long-handle wrench shown in the sketch. It was forged from a piece of ¼-in. round wrought iron, 2½ ft. long. One end was forged into a

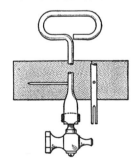

handle and the other was "upset" and slotted to fit the keys by which the drain cocks are opened.—H. W. Offins, Grants Pass, Ore.

Substitute for a Hanger Bolt

Hanger bolts which have a wood screw on one end and a machine screw on the other are not always carried in

Cutting Off the Head of a Wood Screw and Threading the End Provides a Hanger Bolt

stock by hardware dealers. When they cannot be obtained a substitute may be made by sawing off the head of a wood screw and cutting machine threads on this end.

Loosening a Tight Glass Stopper

Heat generated by the friction of a cord drawn rapidly around the neck of

a bottle, as shown in the sketch, will cause the glass to expand and free the stopper. A convenient method of accomplishing this is to tie one end of a cord to a hook in the wall, wind the cord around the neck of the bottle, and hold the other end of the cord as indicated. The bottle may then be drawn quickly back and forth along the cord, causing the neck to become heated.—James M. Kane, Doylestown, Pa.

Making Small Wire Rings

Small wire rings may be made quickly by winding a wire around a rod slightly smaller than the diameter

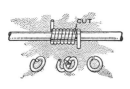

of the rings desired, and cutting the wire into sections. The wire is wound around the rod in a spiral, as though making a spring. A cut is made through the length of the spring, resulting in rings that are sprung open slightly. These may be closed neatly by tapping them upon a bench block, or clamping them in pliers. The sketch shows the method of winding and cutting the wire, as well as rings in process.

Lockstitch Sewing Awl

A satisfactory awl for sewing leather, or repairing harness, may be made by fitting a large-sized darning needle into a handle, as shown in the sketch. The handle should be of hard wood and provided with a ferrule. The eye of the

needle should be of a fair size, and the exposed end should be ground to a sharp point. The awl is used by threading a waxed cord through the eye and driving the needle through the leather. One end of the cord is permitted to extend along the under side where the sewing is done, and the other is locked over it with each stroke of the needle. When the awl is withdrawn from the hole the thread passing through its eye is looped around the lower thread, forming a lockstitch.

Wire Spring Machine-Thread Cleaner

Accumulation of dirt and metal chips in machine threads causes much

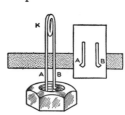

annoyance when threaded parts are to be fitted together quickly and firmly. The illustration shows a simple device made of a wire spring with which such obstructions may be removed from the thread. The spring is coiled at its center as indicated at K; the ends are flattened to a chisel edge and ground to points, as at A and B. The points are inserted in the thread, and the spring action holds them in place while they are scraped through the threads.—George L. Yaste, Lonaconing, Md.

Shop Notes

Spring Bumper for Motorboat Landings

By JOHN E. CAHILL, Jr.

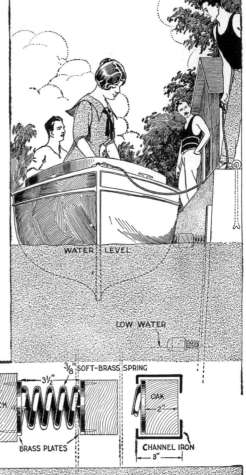

PROTECTION for boats at landings, particularly in rough weather, is afforded by the spring bumper shown in the illustration, applied to a concrete wharf. It adjusts itself readily to varying water levels, is of simple construction, and not readily damaged by boats. It may be removed from the water quickly and easily for storage in winter, or for making repairs. The bumper consists of a yellow-pine timber, 4 in. square, and of suitable length to fit the wharf, provided with heavy soft-brass springs, and fitted to wooden bases which slide vertically in channel irons. The sliding feature permits the bumper to rise and fall with changes in water level. A pad made of a fire hose, filled with granulated cork, is fitted to the outer face of the timber, as a protection to the boats that are brought alongside the dock.

The slides in which the bumper is held against the wharf are built up of two 3-in. channel irons, cut on the outer rib, to admit the springs. The

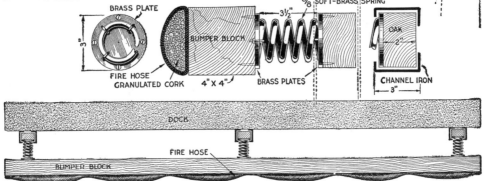

The Floating Bumper Protects Boats That are Docked at the Landing, and Is Readily Adjustable to the Varying Height of Water

guides are fixed to the wharf with screws, their heads being countersunk in the channel irons. The springs are set between brass plates, which are fastened, one to the timber which slides in the channel irons, and the other to the bumper block, at each spring. The sliding timber should be fitted into the guides with plenty of play, so that the bumper may adjust itself to the varying height of the water, or be adjusted with little effort.

Rack for Filing Drawings Vertically

Rolling up of large drawings for storage causes them to curl in an un-

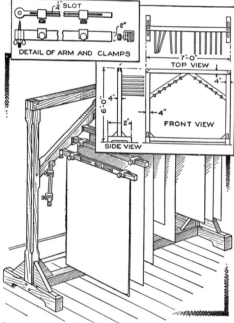

Drawings and Blueprints are Preserved, without Rolling Them, in this Rack. The Arms, in Which the Sheets are Clamped, may be Swung Horizontally, Making Access to the Drawings Convenient

satisfactory manner when they are un-rolled for reference. A filing arrangement that permits the drawings to hang vertically and exposes them so as to be readily available is shown in the sketch. The principle of construction involved may be used for a rack one-half the size of that shown, or may be extended to a larger one. It was designed to care for drawings and blueprints in an architect's office, and was

found especially convenient when drawings were referred to frequently. The rack was placed so that all the draftsmen could reach it with a minimum of effort.

The frame was built of 4 by 4-in. pine, dressed down on all sides. It was strongly joined and pinned at the joints, the floor supports being braced with triangular blocks. The racks on which the drawings are carried are suspended on the upper braces, and are arranged in a series so that the index, or title, on the strips between which the drawings are clamped, may be seen readily. A detail of the arms and the method of supporting them so that they may be swung horizontally, is shown in the small sketch above. Index slides are provided so that the titles of drawings may be inserted as required. The frame shown is substantial enough to carry a second set of racks on the other side. Since it was used against a wall, this feature was omitted. The frame, without a base, may also be fixed to the wall

Concave Mirror Ground from Plane Glass

Desiring a spherical concave mirror of a given focal length, and not being able to find one, I had a lens grinder grind a concave surface of the same curvature that the spherical mirror would have to be, on the face of a plane plate-glass mirror. The concave surface on the plane back gave nearly the same result as would have been obtained by a concave spherical mirror.—Herbert N. Bradstreet, Phoenix, Ariz.

Preventing Screw Eyes from Rusting in Signboard

The screw eyes by which a signboard is suspended, particularly out of doors, become rusted quickly, causing the board to become loosened. White lead applied to the threads of the screw eyes when they are inserted in the wood, will prevent the rusting, which may also spoil the appearance of the sign by streaking it with rust.

Easy Method of Riddling Sand

Riddling sand or gravel for use in making mortar, and other binders, is a tiresome task when the ordinary hand sieve must be used. A good way of lightening the work is to use a rectangular sieve, provided with handles on one end. Nail two strips, about 1 in. square, across the top of the box into which the sand is to be riddled, leaving space enough between them for a roller slightly larger in diameter than the thickness of the strips. By placing such a roller between the strips and drawing the sieve back and forth upon it, the necessity of lifting the sand while riddling it is avoided.—Charles Darlington, Des Moines, Ia.

Screw-Riveting Kink

Occasionally two channel bars, or other members, must be joined together with machine screws in such a way that the heads of the screws will not project as shown in the illustration. Suitable flat-head screws may not be available, and the makeshift method of countersinking the work for another style of screw is not satisfactory. The heads may then be cut off, as indicated at D, Fig. 2. If the screw is driven into place before the nick is made in it, it is difficult to handle the job, because of the obstruction by the flange A. A good method then is to drive the screw into place and mark the portion

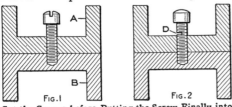

Cut the Groove before Putting the Screw Finally into Place, and Rivet the End After the Head is Broken Off

exposed. Remove the screw, and with a hacksaw cut about halfway through it, as shown. Then replace it and break off the head. The end may then be riveted into place, making a secure joint.—William Philip, South Orange, New Jersey.

Tools Made of Buggy-Top Braces

Many handy tools may be made from the jointed portions of buggy-top braces, and several suggestive uses are

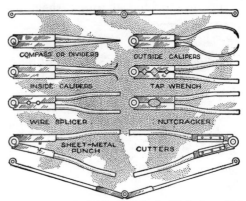

A Variety of Useful Tools may be Made from Old Buggy-Top Braces at Practically No Cost

shown in the sketch. By grinding the ends of the sections to points, a compass or dividers may be made; by forging them slightly, inside calipers, outside calipers, and similar tools may be made. By cutting appropriate notches into the jaws of the sections and fitting them with small pins as required, a nutcracker, wire splicer, sheet-metal punch, and a wrench are possibilities. Various types of cutters and nippers may be constructed from the sections by riveting blades to them, as shown at the right. The braces may also be used as clamps by fitting them with machine screws, or with bolts and wing nuts. By sharpening the points, as for dividers, and bending them slightly inward, the resulting tool may be used for spreading boards in nailing them by setting one point in each adjacent board, and bearing down on the hinge of the brace. Leather straps, or even carpets, may be stretched in this manner by using a board to increase the range of the device.—R. S. Matzen, Fort Collins, Colo.

⟪Emery wheels should be kept dressed up to give the best results, and the seeming waste of the wheel in dressing will be found an economy in time and satisfactory grinding.

Jackscrew Used in Laying Plank Floors

Heavy planks used in the making of floors frequently are not straight, and it is thus difficult to bring them to-

Heavy Planks are Forced into Place, Forming a Tight-Jointed Floor, by Means of the Jackscrew

gether firmly by the usual kinks in drawing them into place, by setting the spikes properly. A small jack, rigged with a chain as shown in the sketch, was used effectively and saved the workmen much time and heavy labor. The jackscrew was fitted on a board having a notch near one end, so that when it was placed on its side the screw was horizontal, with the handle upward, and the head raised so that it could be turned by means of a hand-spike. The chain was placed around the floor joists, and over the handle of the jackscrew. By tightening the chain, with the head of the jackscrew against the plank, the latter was forced into place as firmly as desired. For each plank the chain and rigging was moved forward along the joist. If necessary it may be shifted from one place to another, or two or more jackscrews used at the same time, if the planks are long, and particularly crooked.—James Skelton, Toronto, Canada.

⁋Leather machine belts should be cleaned with gasoline to give a good binding surface, rather than load them with belt grease, when they slip repeatedly.

String Solder Replaces Copper Wire in Battery Room

Considerable trouble was experienced in the storage-battery room because of acid fumes attacking the copper service wires. The life of the unprotected wires strung above the batteries was short; they became brittle and broke easily. To overcome the difficulty, the room was completely rewired, using string solder for conductors. This metal, being immune from acid fumes, was not corroded and showed no tendency to become brittle.—K. M. Coggeshall, Webster Groves, Mo.

Tension Spring for T-Square

The necessity for continual care in keeping the head of a T-square against the edge of the drawing board is obviated by the use of a tension spring on the other end of the square, as shown in the illustration. The action becomes that of a movable straight-edge rigged to remain in a horizontal position, and the T-square may be quickly changed to its common form by removing the spring. The details of the device are shown in the working drawing on the drawing board.

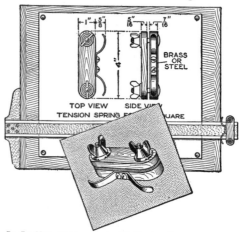

It Is Not Necessary to Hold the Head of the T-Square Firmly against the Board When the Tension Spring is Used

The spring may be of brass or steel. The clamp is held firmly by means of two wing nuts.—Alphonse R. Desjardins, Cheyenne, Wyo.

Cleaning Automobile-Engine Cooling System

To clean the cooling system of an automobile engine, drain off the water from the water jacket and connections, by means of the petcock provided for that purpose. Pour a solution of two handfuls of washing soda to a pail of hot water into the system. Run the engine for a few moments to stir the mixture thoroughly throughout the system, and then drain off the soda solution. Permit clean water to flow through the radiator until it brings no more sediment with it, and then fill the system with clean water. This method removes all rust or grease effectively from the radiator and its connections.

Gauge for Cutting Packing-Box Stock

The gauge shown in Fig. 1 was made to provide a convenient method of measuring duplicate pieces for packing boxes, made from miscellaneous stock from time to time, in a shipping room. The articles to be packed were largely of several standard sizes and the gauge was designed first to fit the necessary boxes. It consisted of two strips of wood joined at right angles, and having indications for the length and width of the pieces. A later development was the attachment of the adjustable

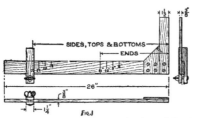

This Simple Gauge Aided in the Cutting of Stock for Boxes of Sizes Much Used

arm, by means of which various odd-sized pieces could be gauged. Figure 2 shows a gauge with metal fittings, and indications readily applicable to various sizes of box stock. Indications for the lengths of pieces for standard-size boxes are shown in the spaces marked "Ends" and "Sides."

Other sizes are gauged by the use of the scale.

The adjustable arm is fitted to slide on the scale rod, and is tightened into place by a knurled thumbscrew. The

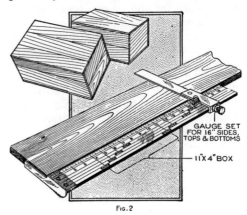

FIG. 2

Stock for a Large Variety of Boxes may be Gauged Quickly with This Device

arm is used as a square in marking the end to be cut off. The metal fittings are of $\frac{1}{16}$-in. sheet brass. The arm is riveted where the portion of the strip looped over the scale rod joins the straightedge. The thumbscrew operates in a hexagonal nut soldered to the end of the loop.—John M. Pipp, Muncie, Ind.

Setting Screws in Making Metal Patches

Liners for revolving or sliding machine parts are usually applied with patch bolts, which sometimes become loosened, causing serious damage. This can be readily prevented by cutting a small notch at the upper edge of the countersunk seat for the head of the bolt, and when the head is in place, riveting the edge of it into the notch. This prevents the bolt from becoming loosened, and, if it is desired to remove it, the riveted portion may be chipped off. Care must be taken not to strike the screw too hard, as the thread may be damaged, only a slight riveting being necessary.

❲The bearings of a magneto should be oiled sparingly.

Simple Tree Repairing

By C. L. MELLER

OFTEN a tree that appears to be ready for the ax can be saved for many a year by the simple process of removing the decayed wood, and, where necessary, strengthening the remaining parts. The nature of the work is such that a person with reasonable skill in the use of carpenter tools can do a satisfactory job, providing he acquaints himself with the fundamental structure of the tree.

The photographs, reproduced in the illustration, show trees repaired by bracing them with wood. Three stages in the process are indicated, for a repair on an upper limb at A, and on the main trunk at B. The stages are: 1, faulty tree; 2, cavity cleaned; 3, cavity filled with wood brace. The part of the tree trunk or limb essential to the tree's life is the thin band of green just below the bark, and a thicker layer of the sapwood behind it. The rest of the inside of a trunk or limb represents strength and does not function in the

or similar substance is good, but requires a technical knowledge that none but an expert along this line possesses. Such work poorly done is worse than useless, and it is not necessary to resort to the filling method to get satisfactory results. The punk and decayed wood must first be removed from the cavity, and the exposed surface permitted to dry out for several days. Then the work should be gone over again, leaving nothing but the soundest of wood with a surface almost as smooth as if it had been dressed down with tools. Painting the cavity with boiled linseed oil, into which a little burnt umber has been stirred, will prove a good protective covering, but needs to be renewed at least once a year to be permanently effective. The burnt umber produces a natural brown color, that makes a hollow in a trunk or limb quite inconspicuous.

If there arises the least suspicion that the cavity leaves the trunk or limb in a condition so weak that it might break under the weight of the tree or the pressure of the wind against the foliage, it can be strengthened by bolting a timber into the cavity, extending the full length of the wound. A four-by-four will generally prove thick enough, though where the cavity is exceedingly large, and the remaining shell of wood is thin.

life process of the tree. That explains why the rotting of the inside of a tree does not interfere with its life. Cutting away the inner wood weakens the tree structurally only, and if this strength can be restored, a tree thus supported will endure for many a year.

Filling cavities made by the removal of decayed wood from a tree with concrete, asphaltum,

Reinforcing a Weak Limb and a Rotted Trunk Is Simple by the Method Shown

a timber of greater dimensions should be used. A sound pole of some of the stronger woods makes an excellent reinforcement. Thus, at times, a small tree that is out of place and is to be cut down may serve as reinforcement for a larger tree that may be saved for a number of years. There is usually sufficient strength at both ends of such a cavity to resist all stress and strains that may be put upon them, while the weakest part is along the middle.

The bolts used should be thick enough to give ample strength, but must not be so thick that the hole required will materially weaken the timber used. They should be no longer than is necessary. Washers are used to provide a good bearing surface, and should be countersunk slightly below the bark. A weakened limb may be further strengthened by tying it to several other limbs with a chain or cable and bolts. In no case, however, must a chain or band of iron encircle a limb. An eyebolt is placed through the limb and the chain attached to it.

An I-Beam Anvil

An I-beam may be made into a serviceable and almost noiseless anvil if

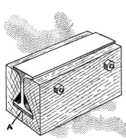

fitted with a wooden casing, as shown in the sketch. A section of the beam, about 2 ft. long, is squared on the ends, the rough edges removed, and two holes for bolts drilled through it, about 6 in. from each end. The case of wood is made from two oak, or other strong wood, blocks, and the inner faces are cut to fit the flanges of the beam, as shown. A pad of leather, A, is fitted under the beam, and the parts are bolted together firmly. If the leather pad is fitted closely and the wooden case is brought up tightly by means of the bolts, there will be little noise produced when the anvil is used.—James E. Noble, Toronto, Can.

An Improvised Lifting Jack

The need of a device for lifting comparatively light objects or constructions while leveling them is often felt, and a jackscrew

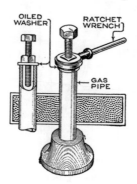

is not always available. Materials at hand in most small shops were used to make the improvised lifting jack shown in the sketch, and it proved satisfactory enough to warrant keeping it for future use. A section of 1-in. pipe was fitted into a wooden block as a base, and a washer was set on top of the pipe. A large machine screw and a nut to fit it were set through the washer, as shown, and a ratchet wrench was applied to the nut. An ordinary plain or monkey wrench may be used, the ratchet wrench being more convenient, and in this instance available.—John Uttley, Hale, Cheshire, Eng.

Revolving Tool Rack

In small shops, or other places where it is desirable to economize tool space, the revolving tool rack shown

in the sketch may be installed to advantage. A round rod was set into a plate fixed on the bench, and its upper end supported by a metal brace, B, fixed to the wall. Two round wooden disks, A, with holes for the tools, are supported on the rod, and may be revolved to make access to the tools convenient. Metal disks may be used, and will be more serviceable than the wooden ones.—H. W. Offins, Grants Pass, Ore.

Temporary Repair for Pipe Leak

Leaks in water pipes, particularly in winter, cause much damage unless stopped promptly. This is often dif-

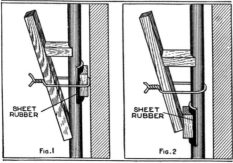

A Leak in a Water Pipe was Stopped Temporarily by the Use of a Simple Clamping Device

ficult, as a plumber's services are not always quickly available. Under such circumstances, the device shown in the sketch was used to stop a leak until a permanent repair was made. A piece of sheet rubber was placed over the leak, and a wooden block was fitted over it, the inner surface being curved to fit the pipe. The block and rubber packing were clamped against the pipe by means of a stick, notched to set against the pipe, and held by a twisted wire, a block being used to wedge the packing and cover block firmly into place. The repair was water-tight and saved much inconvenience and probably considerable damage. The illustration shows the application of this method to two types of leaks, Fig. 1 being a leak difficult of access, against a wall, and that in Fig. 2 on the exposed side of the pipe.—J. W. Cox, Florence, Alabama.

Keeping Auto Top Down Saves Gasoline

The practice of running an automobile with the top up when it is not needed, is costly, according to tests which I made. When the back of the top cannot be rolled up, the resistance is especially great. Six miles more were obtained from a gallon of gasoline with the top rolled and covered, as compared with having the top up with the back closed. When going against the wind, this extra pull is especially heavy, and difficulty in making a hard climb may often be relieved by lowering the top. Careful regulation of the top, using it only when essential, will be found to be a worth-while factor in reducing the gasoline bill.—L. E. Turner, Jamaica, N. Y.

Overcoming Floor Vibration under Scale Platform

Scales, set on the floor of a shop or other place, where machinery, passing traffic, and other disturbances, cause considerable vibration, cannot be used with satisfaction because of this condition. This trouble was overcome by providing the scales with a hollow cast-iron base, having $\frac{3}{8}$-in. walls, so that the scales were raised to a more convenient height for using them, in weighing objects of no great bulk. A square piece of live rubber, $\frac{1}{2}$ in. thick, was placed as a foot at each corner of the base, and this took up the floor vibrations.—M. E. Duggan, Kenosha, Wisconsin.

Making Oil Grooves in Babbitt Bearings

Oil grooves may be provided in babbitt bearings by wrapping a piece of cord around the shafting which is to fit the bearing, as shown in the sketch. The cord should be wrapped spirally in two directions from the center of the bearing toward the ends, so that the oil

Oil Grooves may be Cast in the Bearing by the Use of a Spiral Cord

will be carried toward each end from the oil hole, when the shaft revolves. The babbitt is poured around the shaft and incloses the cord, which is withdrawn when the metal has cooled.

⊄Copper nails and screws are best for boats and other marine purposes.

Machinery Foundations with Anchor-Plate Pockets

By TERRELL CROFT

SETTING heavy machinery, or removing it from foundations, is accomplished more readily when the anchor bolts are arranged to be inserted or taken out after the machine is in place. This may be provided for by pockets in the foundations, so disposed that headless anchor bolts project into them, at their lower ends, the anchor plates and nuts being accessible in the pockets, as shown in Fig. 1. This method of construction is adaptable to a large variety of foundations, of materials in common use; details of several typical applications are indicated in the sketches. The bolts are incased in metal pipes, built into the foundation, and providing a convenient method of inserting them. The pockets may be formed by the use of wooden forms, stone slabs, cast into the foundation, as shown in Fig. 6, bricks and iron slabs, Fig. 8, and, when the number of pockets makes it advisable, pocket castings of iron may be inserted, as shown in Figs. 10, 11, and 12. The method of setting the bolts to fit the bolt holes in the machinery is detailed in Fig. 13, and shown also in other sketches, the upper ends of the bolt casings being set into templates.

The function of an anchor-plate pocket is to permit the withdrawal or insertion of an anchor bolt when desired. The provision of pockets permits the insertion of anchor bolts in a foundation after the foundation has been completed. It is frequently desirable to build a foundation without the anchor bolts in it, so that their projecting ends will not interfere with the installation of the machinery on the foundation. In such instances, the foundation must be "pocketed." Occasionally a foundation bolt is broken and

must be replaced. Such replacements are exceedingly difficult unless pockets are provided. Sometimes it is not feasible to place the anchor bolts in a foundation when it is being constructed because the bolts are not immediately available, and a pocketed foundation must then be used. As is quite evident, pockets are used only where the anchor bolts are removable.

Large foundation installations justify the provision of pockets for the nuts and anchor plates, because with all large foundations it is exceedingly expensive to replace an anchor bolt if one is broken, unless pockets are provided. Anchor bolts in large foundations frequently extend a considerable distance above the top surface of the foundation, and materially interfere with the skidding of the machine onto the foundation. Where bolts are removable, that is, where pockets are provided, such interference can be eliminated.

There are really two kinds of anchor-plate pockets, accessible and inaccessible. An accessible pocket is one that opens to the outside of the foundation, so that the lower end of the anchor bolt is always accessible. An inaccessible pocket is merely a cavity under the anchor plate to accommodate the end of the anchor bolt that extends through the nut. The accessible type is the more frequently used because an inaccessible pocket may become clogged with rubbish, falling in from the top of the foundation, whereby its purpose is defeated. Only pockets of the accessible type are considered in this article. Accessible pockets are sometimes called handholes; they are recesses, or chambers, extending from the side of a foundation, as shown in Figs. 1 and 2, to a point somewhat beyond and directly under the anchor plate and bolt. In the case of a large foundation, instead of extending from the side of the foundation, the chambers may open into a tunnel through the foundation. Such tunnels are frequently provided to admit access to the anchor-plate pockets.

The location of the pockets in a foundation must be determined in each specific installation. It is difficult to outline any general rule. It is usual, however, to make foundation bolts extend almost to the bottom of, or for a distance at least equal to 40 times the diameter of the anchor bolt into, the foundation. This means that the pockets will nearly always be near the bottom of the foundation. Where a foundation is constructed on a footing, as indicated in Fig. 3, the top surface of the footing frequently constitutes the bottom of the pocket cavity. It is obvious that the location of the pockets in a foundation will be in any case largely determined by the length of the foundation bolts.

In removing an anchor bolt from a pocketed foundation it is only necessary to unscrew the anchor bolt. If the pocket is accessible, the nut can then be removed from the pocket, and a new nut substituted, if desirable. Anchor bolts for pocketed foundations consist, in practically every case, of mild-steel rods threaded on both ends. An anchor bolt with a head forged on its lower end could, of course, not be removed.

Pockets in brick foundations are constructed as shown in Fig. 3. In building the foundation, a cavity is left in the brickwork as diagrammed, and from this cavity, extending vertically upward, a shaft, which provides a casing hole for the future insertion of the foundation bolt, is arranged. To support the brickwork above the pocket cavity, a slab of wrought or cast iron, or of stone, is used. If an iron slab is utilized, it should be proportioned of sufficient thickness to constitute an anchor plate, rendering the use of an additional anchor plate unnecessary. Cast-iron anchor plates, of the standard types used in foundations, can often be applied instead of an iron slab. Where the slab is of stone, an anchor plate should be used on the lower end of the foundation bolt, as shown in Fig. 2, to distribute the pressure transmitted from the anchor bolt to the stone slab. Boiler-plate steel, of sufficient thickness, can often be obtained from junk dealers at little cost, and where such can be procured, a rectangular piece, with a hole drilled through it at the proper place, constitutes a splendid roof slab for the pocket in a brick foundation. Pockets in rock or stone foundations are constructed in practically the same manner as those for brick, as illustrated in Fig. 3.

Pockets in concrete foundations are subject to more variation in design and arrangement than are those used in brickwork. Figure 4 shows the arrangement and construction of a typical concrete-foundation pocket. It is usual in concrete foundations to place a footing which covers the entire bottom of the hole that has been excavated for the foundation. Then the foundation proper is built up on this footing. Ordinarily the bottom of the pocket hole is the top of the foundation footing, as shown in Fig. 4. A form is necessary where a pocket is to be cast into a concrete foundation. Forms of different types are shown in the sketches and merit detailed discussion.

A wooden form, for a pocket and a casing hole, is shown in Fig. 5 in position in the foundation, with the concrete cast around it. Where an iron-tube casing is not used for the foundation bolt, the construction suggested in this illustration is a good one. The casing form is supported at its upper end by the template. The top piece of the pocket form is nailed to its lower end, and is supported at its sides, back, and front, with pieces of board, which constitute the form for the pocket walls. While the front board of the pocket form—that at the access side of the pocket—serves partly to support the weight of the concrete, which rests on the top piece at that point, it is always desirable to secure the pocket form to the foundation form by nails

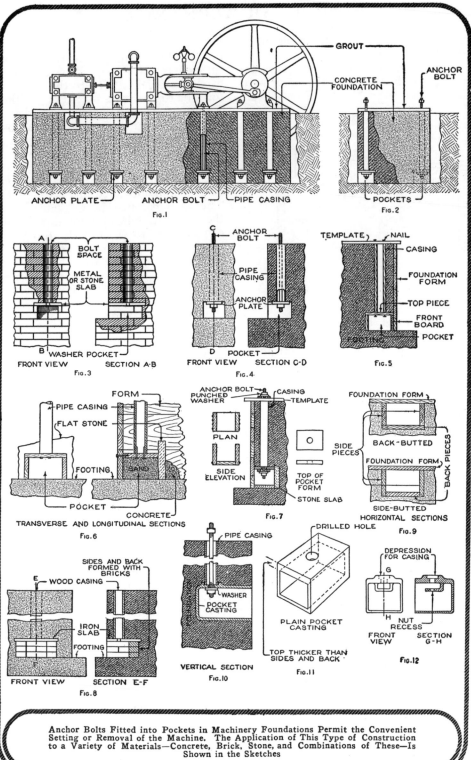

GROUT

ANCHOR BOLT

CONCRETE FOUNDATION

ANCHOR PLATE — ANCHOR BOLT — PIPE CASING

Fɪɢ.1

POCKETS

Fɪɢ.2

BOLT SPACE

METAL OR STONE SLAB

A

B WASHER POCKET

FRONT VIEW   SECTION A-B

Fɪɢ.3

C   ANCHOR BOLT

PIPE CASING

ANCHOR PLATE

D   POCKET

FRONT VIEW   SECTION C-D

Fɪɢ.4

TEMPLATE   NAIL

CASING

FOUNDATION FORM

TOP PIECE

FRONT BOARD

FOOTING   POCKET

Fɪɢ.5

FORM

PIPE CASING

FLAT STONE

FOOTING   SAND

POCKET   CONCRETE

TRANSVERSE AND LONGITUDINAL SECTIONS

Fɪɢ.6

ANCHOR BOLT PUNCHED WASHER   CASING

TEMPLATE

PLAN

SIDE ELEVATION

SIDE PIECES

TOP OF POCKET FORM

STONE SLAB

Fɪɢ.7

FOUNDATION FORM

BACK-BUTTED

FOUNDATION FORM

BACK PIECES

SIDE-BUTTED

HORIZONTAL SECTIONS

Fɪɢ.9

SIDES AND BACK FORMED WITH BRICKS

E   WOOD CASING

IRON SLAB

FOOTING

F

FRONT VIEW   SECTION E-F

Fɪɢ.8

PIPE CASING

FOUNDATION

WASHER

POCKET CASTING

VERTICAL SECTION

Fɪɢ.10

DRILLED HOLE

PLAIN POCKET CASTING

TOP THICKER THAN SIDES AND BACK

Fɪɢ.11

DEPRESSION FOR CASING

G

H   NUT RECESS

FRONT VIEW   SECTION G-H

Fɪɢ.12

Anchor Bolts Fitted into Pockets in Machinery Foundations Permit the Convenient Setting or Removal of the Machine. The Application of This Type of Construction to a Variety of Materials—Concrete, Brick, Stone, and Combinations of These—Is Shown in the Sketches

driven in from the outside, as illustrated in Fig. 3.

Forms for pockets, where a metal casing is to be used for the anchor bolt,

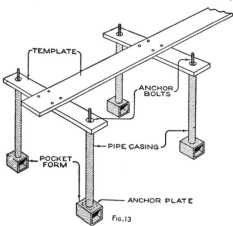

FIG.13

The Pocket Castings are Suspended from the Casings and Bolts, Fitted to the Template

are shown in Figs. 6, 7, and 8. In these examples the form for the pocket is fixed to the bolt casing, so that the latter may serve, in part, as a support for the form.

It is desirable to arrange the pieces of board, constituting the pocket form, so that they can be removed easily after the foundation has set. If, in building a pocket form, it is so constructed that the backboard butts against the ends of the two side pieces, the latter can be removed easily, after the foundation has set, as shown above in Fig. 9. The back piece, however, will probably be difficult of removal, because the concrete will bind at the ends of the piece. If the end pieces are side-butted, as shown below, the pocket form can be pried out of the foundation easily, after the latter has set.

Stone slabs are often used to form the backs of pocket forms, to obviate the difficulty in removing the pieces of the form. Figures 6 and 7 illustrate pocket forms having stone-slab backs. The sides of a pocket can also be made of stone slabs, if slabs of the proper dimensions are available. The stone is, of course, permitted to remain in the foundation permanently.

Sand may be used for filling in pocket

forms, as shown in Fig. 6, to prevent the possible collapse of the form, before the concrete has set. Where sand is used, the form is filled to the brim before the top board is placed in position. Where stone slabs are employed in a pocket form, they can be held in position temporarily by placing a lump of concrete outside of them, as shown in Fig. 6.

The pocket forms and casings may be joined as indicated in Figs. 6 and 7. The casings must be available when the concrete is being poured, and they can be used to support the top board of a pocket form, as shown in Figs. 7 and 13, if the foundation bolts are at hand. The casing is cut to a length exactly equal to the distance between the top of the foundation and the roof of the pocket, as shown in Fig. 7. The upper end of the anchor bolt is located accurately in the foundation form by a template. The casing is arranged concentrically around the bolt, and is clamped between the bottom face of the template and the board which forms the top of the pocket form. If the sides of the pocket form consist of wood pieces, they may be prevented from collapsing, as shown in Fig. 7, by another board nailed between them at the bottom, and by nails driven into them, through the top board.

It should be noted that, with the arrangement described, the anchor-bolt template locates the casings and the positions of the pockets, and that the elevation of the tops of the pocket forms is determined by the length of the casings. If the template is laid out correctly, and the casings are cut accurately to length, the pocket forms locate themselves almost automatically, both laterally and vertically. With this procedure, there is little chance for error, and the concrete men have to make but few measurements.

Bricks can be used to make pocket forms, as shown in Fig. 8. Where this method is utilized, the construction of practically all form work is avoided. A metal slab may be used as a form for the roof of the pocket. It can be supported by an anchor bolt. In building a pocket of this type, the bolt casing and the slab constituting the top of the form, are first suspended from the template. Then the brickwork—sides and back—is built around the edges of the slab. The sides are built first and braced inside with bricks temporarily placed, or with pieces of board. Then the back is built.

Cast-iron pockets can be used, as shown in Fig. 10. These pockets, or castings, detailed in Figs. 11 and 12, may be made to serve both as pocket forms and anchor plates. They, of course, remain in the foundation permanently. The simplest type of anchor-bolt pocket casting is shown in Fig. 11. It is merely a cast-iron box, with one open side, and a hole drilled in its top for the accommodation of the anchor bolt. Where such a casting must also act as an anchor plate, its top should be thicker than the sides and bottom, as suggested in the illustration, so that it will withstand successfully the stresses imposed when the anchor-bolt nuts are tightened. A more elaborate casting is shown in Fig. 12. This has a recess for the anchor-bolt nut and a circular depression on its upper side to accommodate a tubular casing. The design shown in Fig. 11 is most frequently used, because one pattern of this design can be used in combination with anchor bolts of several different diameters. However, with the casting shown in Fig. 12, the dimensions of the nut recess and of the casing depression should be different for each size bolt. Hence, it does not pay to make a pattern for a casting like that of Fig. 12 unless many bolts of the same diameter are to be installed.

In constructing a concrete foundation where pocket castings are to be used, the castings can be suspended from the template and held in place by the castings and anchor bolts as shown in Fig. 13. The template thus serves to locate the pockets and also the bolts. The casings, if cut to proper length, will maintain the pocket castings at the correct elevation, and they need only be steadied when the concrete is poured.

Rack for Raising Crossbar on Vaulting Standards

Placing the crossbar upon the vaulting standards consumes considerable

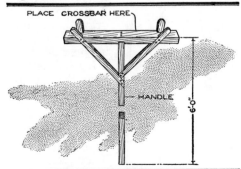

Place the Crossbar on the Rack and Raise It into Place Quickly and Accurately

time and frequently causes annoyance to participants and officials at track meets. This is particularly true in pole vaulting at a considerable height. The device shown in the sketch was made to overcome this difficulty. The crossbar is placed between the projecting strips and raised into place easily. This also insures accurate placing of the bar on the standards, and prevents the possibility of the bar falling accidentally and ruining a trial which might have been successful.—A. B. Wegener, Madison, N. J.

Wire Straightener Made of Spools

An effective wire straightener may be made by bolting several spools to a board in a row, as shown in the illustration. The wire to be straightened is threaded between the spools and drawn through them as indicated by the arrows. This device is very con-

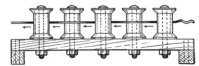

Draw the Wire through the Spools in Order to Straighten It

venient when coils are to be wound, as it will keep wire taut without putting undue strain on it.—Thomas W. Benson, Hastings upon Hudson, N. Y.

An Adjustable Taper Gauge

The taper gauge illustrated was designed to fit a large variety of taper work. The body 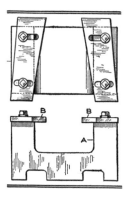 A is a casting of gray iron, machined on the upper surface. The adjustable jaws B are made of machine steel, and should have at least one face and the inner edge machined. They may be made of various widths and ranges of adjustment, to suit the work. The jaws are clamped securely by means of the machine screws, which should be of standard-size head, to fit a socket wrench. A convenient size is that used on lathes in the shop where the gauge is to be used.—C. Anderson, Worcester, Mass.

Testing Judgment of Short Distances

Mechanics often pride themselves on their ability to judge and to compare 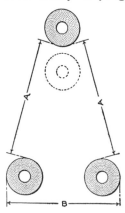 distances accurately. An interesting test of this ability is shown in the illustration. The test is as follows: Arrange three coins, washers, or similar disks in triangular form so that the distances A are equal to the distance B. Almost invariably the third washer, at the apex of the triangle, will be placed in a position as indicated by the dotted outline. Even after the washers have been placed correctly by measurement, the distances A appear to be longer than the distance B.

Handle for Cellar or Floor Doors

Doors of the old-fashioned slanting cellar type are quickly pulled out of shape or loosened at the hinges when raised by means of a small handle. If a block is nailed to the door at each end of the edge at which it opens, and a strip nailed across the blocks, the handle may be grasped at any convenient point, and the strain will be distributed over the door properly, with a minimum of damage to it. This type of handle is useful on trapdoors leading down into a cellar, or on doors leading up from a stairway into lofts and attics.

Leather Cover for an Automobile Pedal

An extremely useful attachment for one's automobile is a form of leather 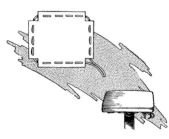 boot to cover the pedal pads. The pads, or boots, can be readily made from a piece of thin leather cut to the shape shown, and are held in position by a leather thong. The pad will be found very useful in cold and snowy weather in keeping the foot on the pedal.

Electric Light Warms Carburetor in Winter

A certain, cheap, and convenient way of starting a motor car, which has saved me much annoyance the past winter, is to use an incandescent lamp with an extension cord to warm the carburetor. An old carbon lamp of eight candlepower was used, by simply putting the lamp under the carburetor and in the morning turning on the current from the house about ten minutes before the car is needed.—E. P. Feate, Spokane, Wash.

Shop Notes

Ventilating a Mine Tunnel

By GEORGE N. STEUART

EXCELLENT ventilation was provided in a mine during the winter seasons, with one shift working, by the installation of the pipe system shown in the sketch. During the summer water power is available from a lake 352 ft. above the tunnel, this fall operating a compressor and water wheel, a 10-in. fan providing air for use at the forge and in the mine. In the winter the water from the lake is not available, and this source of power is cut off until the melting of the snow raises the water in the lake basin.

To provide ventilation in winter, the 10-in. ventilation pipe is connected with the 10-in. water pipe, the water intake being closed. A standpipe with a ventilator head is provided at the lake end of the water pipe, as shown in the illustration. The air moves freely from the ventilator, being aided by the action of the wind, and the fact that the warm air at the tunnel breast will have a tendency to rise in the pipe.

The pipe line from the power house to the lake is 1,600 ft., the tunnel is cut into the hillside 1,320 ft., and 100 ft. of pipe was required to connect the line from the portal of the tunnel to the lower end of the water pipe. After blasting down the rock, the powder fumes come from the ventilator quickly, and by morning, when the shift is ready to resume operations, the entire mine—2,400 ft. of workings, closed stopes, or chambers in which the rock is blasted from overhead, with manways, and 50 ft. of stoping—is clear of gas and thoroughly ventilated.

This ventilating system was inexpensive under the conditions, and is suggestive for adaptation in many other similar mining or tunneling operations. The fact that the water pipe is used for a ventilating shaft is a considerable economy, but even if installed complete for the special purpose of ventilation, it should prove efficient and worth while, particularly where no cheap power is available. For mining operations with more than a single shift, forced draft would be necessary to provide adequate ventilation. The pipes should be run up to a sufficient height for proper draft, by the shortest route available.

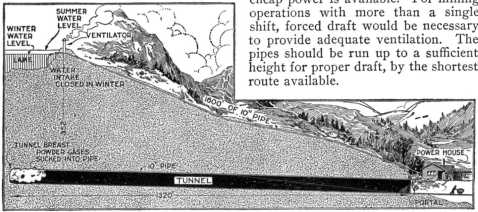

In Summer the Mine is Ventilated by a Fan Driven by Water Power, and in Winter the Unused Water Line is Connected with the Air Pipe, Providing a Draft Which Removes Powder Gases

Drill Press Used as a Vertical Miller

A large number of pulleys were in process of finishing when it was discovered that an error had been made

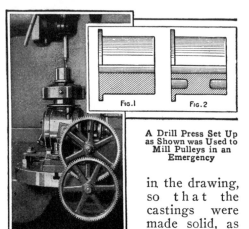

Fig.1　　Fig.2

A Drill Press Set Up as Shown was Used to Mill Pulleys in an Emergency

in the drawing, so that the castings were made solid, as shown in Fig. 1, instead of with a web, as in Fig. 2. In order to use the castings it was decided to machine them to the proper shape, on the only machine available, a drill press. The dividing head from the milling machine was not in use on the job which tied up the milling machine, and it was set up on the drill press, as shown in the photograph reproduced. A socket was made to fit the taper of the drill-press spindle, and its other end was fitted to take an end mill. It was necessary to feed or revolve the work by hand, and to avoid the danger of crowding the cutter, the gears were arranged as shown. In this way, by hand-turning, the gear could be moved rapidly without endangering the cutter.—Harvey Mead, Scranton, Pennsylvania.

Stretching Fence Wire with an Automobile

It was desired to build about three miles of three-strand barbed-wire fence, and fence-building equipment was not available. An automobile was pressed into service and the work was accomplished satisfactorily in the following manner: The posts were set ready to receive the wire. The rolls of wire were hauled to the place at which the wiring was to begin. Two posts were set in the ground, one on each side of the end of the fence, and the three spools of barbed wire were supported upon them by means of pipe. The spools could revolve as on a reel and were set at the height at which it was desired to fasten the wire on the fence posts. The free end of one coil was fixed to the automobile, the wire was unreeled, and by driving slowly it was drawn to the desired tension. It was then stapled to the post. In this way the other two strands were also fastened. The result was a fence having the wire drawn tightly and made in comparatively short time.—J. E. King, Dallas, Tex.

Self-Locking Swinging Stanchion

The handling of a large number of cattle in a stable may be facilitated by the use of stanchions which will lock the cows into their places without assistance from the herdsman. Such a device, designed to be made in the farm workshop, is shown in the illustration. It is free to swing, making it

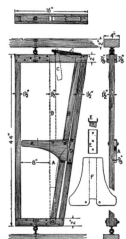

comfortable for cattle, and may be fitted into the old wooden standards in combination with other types of stanchions. The trigger may be made of wood or of sheet metal, cut to the proper shape and bent to fit the movable bar.

The stanchion is suspended between the standards by means of eyebolts. The frame is built of hard wood, 1½ in. square, and joined with countersunk screws. At the top and bottom the crosspieces are of ⅞-in. stuff, and the movable bar B is fitted between them. The movable bar is pivoted on a bolt at its lower end and engages a key, C, at its upper end. The key holds the bar back until the trigger A is sprung by the cow, in placing the head into the stanchion. The trigger operates against a block, D, fixed to the side of the frame.

The construction of a metal trigger is shown at F. The sheet metal is cut to the shape shown and folded on the dotted lines. A guide of sheet metal, E, is fixed to the frame to engage the end of the metal trigger. Cattle are released from the stanchion by raising the trigger, the device then being in position for locking automatically when again occupied.—F. H. Sweet, Waynesboro, Va.

Lever Holds Planer Tool Block on Backstroke

While planing a considerable number of large pieces in a machine shop, and also some long T-slots, I found that my arm became quite lame from lifting the tool block on the planer on the backstroke. I devised the lever shown in the sketch and fitted it on the tool block, making it unnecessary to lift the block. During the cutting stroke the lever is in the position indicated in Fig. 1, and by raising it on its cam surface, as shown in Fig. 2, the tool is held up on the backstroke. The lever is shown in detail in Fig. 3. For rais-

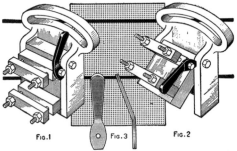

The Lever with a Cam End Makes the Holding of the Tool Block on the Backstroke Unnecessary

ing the tool only slightly above the work, the lever may be attached at the lower end of the block.—Richard H. Jehlicka, Worcester, Mass.

Reel and Cutter for Sandpaper and Emery Cloth

Emery cloth and sandpaper are used in rolls in many factories and shops; much waste results when the roll is

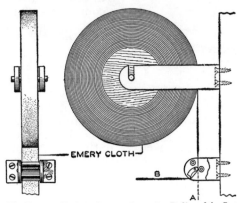

The Emery Cloth is Drawn from the Roll and is Cut Off Squarely by the Cutter

not properly cared for, so that the workmen may take only such pieces as are required for the work in hand. The reel and cutter shown in the sketch was built to economize emery cloth, which was used in strips. It is simple in construction and may be adapted to rolls of various widths. The roll is carried on a wooden disk, in which an iron rod is mounted as a bearing shaft. The latter rests in a metal bracket, fixed to the wall. Below the reel, and in line with the edge of the roll near the wall, is the cutting device, through which the strip is drawn from the roll. The strip is drawn toward A over a small roller, and then brought to the position B, when it is cut off.— Stephen Bona, Union City, Conn.

An Emergency Pipe Wrench

Pipes can be handled with an ordinary monkey wrench nearly as satisfactorily as with a pipe wrench, if a small bolt, threaded the full length, is placed between the lower jaw of the wrench and the pipe to be turned. The jaws of the wrench must be drawn up closely before attempting to turn the pipe.—George L. Yaste, Lonaconing, Maryland.

Clip for Pocket Scale

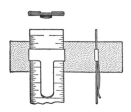

The annoyance of having a scale slip from the pocket is experienced by most mechanics, and in order to overcome this nuisance, I made a clip of sheet brass, $\frac{1}{32}$ in. thick, like that shown in the sketch. It was clamped securely to the end of the scale and prevented the latter from falling out of the pocket. Others in the shop thought so well of it that in a short time many had made clips similar to mine.—John I. Blaker, Worcester, Massachusetts.

Tray for Counter Advertising Matter

Handbills, or other small printed matter for distribution on counters in stores, easily get out of order, both through carelessness and the likelihood of drafts blowing the paper about. The holder shown in the sketch attracts attention to the handbills and keeps them readily available, yet in a neat pile that cannot be easily disturbed.—J. J. O'Brien, Buffalo, N. Y.

Key-Ring Riveter

The small riveter shown in the sketch was made to be carried on a key ring in the pocket, and is convenient for use with hollow or tubular rivets. It was made of a piece of steel, $\frac{1}{2}$ in. in diameter, turned in a lathe to the shape shown at A, on one end. A groove was turned around the piece, at B, and a stiff $\frac{1}{8}$-in. wire

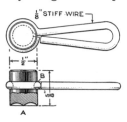

was fixed around it and a handle formed on the other end. The handle is slipped onto the key ring, and the device may be used without removing it from the latter. A sharp blow from a hammer on the upper end of the riveter causes the rivet to spread neatly.—R. S. Matzen, Fort Collins, Colorado.

Device for Punching Holes in Sheet Metal

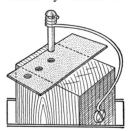

A $\frac{1}{2}$-in. bolt held above a wooden block by means of a wire, as shown in the sketch, was used to punch holes in No. 24-gauge sheet iron, and smoothly cut holes resulted. The block was of hard wood and a $\frac{1}{2}$-in. hole was bored into the end grain to act as a die for the bolt. The wire was convenient in that it held the bolt out of the way while the strip of metal was shifted. A better die could be provided by placing an iron plate with a $\frac{1}{2}$-in. hole through it on top of a block, arranging it so that the bolt registers over the hole.

Hard-Rubber Bushing Made without Lathe

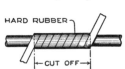

A narrow strip of sheet hard rubber, wound spirally around a rod of appropriate diameter, can be used to make a bushing for electrical work, nearly as useful as one turned up on a lathe. When the work is begun, the rubber and the rod should be heated slightly. Hold the ends of the rubber until it cools, and it will remain in shape as shown in the cut. The ends may either be filed off or nicked with a sharp knife and broken at the dotted lines.—Frank L. Whitaker, Clay City, Ind.

Lights behind Storage Batteries Indicate Charging Periods

The storage-battery room for most office telephone exchanges is situated in a compartment which has to be artificially lighted. It is difficult, therefore, to ascertain when a battery is charging or what the condition of its plates and solution is without an examination with a flash light. An electrician in charge of such a battery room placed a row of miniature incandescent lamps behind the line of batteries. Each shelf of batteries has its row of lamps. These lamps are switched on, a row at a time, and the batteries examined. The light shining through the solution shows the bubbles rising when the battery is charging properly. Any buckling of the plates can be seen at a glance and the trouble remedied before further damage is done.

Preventing Snow from Clinging to Shovel

A coating of paraffin on an ordinary snow shovel, of metal or wood, will prevent the snow from sticking to it, and will give service for heavy shoveling for a number of hours. The paraffin may be applied to a metal shovel by heating the latter over a stove and flowing on the protective covering. The molten paraffin may be brushed over a wooden shovel easily if the shovel is warmed.—C. D. Ryan, Seattle, Wash.

Sound-Proof Pump Connection

Windmill pumps are sometimes troublesome in that the pumping noises are communicated to the house, causing a monotonous dull thumping whenever the mill is in operation. Metallic pipe lines are good conductors of sound, and by interrupting the metal lines, sound transmission will be interfered with. A short piece of rubber hose at the pump, to connect it with the pipe line, will effectively overcome the transmission of the noises.

Elevated Bin Makes Ash Disposal Convenient

An apartment house in a section of the city in which collections of ashes are made only once or twice a week was provided with a practical

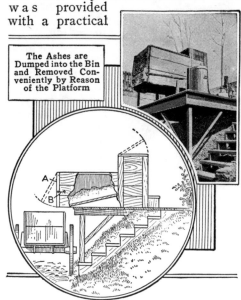

The Ashes are Dumped into the Bin and Removed Conveniently by Reason of the Platform

container for the ashes, which saved both space and labor. A large box was built on a platform, as shown in the illustration. The ashes are poured into it from day to day at the hinged lid. The bottom of the box slants down toward the alley, so that when the wagon drives alongside the platform, it is only necessary for the driver of the ash wagon to open the door A, by lifting the hook B, and the ashes are discharged into the wagon with a minimum of handling.—Hamilton A. Hooper, Baltimore, Md.

Keeping the Point of a Nail Set in Shape

Not infrequently woodwork and often fingers are damaged by the use of a nail set having a smooth point. A simple way to overcome this difficulty without attempting to make a cup point, as on commercial nail sets, is to file grooves at right angles into the point, with a triangular file.

Chain-Rivet Extracting Tool

Roller-chain links are easily injured when gripped in the jaws of a vise in order to remove the rivets. The tool shown in the sketch was forged in a garage from a piece of scrap steel, and is useful in handling links without injuring them. The rollers of the link to be repaired are placed in the recesses of the device, as shown in the sketch, and the whole is then clamped into the vise, for the removal of the rivets.—H. W. Offins, Grants Pass, Ore.

To Repair a Worn-Out Spigot

When new washers do not remedy a leaky spigot, the valve seat has usually been worn rough from sand or other particles. It can be reground in the following manner, with little difficulty or expense: A 2-in., 8-32 round-head machine screw and nut, a small piece of No. 1 emery cloth, a washer of the proper size to fit the spigot, and an ordinary hand drill are needed for the work. First cut a round piece from the emery cloth, slightly larger than the spigot washer, punch a hole in the center, and place it on the machine screw, with the abrasive side facing the head. Then put on the washer and nut, tightening the latter. The end of the screw should then be fastened in the drill chuck, and the valve grinder will be ready for use.

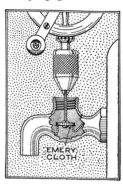

Turn off the water supply, remove the valve plunger, and dry the inside of the spigot with a cloth. The grinder should then be inserted and firmly held erect, as shown in the sketch, and the crank turned at a fair speed until the valve seat is ground smooth and free from pits. By treating it in this manner and reassembling with a new washer, any spigot can be repaired to be practically as good as new.—Edwin L. Powell, Takoma Park, Md.

Brake-Lever Rod Guide

The pull rod on the brake lever of an automobile was a source of constant annoyance resulting from its continuous rattling against the lever. A piece of strip steel, A, was bent in the shape indicated in the sketch, and was then riveted to the lever midway between the ends of the rod. This little guide prevented the lever and the rod from touching each other, and the trouble was eliminated.—Adolph Klein, New York City.

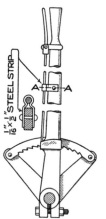

Sand Racks for Storage Batteries

In a storage-battery room considerable damage resulted from the acid which frequently leaked or spilled from the jars. The jars were placed in long rows on wooden racks, and, due to the destructive effect of the acid, the wood soon decayed. To eliminate the expense of frequently renewing the racks, larger shelves were built with sides 3 in. high. Into these boxlike racks sand was placed to a depth of 2 in. The glass storage-battery jars were then placed on this sand bed, and more sand was packed around them to a further depth of 1 in. Acid escaping from the jars was thus absorbed by the sand, leaving the wooden containers undamaged.—K. M. Coggeshall, Webster Groves, Mo.

Sander Attachment for a Lathe

In a small shop, where the sanding to be done did not warrant the purchase of a sander, the device illustrated was fitted into a lathe and performed its work to thorough satisfaction. The dimensions of the table and roller will be determined largely by the size of the lathe to which the device is to be fitted. The drum carrying the sandpaper should be about 6 in. in diameter, in order to give the necessary speed for good work in sanding. A medium grade of garnet sandpaper was used for all ordinary work, but other grades may be used if a specially fine finish or heavy cutting is required. The sandpaper is fitted to the drum by drawing it around tightly and clamping it into place by means of the V-shaped spline fitted into a groove, and fastened with countersunk screws. The sandpaper may also be glued to the drum instead of using the strip-and-groove device.

The roller is supported in a strong frame, built of hard wood. Its ends are fitted to the fixed support of the headstock and of the tailstock, and the device clamped firmly to the lathe bed by means of the rod, plate, and clamping wheel, below. The projection of the roller above the surface of the table may be regulated by supporting the back of the table on a wooden rest, ad-

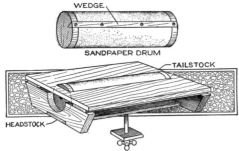

The Roller and Table are Fitted to a Lathe for Use in Sanding Wood to a Finish in Shops Where It Is Impracticable to Purchase a Sander

justable, vertically, on two machine screws engaging nuts set into the rest. The roller must be set in the lathe between centers carefully, and the tailstock center kept oiled.

Improved Emery-Wheel Arbor

An arbor for use with emery wheels, or similar grinding wheels and disks, is shown in the illustration in compari-

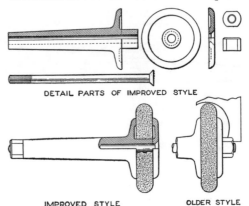

DETAIL PARTS OF IMPROVED STYLE

IMPROVED STYLE   OLDER STYLE

The Improved Style of Arbor for Emery Wheels Gives an Unobstructed End and Grips the Wheel Firmly

son with a type commonly used. The improved type insures a firm grip on the wheel, causing it to run more steadily and true in spite of frequent change of wheels. With the older type, in which the wheel is held in place by a flange and nut, set on the end of the arbor, the nut interferes with certain kinds of grinding, and is an obstruction in working from the side of the wheel.

The improved style of arbor overcomes these difficulties, clamps the wheel securely, with a smooth, unobstructed face on the side of the wheel and flange. The undercut flanges give a better fit to the surface of the emery wheel, and aid in keeping the wheel running true. The arbor, as shown in the detailed sketches, is bored out through its center, and a steel rod, threaded on one end, and with a flat head on the other, is fitted to it. The arbor and inner flange, as well as the bearing shaft for the wheel, are in one piece. The outer flange is bored and countersunk to fit the center rod, and the wheel is clamped between the flanges by means of a nut drawn up on the opposite end of the arbor rod. The arbor is, of course, tapered to fit the socket in which it is used.—Andrew J. Rutz, New Haven, Conn.

Stove-Lifting Truck of Varied Uses

The moving or setting up of a stove is often a difficult task, especially in the home where it is undertaken by one

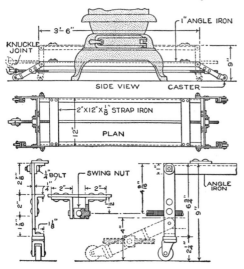

The Truck is Lowered, Rolled under the Stove, and Raised Until the Stove is Lifted from the Floor

man. Damage to woodwork and floors results, with the possibility of damage to the stove and injury to the householder. The truck shown in the illustration was built particularly for the lifting and moving of stoves, but may be used for many similar purposes, such as the transportation of heavy boxes, trunks, and furniture. It is useful in stores and shops as well as in the home. It is set low enough to permit rolling it under the stove, as indicated in the upper sketch, and by turning the removable tongue by which it is drawn, the truck is raised until it lifts the stove from the floor. The large ball-bearing casters will not mar the floor, except under very heavy loads, in which case it is desirable to protect the floor with strips of wood or even heavy cardboard.

The truck is strongly built, and consists of a frame made of 1-in. angle iron, braced near the ends with two pieces of ⅛ by 2 by 12-in. strap iron, as shown in the plan. The end supports of the truck are pivoted where they join the top, a detail of the joint being shown

in the lower sketches. A strap of iron extends across each end of the truck, and at the center of each strap is a swing nut, threaded to receive the long round rod, which is supported at each end, and turned by means of the tongue. One end of the rod is threaded with a right and the other with a left-hand thread, so that the raising and lowering action is equal at both ends of the truck. The fixed joints of the frame and connections are riveted and the others are fitted with stove bolts.
—P. J. Backus, Delphos, Ohio.

Kink for Lacing Machine Belts

Frequently, in lacing machine belts on revolving shafting, or among pulleys at the ceiling, it is dangerous to attempt the work without the aid of some one to hold the ends, to prevent the belt from turning when the power is on. To shut off the power is sometimes undesirable. A convenient method of holding the belt ends, so that one man may lace them, is to apply a clamp, as shown in the diagram, the belt being looped around the shafts in its usual position. When the lacing is completed the belt is replaced on the pulleys, the safe method being

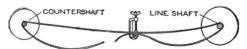

The Clamp Holds the Belt so That One may Lace It

to stop the machinery, although an experienced man can easily replace it while the shafts are in operation.—J. Harger, Honolulu, Hawaii.

Removing Fence Posts Easily

Fence posts of considerable size may be removed readily by hitching a chain around the post near the ground and passing it over a piece of two-by-four stock set at a slant against the post. A horse hitched to the chain can withdraw large posts by means of the leverage on the chain and the piece of wood.
—Will Chapel, Manchester, Ia.

Hand-Operated Wire-Forming Fixtures

By GEORGE P. BREITSCHMID

PRODUCTION of machine parts, and other small devices of formed wire, is often more economical by the use of hand-operated fixtures than by the installation of more or less automatic machines. This is the case especially where a small number of pieces are to be made, for a small order, or for the replacing of broken parts from time to time. The hand-operated wire-forming fixtures shown in the illustrations were designed primarily for the making of a stopping lever, the function of which is to stop automatically a machine for winding thread, when the thread breaks or the bobbin is empty. They are directly adaptable to a large variety of similar work, by the addition of special plates and parts, two of which are suggested. By application of the principles of design involved, fixtures for the making of wire parts for sewing machines, typewriters, adding, stamping, sealing, and vending machines, toys, loose-leaf appliances, household utensils, and similar work, may be devised. The operation of the fixtures and the wire lever which is formed in them, are shown in the diagram. On the page plate are shown the detailed working drawings of the fixtures and their parts, a sketch of the main device in use, Fig. 6, and two adaptations useful in the making of formed parts similar to that shown: a right-angle plate, and a stop arrangement for bending wire at various angles in the fixture, in Fig. 7. The base is clamped in a vise, as shown in Fig. 6, and the wire is formed by setting it in the proper grooves, so that the revolving anvil may be brought against it by means of the handle. The device is of small size, being about 2½ by 2½ by 4 in. in over-all dimensions.

Before attempting to study the construction in detail, it is desirable to identify the main parts and to trace their operation in forming the stopping

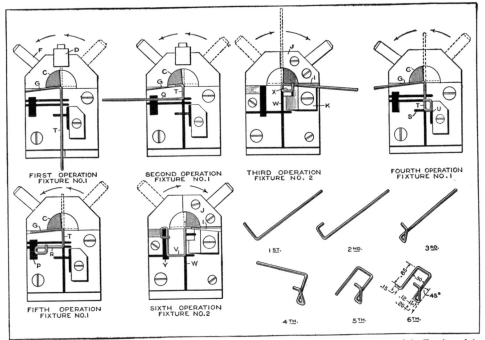

FIRST OPERATION FIXTURE NO. 1

SECOND OPERATION FIXTURE NO. 1

THIRD OPERATION FIXTURE NO. 2

FOURTH OPERATION FIXTURE NO. 1

FIFTH OPERATION FIXTURE NO. 1

SIXTH OPERATION FIXTURE NO. 2

1ST. 2ND. 3RD. 4TH. 5TH. 6TH.

The Operations Necessary for the Forming of the Stopping Lever are Shown in Detail, and the Tracing of the Process through the Diagrams Makes Them Strikingly Clear. The Dotted Lines Indicate the Original Position of the Wire, the Handle, and the Wiper, and the Arrows Show the Direction of the Bending Force

lever through the six operations required, as shown in the diagram. The lever is shown finished and with dimensions, as the result of the sixth operation. As indicated by the minute decimal dimensions, it must be made accurately, No. 26 music wire, .063 in. in diameter, being used. Referring to Fig. 1 of the page plate, the chief parts are designated by the letters A to F, slightly larger than those indicating the minor parts. A cast-iron base, A, carries the other parts. The forming plate B, of tool steel, hardened, is fixed to the top of the base with flat-head machine screws. The forming wiper C, with its upper end formed into a sectorlike anvil, also of tool steel, hardened, rests in the base on its upper shouldered portion, and projects below it, providing a fastening for the handle F. The gauge D is used in placing the wire properly, and is made of case-hardened, soft machine steel. The gauge E is made of tool steel, hardened, and is held in place on the plate B by means of a flat-head machine screw and two small pins. The handle is a piece of cold-rolled wire, $\frac{5}{16}$ in. in diameter and 6 in. long. Two forming plates are required, one being used for the first, second, fourth, and fifth operations, and the other for the third and sixth operations, as shown in the diagram. In connection with the second forming plate, shown in Fig. 5, a special rest, K, of tool steel, is provided, in order to make the 45° bend in the lever. The special rest J, also of tool steel, is added to give a bearing for the wire during the third operation.

The six operations, as indicated in the diagram, result in the shapes of the wire marked correspondingly. The pieces from which the lever is formed are cut to a length of $3\frac{1}{4}$ in. A piece of wire of this length is inserted into groove T for the first operation, the gauge D being set so that the portion bent to a right angle is sufficient for the making of the additional bends, as indicated by the detailed dimensioning of the lever. This was determined in part by experiment. The handle F is brought from the position indicated by the dotted lines, carrying the wiper C with it, as indicated by the arrows. The portion bent is carried slightly beyond a right angle in each instance, against the beveled edge G, to allow for the return spring of the wire. This must also be determined in part by experiment, for the particular stock used.

The wire is placed in slots Q and T for the second operation, the projecting end to be bent being shown by the dotted lines opposite the slot T. Fixture No. 2, with the forming plate shown in Fig. 5, is used in the third operation. The portion of the wire previously bent is rested in the grooves W and X, the latter in the rest K, and the straight portion is extended to rest upon the rest J. The handle is drawn as indicated by the arrows, and the bend is made against the beveled edge I. Reference to the sketch showing the shape of the wire after the third operation will make this clear. The fourth operation is performed on fixture No. 1. The wire is set as shown, with the straight end extending as indicated by the dotted lines opposite the groove T, and with other portions of the wire in grooves S and U. It is bent against the beveled edge G.

The bent portions of the wire are set into grooves R and T, and into the clearance hole P, for the fifth operation. The bend is made in the same direction as in the fourth operation. The sixth operation is performed on fixture No. 2. The wire is placed in the grooves V and W, with the 45° end in the clearance hole Y, and the portion to be bent extending beyond the end of groove W, as indicated by the dotted lines. The bend is made against the beveled edge I. This completes the forming operations, and the stopping lever is shaped to the form shown with dimensions.

The details of the various parts of the forming fixtures are shown in the page plate. The general arrangement and method of joining the parts is shown in the top and side views, Fig. 1. A detail of the plate B is shown in

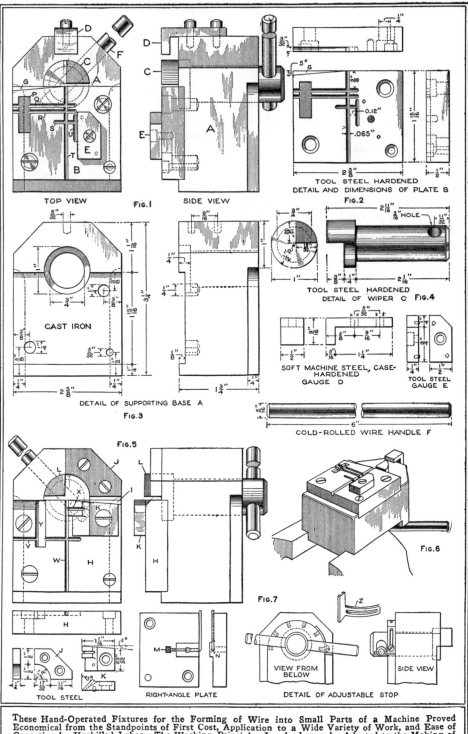

TOP VIEW   FIG.1   SIDE VIEW

TOOL STEEL HARDENED
DETAIL AND DIMENSIONS OF PLATE B   FIG.2

TOOL STEEL HARDENED
DETAIL OF WIPER C   FIG.4

CAST IRON

SOFT MACHINE STEEL, CASE-
HARDENED
GAUGE D

TOOL STEEL
GAUGE E

DETAIL OF SUPPORTING BASE A

FIG.3

COLD-ROLLED WIRE HANDLE F

FIG.5

FIG.6

TOOL STEEL

RIGHT-ANGLE PLATE

FIG.7

VIEW FROM
BELOW

SIDE VIEW

DETAIL OF ADJUSTABLE STOP

These Hand-Operated Fixtures for the Forming of Wire into Small Parts of a Machine Proved
Economical from the Standpoints of First Cost, Application to a Wide Variety of Work, and Ease of
Operation by Unskilled Labor. The Working Principles Involved may be Adapted to the Making of
Wire Parts for Many Kinds of Machines. The Details of the First of the Two Fixtures Used are
Shown in Fig. 1; Those for the Second Fixture, in Fig. 5. The Parts are Shown in Figs. 2, 3, and 4.
Two Additional Features are Suggested in Fig. 7

Fig. 2. The grooves are milled accurately in the face of the plate to a depth of ³⁄₃₂ in., and a width of .065 in., so as to accommodate the wire snugly, it being .063 in. in diameter. A bevel, G, of 5°, is milled on the corner, as shown. The plate is bored for three fillister-head machine screws, and hardened, to withstand the wear. In this, as well as in the other detail drawings, the dimensions are not given in great detail, as they would be of interest only in reproducing a set of parts for the making of the particular stopping lever described; essential dimensions for the application of the fixtures to other wire parts are given.

The supporting base A is shown in Fig. 3, in top and side views. It is of cast iron, milled to receive the plate B, and also to provide a shoulder on each side, for gripping the base in the vise, as shown in Fig. 6. The wiper C, which fits into the base, is shown in Fig. 4. It is of tool steel, hardened, and at its upper end is an anvil portion, which is forced against the wire in bending it. The anvil is not one-fourth of the area of the top of the wiper, but is ¹⁵⁄₃₂ in. in width on each side. This is to provide clearance, between the wiper and the edges against which it bends the wire, for the latter. Other parts, also shown in detail in Fig. 4, are the gauge D, of soft machine steel, casehardened; the gauge E, of tool steel, and the handle F. Two small pins are riveted into the lower surface of the gauge E, which fit into holes in the top of the plate B, so that the gauge will not shift when tightened into place by means of the machine screw.

The arrangement of parts and the details of fixture No. 2 and its fittings are shown in Fig. 5. The grooves V and W, and the clearance hole Y, are spaced in the forming plate H, to accommodate the partly formed wire in the third and sixth operations. The anvil L is similar to that used in the first fixture, and the rest J is provided for use in the third operation. Its upper surface is on a level with the bottom of the grooves, so that the wire

placed in the grooves will rest squarely upon it, as indicated in the side view. It is shown in detail in the sketch below the top view. The rest K is a distinctive feature of this fixture. It is used in forming the wire to the 45° angle, in the third operation. It has a slanting side to conform to the 5° angle on the edge of the forming plate, and at the wedge-shaped end is a groove X. The detail drawing of this gauge is shown below the top view of Fig. 5.

Two simple devices for use in connection with the forming fixtures described are shown in Fig. 7. The right-angle plate is used in bending wires to forms requiring only simple right-angular bends, and may be used to do preliminary work for the other fixtures, especially on rush jobs. The knurled thumbscrew M is set in the slot N so that the proper length of wire is bent, by forcing it against the side of the plate, as shown. The plate may be used separately or be fixed into a base with the wiper, as in Fig. 1.

If it is desired to use the fixtures described for bending angles other than right angles, a device for gauging the angle by one setting of a stop is convenient. Two stops, as shown at Z, Fig. 7, one right and one left, are required for the arrangement shown. The view at the left shows the fixture as seen from below, with the stop in place. The shoulder milled into the base, to provide a firm grip in the vise, is continued around the end of the base, forming a semicircular shoulder as a slide for the stop. The vertical edge of the shoulder is drilled and tapped to receive a round-head machine screw, by which the stop is fixed into place. If desired, indications of degrees may be made on the edge of the shoulder, to aid in setting the stop for the bending of various angles. The stop is made of soft steel, hardened, and is provided with a slot for finer adjustment, when the machine screw has been set into one of the holes in the shoulder. These simple additions to the fixtures will suggest other adaptations for use on particular jobs.

The considerations which resulted in the making of the fixtures described may be of interest in applying them to other work. The aim was to produce the special wire forms with the smallest possible expense, not only from the standpoint of labor cost, but also from that of cost of making the necessary tools. Hand-operated fixtures were determined upon, and it was decided that six operations were required for the job. The small size of the tools and fixtures, their comparatively small cost, and the fact that they are always ready for use without being specially set up, were points in their favor. Expert mechanics are not required to operate or set up the devices, and they can be operated successfully by unskilled labor with brief instruction.

Device Facilitates Handling of Long List of Names

Frequent consultation of a long list of names made it necessary that some means be devised by which the list could be handled quickly; the device shown in the sketch was constructed for the purpose and proved satisfactory. Two rollers, with supports, were made to carry a long roll of finished-surface white cloth, on which the list of names was typewritten. A line guide was made to fit the roll of cloth, and mounted at a convenient point over it. By drawing on the roll the desired name is brought to the opening in the guide, and the user is enabled to obtain the name quickly and accurately. The device may be adapted to a wide range of uses, and paper strips may be used instead of cloth.

Electrical Finder for Submerged Metal Objects

Great difficulty is sometimes experienced in finding a gun, ax, or other heavy metal object, which has been lost in water. They sink into the soft mud, and diving fails to give any trace of them. The device shown in the sketch was made to locate such objects by the ringing of a bell when the electrical contact wires of the device are touched against the metal of the object sought. The device consists of a bamboo pole on which an ordinary doorbell with a dry battery is attached. Copper

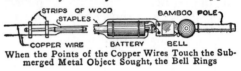
When the Points of the Copper Wires Touch the Submerged Metal Object Sought, the Bell Rings

wires, stiff enough to stand the probing on the water bottom, are conducted from the battery and bell to the end of the pole. They are fixed to two strips of wood, which are pivoted on the pole. When the copper-wire points strike the surface of an irregular object they adjust themselves to the surface, by the movement of the pivoted wooden strips. Contact of both points with a metal object causes a current to pass and the bell rings, thus indicating the point at which the object sought is submerged.—W. S. Wilson, Cascades, Quebec, Can.

Ferrule for Tool Handle Made of Hose Coupling

The threaded section of a brass hose coupling makes a better ferrule for a heavy tool handle than the ordinary smooth-bore variety, since it can be tightened and will not slip off. It also gives a finished appearance to the handle, as the brass will keep polished with use. —James M. Kane, Doylestown, Pa.

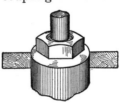

❏Brass should be turned in a lathe at higher speed than iron or steel.

Enlarging a Pulley for Emergency Use

It was necessary to provide a 14-in. pulley on a shaft, and, in order to remove the 10-in.

pulley at that point, it must either be broken or an entire line of shafting taken down to insert a new pulley. The engineer fitted the device shown in the sketch to the 10-in. pulley, making the outer rim 14 in. in diameter, as required. It was intended as an emergency method but has been in use several years. Wooden blocks were fitted around the pulley, and a split band clamped over them, screws holding the blocks fast to the band, as indicated at A. The band is tightened by means of the shoulders and bolts, at B, thus insuring a firm grip on the pulley, if attended to occasionally. Care must be taken in fitting the parts, and the pulley must not be used permanently under severe conditions.—James E. Noble, Toronto, Ont.

Nippers for Removing Insulation from Wire

Removing the cotton insulation from armature-coil leads, when connecting the coils to the commutator segments, is often a tiresome job. The accompanying

sketch shows a handy tool which does the work very nicely. It is made of a piece of 1/16 by 3/4-in. steel, ground and tempered at the cutting edge. To protect the hand, a piece of leather can be cemented or riveted on, as shown. This tool is also convenient for use in removing insulation from various kinds of other electrical wire.—R. L. Hervey, Washington, D. C.

Noiseless Rubber Tips for Bench-Vise Handles

The wooden tips usually furnished with the handles of a bench vise do not last very long. For this reason they are sometimes replaced by iron tips or ferrules. These are noisy, make the handle heavy, and are likely to bruise a finger when the handle has been left raised and then slips. A better tip is made as follows: Cut two pieces, 2 in. long, from 3/4-in. garden hose, slip one over each end of the handle, and fasten them with three or four tacks each. Besides costing nothing and being easy to put on, these tips last for years and make the handle noiseless.—Henry Simon, Laguna Beach, Calif.

Eliminating End Thrust on a Rear Automobile Axle

The two drive shafts on the rear axle of an automobile were subjected to an excessive amount of end thrust, and it was extremely important to take up the looseness to prevent the differential gears from being thrown out of line, as this would cause serious trouble with the entire axle. It was decided to fit two hardened-steel end collars, as shown in the illustration, the

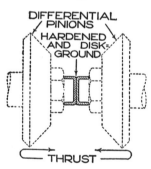

clearance between the two not exceeding .01 in. The collars were pressed tightly on the ends of the shafts, then carefully hardened and ground on a disk grinder. The repair was so perfect that it was not necessary to replace the collars until the car had traveled over 4,000 miles.

¶A spark plug should not be turned firmly into a hot engine cylinder, as it will be difficult to remove it when the engine cools.

Shop Notes

Homemade Joist-Boring Machine

By CHARLES H. TRAPP

AN easily constructed joist-boring machine, which is particularly adapted for boring holes for knob-and-tube wiring in basements, is shown in the illustration. The ordinary joist-boring machine is usually too long for convenient use in a basement, hence the especial value of the one described. The machine is of one-piece construction, that is, it is not jointed as are some borers, which makes it light, and easily transported and handled. It consists essentially of a piece of 1-in. conduit, 6 ft. 6 in. long, two sprockets, 13 ft. of bicycle chain, and a twist bit, these materials being inexpensive and readily obtainable.

The head sprocket, as shown in detail, is mounted on a shaft contained in the bearing of the driving sprocket, head sprocket is smaller than the bottom one, the machine will "feed" faster, with the same number of revolutions of the bottom sprocket, than when the sprockets are the same. The bearing for the head sprocket being taken from an old bicycle, the shaft to which the sprocket is attached revolves on ball bearings and is adjusted and held in place by cones, washers, collars, and keys. The column supporting the bearing is telescoped into the 1-in. conduit. It is about 1 ft. 6 in. long, and is riveted into place.

The twist bit is inserted into a hole, $1\frac{1}{2}$ in. deep, drilled into the shaft or axle, as shown at the left, and is held rigidly in place by a key driven through the collar. The shank of the bit is first cut off, as shown, and then filed

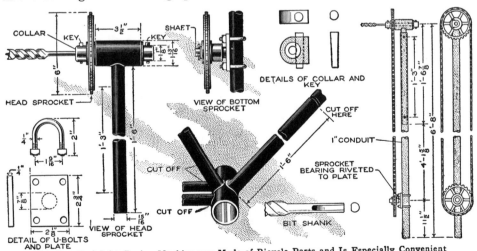

This Practical Joist-Boring Machine was Made of Bicycle Parts and Is Especially Convenient in Knob-and-Tube Work

cut from an old bicycle frame. It is 6 in. in diameter, the same size as the bottom sprocket. Obviously, if the flat. The bit is inserted in the hole in the shaft, and the key, which also has a flat side, is driven through the collar so that the flat side of the key rests tightly against the flat side of the bit shank, holding the bit firmly in place.

The bottom-sprocket bearing is riveted to a ¼ by 2⅛ by 2¾-in. iron plate, drilled in each corner for ¼-in. bolts. The plate is then attached to the conduit frame with two ¼-in. U-bolts, shown in the sketch. The bottom sprocket is held in place on the bearing and shaft with a nut and washer, secured further by a spring cotter.

When assembling the machine, the head sprocket should first be fixed into place. Then the chain should be assembled and placed over the head sprocket and the bottom sprocket should be adjusted at such a distance from the head sprocket that the chain will be reasonably taut when the machine is operated. It is well to make the borer of such a height—about 6 ft. 8 in. is satisfactory—that it can be used conveniently in basements with low ceilings. If the borer is too short for use in some basements, it can be raised by inserting a rod, of suitable length, in the bottom end of the conduit.

To operate the machine, make the proper adjustments as to height, set it up at the joist to be bored, grasp the conduit frame firmly with the left hand and feed the bit into the joist by pulling down on the chain with the right hand. While boring, pressure should be exerted against the machine with the left hand. This will, of course, cause it to feed faster. When the hole is bored, the machine, still held by the left hand, should be pulled toward the operator while the chain is moved quickly up and down with the right hand, making it easier to remove the bit, and giving a clean-cut hole.

Stairs for Climbing over Fence

Modern farm fencing is not well adapted for providing a foothold to

The Stairs Built into the Fence Provides a Convenient Method of Climbing over the Barrier

climb over it, and the adaptation of an idea, not altogether new, shown in the sketch, might be used with profit in many places. When a convenient means of climbing over a fence is provided, damage to the fence by careless climbers is avoided. A stairs built to extend on both sides of the fence is a simple and practical means of travel between adjoining grounds. It is a barrier to stock, and if well made it will prove serviceable and inexpensive.— J. H. Moore, Hamilton, Canada.

Kink in Overhauling a Gasoline Engine

When overhauling an automobile, or other gasoline, engine extreme care should be taken that the valves be numbered and reassembled to their proper valve stems. Trouble in assembling may thus be avoided, for in not a few instances noisy and sticky valves are traced to errors in assembling apparently identical parts. The valves and parts to which they are fitted are numbered in many engines; when this is not the case, a good plan is to tie numbered paper tags to the parts which correspond as they are separated.—Adolph Klein, New York, N. Y.

Gauge for Spacing Steel-Marking Punches

Names, or other indications on tools, punched into the surface by the use of individual punches, are often unsightly because it is difficult to aline them properly. The device shown in the illustration provides a simple and accurate means of gauging the spacing of the letters or figures, and can be adapted to various sizes of punches.

I have two alphabets, 1/16 in. and 1/4 in. in height, and for the former I found that a spacing of 12 letters to the inch is satisfactory; for the latter I use five letters to the inch. I made a sliding piece, A, of brass, and brazed an angle, B, to it, as shown. The steel punches fit into the angle, which acts as a guide in conjunction with the spacing gauge marked on the forward strip of the frame. The vertical angle is 1/2 in. shorter than the punches and its lower edge is flush with that of the sliding piece. The frame was made of hardwood strips, the end pieces D being fastened to the sidepieces E by means of screws, countersunk. The indications for the spacing of the two sizes of letters were made on the frame and a small pin was fitted to the sliding

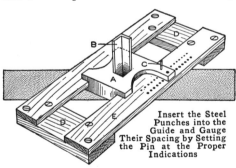

Insert the Steel Punches into the Guide and Gauge Their Spacing by Setting the Pin at the Proper Indications

piece to engage the holes. This insures the accurate spacing of the letters, both as to being in a straight line and as to distance apart.—Harry G. Fesenfeld, Black Earth, Wis.

❧To split off a tight machine nut with a cold chisel is sometimes more economical than to risk ruining the bolt threads.

Drafting Table Made of Pipes and Fittings

I made and used a drafting table like that shown in the illustration, and

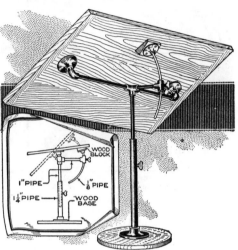

The Height and Slant of the Board may be Adjusted over a Wide Range by Means of the Thumbscrews

it has given complete satisfaction; in fact, I find it as convenient as any commercial table I have ever used. It was made for a large drawing board, but can be adapted to a board of any of the sizes ordinarily used. The base was made of a wooden disk, 20 in. in diameter. A flange and a 1¼-in. pipe was used for the lower section, and 1-in. pipe for the upper parts of the support. The curved part by which the slant of the top is adjusted was made of a ⅛-in. pipe screwed into a flange which was fastened to the board as shown. The pipes were drilled and tapped for thumbscrews, by means of which the board is held at the desired angle and height.—Armydis E. Sturdivant, Newcastle, Ind.

Bushing Avoids Marring of Work in Lathe Dog or Chuck

It is frequently necessary to grip highly polished work, such as ground spindles and polished brass pieces, in lathe dogs or chucks. To prevent their marring by the setscrew of the dog or the jaws of the chuck, I have found the following method to be superior to many others I have tried: A bushing of soft steel is bored and reamed smooth to a push fit, on the shaft or

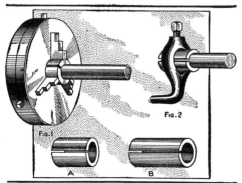

The Smoothly Turned Split Bushings Protect Highly Polished Spindles in the Chuck or Lathe Dog

spindle to be held. This is mounted on an arbor and turned down so as to leave the walls of the bushing ⁵⁄₁₆ in. thick. A ¹⁄₁₆-in. slot is cut through the bushing, as shown in the sketch at A and B, two useful sizes. The burr is removed and the bushing smoothed carefully with emery cloth. Fig. 1 shows the bushing in use in a chuck, and Fig. 2 in a lathe dog. Where much of this work is done it is desirable to provide several such bushings of standard sizes.—Richard H. Jehlicka, Worcester, Mass.

A Valve-Cap Wrench

The valve-cap wrench illustrated was made after two other types had

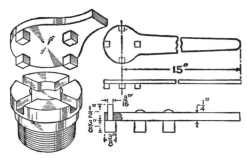

Wrench Made Similar to a Spanner for Turning Valve Caps In and Out of Place

proved failures. The body of the wrench is constructed of ¼-in. cold-

rolled steel, 16¼ in. long, and the pegs for gripping the slots in the valve cap are made of ⅜-in. square drill rod. The pegs are shouldered so that they can be riveted to the handle. It is a good plan to harden the square end of the pegs, but care should be taken to harden them to a very slight depth.

Making Small Steel Scales

The mechanic will ordinarily profit by purchasing reliable scales or other precision instruments, but if care is taken and the satisfaction of having an accurate homemade scale, of steel, is appreciated, my experience may be of interest. I use a 2-ft. four-fold scale, accurate enough for all ordinary purposes as a pocket rule, made from corset stays, etched and polished to a finish like that of commercial steel rules. The stays are straightened, polished, and covered with a thin layer of paraffin. The indications are carefully scratched upon them, including the numerals for the inch marks. The strips are then placed in a bath of one part nitric acid, one part sulphuric acid, and 12 parts rain water, and permitted to remain until the indications are etched to a sufficient depth. The holes at the ends of the strips are located carefully and rivets placed in them, making the joints tight enough so that the rule remains extended when unfolded.—R. S. Matzen, Fort Collins, Colorado.

Self-Acting Blowpipe

The steadiness of the flame is an important factor in successful blowpipe work; thus, in hard-soldering, the point of fusion may be almost reached, when the withdrawal of the flame for the fraction of a second between breaths will cause quite an appreciable cooling. The knack of maintaining a constant air supply without interruption through the breathing of the operator can be acquired only after long experience. In addition to this difficulty, the mouth blowpipe has the further disadvantage of being insanitary, and it is sometimes awkward to reach certain portions of the work with it.

The simple nozzle, or burner, shown in the sketch was devised to overcome these disadvantages. It may be slipped into the end of a ¼-in. rubber tube connected with the gas supply and will produce, without blowing, a long, narrow pencil of blue flame sufficiently hot to melt pins or copper wire quickly. It is apparent that when the tubing is 3 or 4 ft. long, the burner may be used in many positions, and permits one to give undivided attention to the work in hand.

The burner is made from a piece of seamless brass tubing, 5 in. long and ⅛ to ¼ in. in diameter, depending on the size of flame desired. For general soldering, or hard-soldering small work, a tube of ⅛-in. diameter is used. This will produce a flame about 2 in. long. About 1 in. from the forward end, two rectangular openings, ⅛ in. long, are made opposite one another by filing across the tube with the edge of a flat file. A brass plug is then prepared, with a diameter that will just permit its being pushed into the tube, and a tapering hole through the center, with the forward end half as large as an ordinary pin, and is inserted into the tube at the holes, as shown in the upper view. To do this, tin the plug, slip it into place directly back of the air openings, apply a little soldering acid, and solder it in place over a flame. If the tube is too small to make a good

The Use of This Easily Made Blowpipe Obviates the Difficulty of One Operated by the Breath

connection with the gas tubing, build up the back end for about ¾ in. The flame should be bluish, and if it appears yellow, the small hole is too large, hence it is well to make the hole very small and enlarge it if necessary.
—John D. Adams, Phoenix, Ariz.

Apparatus for Removing Dust in Sand

In railroad shops, and elsewhere where clean sand is required, the

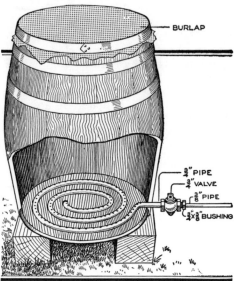

Sand to be Cleaned is Placed in the Barrel, the Air is Turned On, and the Dust Blown Out through the Burlap Covering

apparatus shown in the illustration will be found useful. A strong barrel was fitted with a plugged coil of ¾-in. pipe, in the upper surface of which ¼-in. holes were drilled 1 in. apart. The coil was connected to a compressed-air supply, regulated by a valve. The sand is poured into the barrel, a covering of burlap is fitted over the top by means of the upper hoop, and the air is turned on. The dust is blown out through the burlap, cleaning the sand thoroughly.—J. K. Long, Renovo, Pennsylvania.

Keeping Automobile Warm in Winter

Considerable heat from an automobile engine ordinarily is wasted, and may be utilized in cold weather for heating the tonneau. It is necessary only to remove the floor board back of the engine and permit the heat to pass up into the car. It is not desirable, of course, to close the car so tightly that there is little or no ventilation, since the heated air from the engine is not pure.—Fred Reschke, Racine, Wis.

A Wing-Joist Frame Barn

By W. E. Frudden

RISING land values and prosperity on the farm are reflected in the farm buildings, the barn as well as the home, and farms generally are provided with better barns for the storage of crops and the housing of animals than a generation ago. However, the construction of farm buildings, especially large barns, has undergone a great change, due largely to the increased cost of labor and the growing scarcity of lumber. The old-fashioned heavy-timber barns built years ago required sufficient lumber for two barns of the type shown in the illustration, and were usually built by a large number of men, gathered for the occasion at the familiar "barn raising." The building of a wing-joist barn requires only a small crew of men, and is economical of lumber. As a result a time-honored neighborly institution is becoming obsolete.

Every piece of lumber that is a part of the barn described is essential to its construction, yet the factors of safety, wind strain, snow loads, and other structural considerations, are amply provided for. The heaviest lumber used in it is 2 in. thick. The frames and other heavier parts are built up of plank, and the small parts may be made of short sections of stock, the waste being thus reduced to a minimum. The truss system used permits construction without crossbeams in the barn, so that the floor is clear except for the braces, and the haymows are free from obstructions. Standard methods are used throughout in the construction, so that any competent carpenter contractor and his men can build the barn properly. The lumber used is of commercial sizes available even in small country lumberyards.

While the wing-joist type of construction is not new, several features of the design shown are interesting and practical. In most barns of this type the floor joists extend crosswise of the structure, whereas those of the barn described are set lengthwise, on built-up plank girders, set on 14-ft. centers across the barn. The joists near the center, which must bear the greatest load, are spaced 20 in. on centers, and those at the sides are set 2 ft. apart. The trusses are set on 14-ft. centers, and can, of course, be adjusted under this distance to accommodate the spacing to various lengths of barns. They are built on the ground, the parts being cut in batches according to their size and shape, for all of the trusses, before assembling them. This process can be applied profitably to all of the construction, where a number of sections are built up in duplicate. As the parts for the trusses are assembled, they are piled up on the ground, and placed in position on the barn floor, when that stage has been reached in the raising of the barn. The barn is sided and shingled in the ordinary manner. The siding extends vertically, as indicated in the shaded portions of the sketches, and is nailed to the 2 by 8-in. braces, extending horizontally around the barn, as shown in the side and end-framing sketches.

Concrete foundations, upon which the ground floor of the barn is built, as shown in the cross section, are generally used instead of stone. The foundation must, of course, be proportioned to the structure to be placed upon it. That shown in the detail view is designed for a structure 36 ft. wide and 56 ft. long, built as indicated. It should be given a wide footing, at least 2 ft. as suggested, and wider if the ground is not well suited for a foundation. The foundation is run up above the ground sufficiently to keep the lower part of the wooden structure from the soil moisture and drippings from the roof. The sill is anchored to the foundation by means of bolts, the across the forms for the concrete. Care should be taken that the upper ends, which are threaded, project above the

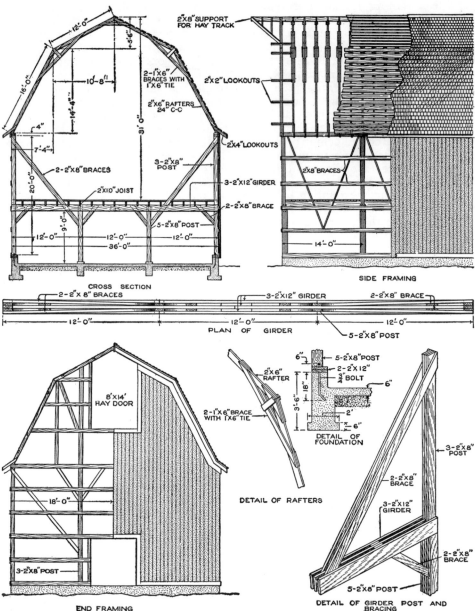

The Heaviest Lumber Used in This Barn Frame Is 2-Inch Plank, of Which the Heavier Parts are Built Up. This Method of Construction Is Economical of Lumber and the Structure can be Built by Only a Few Men. The 14-Foot Sections may be Figured as Standard Units in the Designing of Similar Barns of Various Lengths

lower ends of which are bent to give a better hold in the concrete. They are set in the concrete when it is placed, and held by templates nailed foundation sufficiently to pass through the double-plank sill, and provide for the nuts. The concrete floor should be 6 in. thick, finished smooth. It is desirable to place an 8-in. layer of cinders, or coarse gravel, under the barn floor, to afford good drainage and to provide a footing for animals that is not unduly damp.

Posts built up of five 2 by 8-in. planks support the girders under the floor. They are set on 14-ft. centers, as shown in the side-framing sketch. Their upper ends are arranged so that two of the planks extend between the planks making up the girder, and the others are butted under the lower edges of the outer and center planks of the girder. They are strongly braced by short braces extending to the girders in the center section of the barn, and by long braces extending between the planks of the girder, and fastened to them and to the upper ends of vertical built-up studs or posts along the side of the barn. The construction of the girder is shown in detail in the plan. The long braces are shown in relation to the studs, or side posts, in the detail of the girder post and bracing. The center plank of the stud butts above and below the center plank of the girder. The two outer planks of the stud extend the full length from the eaves to the sills. The outer planks of the girder are nailed over the outer planks of the stud. Cross braces of 2 by 8-in. stuff are placed between the studs to afford support for the nailing of the siding.

The trusses are formed of two rafters, built up of 2 by 6-in. stuff. They are set on 24-in. centers and strongly braced, as shown in the cross section and the side-framing sketch. Lookouts of 2 by 2-in. stock are fixed to the double rafter at the end and to the one adjoining it. Short braced rafters afford a support for the hay-lifting rigging at the end of the ridge. The ridge pole is of 2 by 8-in. plank, and the trolley track for the hay and grain carrier is suspended from the cross braces immediately below it.

The framing of the ends is shown in the lower sketch, and is better understood by referring also to the sketch showing the side framing, to observe the method of building up the corner

posts. They are of five planks below the floor and three planks from the floor to the eaves plates.

The other details of the structure are standard, or may be made in various ways in common use. An 8 by 14-ft. hay door is provided in each gable, and double doors give entrance to the ground story. The roof is made of rough boards covered with shingles or other suitable roofing material.

As a basis for computing the materials required for a barn of this type, a 14-ft. section as shown should be listed. The ends are considered separately and must in each case be added to the amount required for a given number of sections. Two thousand feet of dimension lumber is necessary for each end, and 2,200 ft. of siding. The cost of two ends is approximately $300, including the foundation. Each truss complete requires about 560 ft. of lumber. The total cost of a 14-ft. section is about $225, including the foundation, floor, siding, and shingles. The detailed list for a section is as follows:

```
 8 pieces, 2 by 8 in. by 14 ft., for sills.
 6 pieces, 2 by 8 in. by 14 ft., for plates.
 6 pieces, 2 by 6 in. by 14 ft., for nailing braces.
 4 pieces, 2 by 6 in. by 16 ft., for braces.
20 pieces, 2 by 12 in. by 14 ft., for joists.
14 pieces, 2 by 6 in. by 16 ft., for rafters.
14 pieces, 2 by 6 in. by 12 ft., for rafters.
28 pieces, 1 by 8 in. by 12 ft., for hip braces.
 7 pieces, 2 by 6 in. by 6 ft., for collar beams.
```

The total dimension lumber required is about 1,600 ft.; siding 470 ft.; shiplap flooring 600 ft., and 7,000 shingles.

Coal Chute Built into Bin

In building a new house I provided a chute into the coal bin that extends from the coal window to the center of the roof of the bin. Instead of it being necessary to enter the bin and shovel the coal away from the wall near the window, as is usually the case, the coal is now distributed evenly in the bin, with the high point of the pile like a pyramid. When the coal is removed from the opening at the lower, inner side nearly the entire pile may be removed without the necessity of shoveling the coal near to the opening. —A. E. Holaday, Naugatuck, Conn.

Hinge Plates and Escutcheon for Door

An interesting feature of exterior doors on craftsman or colonial-style houses is the heavy hardware, consisting of hinge plates, escutcheon, and knocker plate, made of soft sheet iron. These fittings may be made specially for the particular job, of a design suited to the surroundings and the individual taste. The design suggested in the illustration is suited to both of these types and may be readily modified. The stock is 3/16 in. thick, may be cut easily with a hacksaw, and finished on an emery wheel or with a file. The pieces should be cut to the proper width and then laid out, with the points for the holes to be drilled punched with a center punch. The holes are to be countersunk for flat-head wood screws as indicated. The door is supported by its hinges, and the hinge plates are fixed in place at them, the plate at the left being fixed to the frame and the T-shaped strap to the door. An easy method of marking the shape of the pieces on the metal is to lay them out and cut patterns from cardboard, tracing around them to transfer the shape to the iron. Black metal paint protects

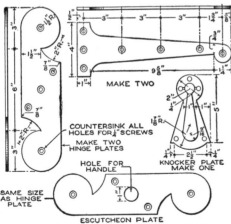

MAKE TWO

COUNTERSINK ALL HOLES FOR 1/4" SCREWS

MAKE TWO HINGE PLATES

HOLE FOR HANDLE

KNOCKER PLATE MAKE ONE

SAME SIZE AS HINGE PLATE

ESCUTCHEON PLATE

Patterns of Cardboard may be Made for the Pieces, Which are Cut with a Hacksaw

the metal and gives a strong contrast with the door, which may be painted white or stained a rich brown shade.—John E. Cahill, Jr., New York City.

Pump Operated by Distant Windmill

A California farmer had good locations for a windmill and for a well, but they were situated at different points. The well was located at the bottom of a small cañon, or creek, bed, where there was plenty of water but where the heavy growth of trees and brush formed an effective windbreak. Above the well was a bare knoll of considerable height, and the area surrounding it was clear of trees. The sketch shows how the windmill, located on the knoll, was connected with the pump by the use

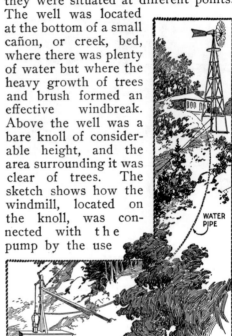

WATER PIPE

The Power from the Windmill is Applied to the Pump by Means of Wires and Levers

of wires and levers. A lever, shaped somewhat like the letter "T," was fixed to the rod of the pump and supported at its center on a framework set above the well. A similar lever was applied to the power shaft of the windmill. The ends of the upper bars of the levers were connected by wires, as shown, held taut with turnbuckles. This arrangement transmitted the power effectively and was quite simple to install.—John Hoeck, Alameda, Calif.

Clamp Enables One Man to Nail Siding Readily

It is difficult for one man to nail siding on a house because he must hold the board in place while starting the first nail, as well as when marking and cutting the stock. The device shown in the sketch overcomes this difficulty, and is made of a steel bar fitted to a weighted section of pipe. The end of the bar is hooked to the studding and clamps the board securely.

The clamp is made as follows: Pro-

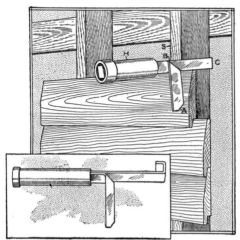

The Clamp Holds the Board Securely While the Workman Marks, Saws, or Nails It

cure a piece of soft galvanized steel bar, 1/8 by 1 by 30 in. Bend it together 14 in. from one end, and then bend the shorter part to a right angle, 5 in. from the end, at B. Studding is usually 1¾ by 3¾ in., and the end of the longer part of the bar should be bent to the shape shown, so as to hook around the studding S, at C. Allowance must be made for the thickness of the siding—usually 7/8 in.—and 1/4 in. additional to give a proper clamping force at A. The handle H is a piece of pipe, 7 in. long. After fitting it over the folded bar, weight it with about 3 lb. of lead.

When the piece of siding is to be fitted into place, hook the clamp on the studding and drop it to bind at A. It will hold boards while marking and sawing them. For long boards, place the clamp near the middle, and in moving boards do not remove the clamp but slide them under it. They will not be scratched if the end is trimmed off at A as shown.—L. M. Drake, Daytona, Fla.

⟨Remove burrs from the slots of screws after driving them in, as they are dangerous to the hands.

Determining Strength of Rope

The practical method of determining the strength of rope is to put it under strain and run it over a pulley. Used rope, especially, is deceiving, from outside appearance, as it is often dried out and the inner fibers broken. A breaking strain at one end of the rope will not serve to determine its ability, since the ends are least likely to be worn, and a weak spot in the middle may cause disaster. By running the rope over a pulley, however, and raising a weight considerably in excess of that which is to be handled in actual use, every point can be tested out thoroughly.—J. C. Grindell, St. Louis, Mo.

Adjustable Jig for Drilling Radial Holes

When a number of radial holes are to be drilled accurately in pulleys, or similar machine parts, the jig shown in two forms in the sketch will be found convenient. It was devised for the drilling of holes in a boss, A, as shown in Fig. 1. The jig shown in Fig. 2 was made of a piece of cast iron, drilled at C to fit the boss, and provided with a tempered-steel collar to guide the drill. The lug D was provided to fit into the hole B, as a guide in drilling the hole in the boss. An adaptation of the jig,

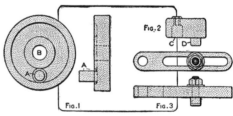

Radial Holes in Pulleys, or Similar Machine Parts, may be Drilled Accurately by the Use of This Jig

which may be adjusted for various sizes of pulleys, or other radial drilled work, is shown in Fig. 3. If holes of various sizes are to be drilled, bushings may be fitted into the guide hole at the end of the jig.—C. Anderson, Worcester, Mass.

Building an Electrical Generator

By B. FRANCIS DASHIELL

THE making of a small electrical generator affords experience in mechanical and electrical construction that is both interesting and practical. The generator described in this article and shown in detail in the illustrations was designed to be made with comparatively simple machine processes and a minimum use of special tools or devices. It is a 100-watt, direct-current, shunt-wound machine, and the parts are worked out to give a high standard of mechanical practice as well as to withstand hard service. If machine-shop facilities are not directly available, the machining may be done in a commercial shop at small cost. The materials are those in common use for such work, and readily available from dealers.

The making of the patterns and castings should be undertaken first, and only after a close examination of the working drawings in the page plate has been made. The perspective sketch and the assembly views, Figs. 9 and 10, show the general construction and the arrangement of the parts. The patterns are of simple design, and may be made by one familiar with the use of ordinary woodworking tools. Patternmakers' white pine is required for the patterns; glue, screws, brads, and other common means of fastening wooden parts, may be used for this purpose. All nail or other holes in the surfaces must be plugged carefully. The pattern for the field-magnet casting, Figs. 1 and 2, should be made first. It is built up of five parts: the yoke A; the two cylindrical magnet cores B, and the two poles C, which form the sides of the armature tunnel, in which the armature revolves. The dimensions on the drawing are for the finished parts, and allowance must therefore be made for machining the tunnel. Machining is indicated by the standard mark *"f."* The pattern is cast with the parting of the mold on the center line DE in Fig. 2, hence the tunnel and the flat exterior surfaces must be given a slight draft, to make removal from the sand conven-ient. The draft is produced by slanting the surfaces from the center line toward the edges, to form a slight crown, like that on the face of a pulley.

The bearings, shown in Fig. 3,

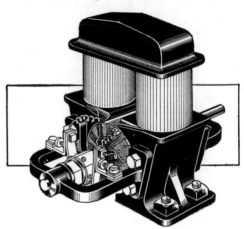

This Direct-Current Generator was Designed to be Made with Comparatively Simple Machine Processes

appear similar in the top view H, but that shown at F is 1⅞ in. wide, and that at G, 3⅜ in. wide. They are built up of five parts each, as indicated, and allowance must be made for finishing the castings to the dimensions shown.

The field magnet is cast from the pattern in gray iron of a fine texture, and the bearings are cast in hard bronze. Iron bearings must not be used under any circumstances. Examine the castings thoroughly and reject them if they have flaws.

The castings must then be machined to the dimensions indicated. This work must be done carefully to insure satisfactory operation of the generator. The sides of the poles C are planed parallel, to give them a width of 3 in., as shown in Fig. 2. Then place the field in a lathe chuck and bore out the armature tunnel to a 3-in. diameter, and exactly perpendicular to the planed sides. Too much care cannot be taken in this work.

The machine work on the bearings is slight. Machine the flat faces at the bases; they are to be fitted to the sides of the field magnet. Set the bearings upright on their bases and drill ⅜-in. holes in the shaft-bearing hubs. Then drill the two holes in each of the bases to fit the ⁵⁄₁₆-in. cap screw J, to provide for the fastening of the bearings to the poles.

The commutator, detailed in Fig. 7, is made as follows: Select a piece of round hard-rubber rod, 1 in. long and 1 in. in diameter. Drill a ½-in. hole through the center for the shaft. Force a piece of brass or copper tube, of ⅛-in. wall and 1-in. inside diameter, over this core. Tap the tube and core to receive 12 No. 4 .11-in. diameter standard fillister-head machine screws. Place six of them at each of the ends, ⅛ in. in, and space them equally, 60° apart. The screws are like that shown at K. Divide the tube into six equal segments by making kerfs with a hacksaw, lengthwise between the screws. Each segment is thus insulated from the others by air gaps.

The armature and shaft assembly are detailed in Fig. 6. The armature is built up of laminations in the form of disks, cut from thin sheet iron, 2¹⁵⁄₁₆ in. in diameter, as shown in Fig. 5. Each disk has twelve ⅜ by ⅜-in. openings cut into its edge, spaced equidistant, 30° apart on center radii. Punch a ½-in. hole in the center of each and stack them up to form a compact pile, 3 in. high. Place them in a charcoal fire and heat them to a bright red. Cover them with ashes and permit the fire to die out slowly. On removing the disks they are annealed. Clean them with emery cloth, dip them into a thin solution of shellac, and spread them out so that the shellac can dry hard.

The armature shaft is shown in Fig. 6. It is a rolled-steel shafting, ½ in. in diameter and 10 in. long. Turn the ends down to ⅜-in. diameter, one end 1⅜ and the other 2⅝ in. Thread the ends of the center portion to receive the ½-in. hexagonal steel nuts. Assemble the armature disks on the shaft and clamp them between the washers and nuts. Fix the commutator into place similarly.

The bearings must be located on the machined sides of the poles with accuracy. If the armature is found to be out of balance, cut it down or file it slightly in a lathe. Wrap a piece of heavy paper around the armature and fit it into the tunnel snugly. Slip the bearings on the shaft ends, and fit them against the surfaces. Taking care that they do not slip or become displaced, slightly mark the centers of the fastening holes in the pole surfaces with a center punch inserted in the holes. Drill and tap the holes for the screws J. The armature should rotate freely when the bearings are fitted into place. Drill oil holes into the hubs from the upper side, and fit them with cups if desired.

The brushes and brush holders used on this generator are of interesting design, as shown in Figs. 4 and 8. Make the holder of a piece of copper or brass angle, ½ in. wide. Solder together three or four strips of thin phosphor bronze at their top edges and drill and tap them for an 8-32 machine screw. Bolt this to the vertical leg of the holder. Drill and tap the lower end of the same leg similarly for an adjusting thumbscrew, with which to move the brush to or from the commutator. Drill the other leg as shown in Fig. 8, for a machine screw, as in Fig. 4, at L. The method of insulating the brush is indicated in Fig. 8. Two fiber, or hard-rubber washers are placed on either side of the holder arm; a short piece of fiber, or hard-rubber tube is slipped over the screw. Place a metal washer under the head to prevent cutting the insulation. Screw the holders tightly to the arms of the bearing, in the holes tapped, as shown in Fig. 3.

The winding of the field magnet is next in order. Cut two strips of heavy paper of sufficient width to cover the magnet cores and long enough to be wrapped twice around them. Paste them on the cores with thick shellac. Cut out four heavy blotting-paper washers, 2½ in. in diameter with 1¾-in. holes. Cut them in half and join the pieces in pasting them to the upper and lower inner surfaces of the cores, brushing them over thoroughly with

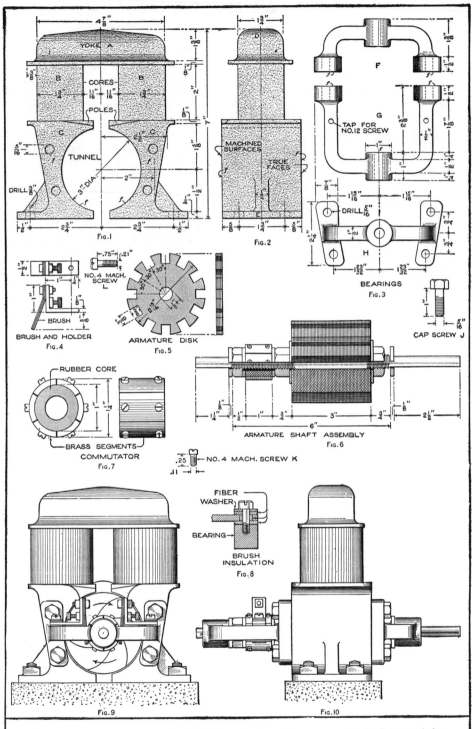

The Assembly Drawings, Figs. 9 and 10, Show the General Arrangement of the Parts, and the Working Drawings Present the Details of Construction. The Pattern for the Field Magnet, Shown in Fig. 1, is Built Up of Five Parts: The Yoke, Cores, and Poles. It is Cast in Gray Iron of Fine Texture, and the Bearings, Shown in Fig. 3, are Cast in Hard Bronze

shellac. The cores are thus provided with an insulating cover. Permit the shellac to dry before winding the coils.

Prepare the armature core by pasting a circle of heavy paper to each end of

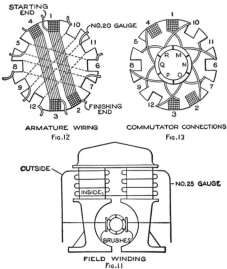

ARMATURE WIRING
Fig. 12

COMMUTATOR CONNECTIONS
Fig. 13

FIELD WINDING
Fig. 11

The Field Winding is Indicated in Fig. 11; the Winding of the Coils around the Armature Core is Shown in Fig. 12; and the Connections of the Armature Coils and the Commutator are Shown in Fig. 13

it with shellac. When dry, cut out the square slots. Paste strips of paper, shellacked thoroughly, into the slots their full length, and cover similarly any other exposed parts that may come in contact with the wire in winding.

The winding of the field magnet may now be undertaken. Use No. 25 gauge double cotton-covered copper wire. Wind 16 layers on each magnet core, as shown in the field-wiring diagram, Fig. 11. The wire must be started at the bottom of the core and finished at the lower part of it.

The wiring diagrams must be examined carefully so that errors may be avoided which may require the undoing of considerable work. With this precaution the windings are not difficult to accomplish, even to one inexperienced in this class of work. The two inner ends of the windings are connected, and the two outer ends are wired to the brush connections, as indicated. The inside, or beginning, ends of the wires should have a small rubber tube slipped over them to prevent breaking and to provide proper insulation.

The winding of the armature is more complicated than that of the field magnet, but should present no serious difficulties if the directions are observed step by step. The process, as shown in Fig. 12, is as follows: The armature is held with the commutator end toward the body of the worker, and the roll of wire is placed conveniently on the workbench. Procure 1¾ lb. No. 20 gauge single cotton-covered wire for this purpose. Start the winding in slot No. 1, passing the wire away from the body through the length of the slot, over the opposite end of the armature, and returning the wire in slot No. 2. Continue this winding until the slots are full, which requires about 80 turns. None of the wires must be above the slots or they will interfere when the armature is placed in the tunnel. Turn the armature halfway around to bring slot No. 3 uppermost. Wind as before, passing the wire around the armature in slots 3 and 4, beginning at No. 3. Repeat this process in the slots paired off, as follows: 5 to 6; 7 to 8; 9 to 10; 11 to 12. Turn the armature part way around in each case so that the first of the two slots being used in winding is uppermost. All of the wires must begin at the bottoms of the odd-numbered slots, and end at the tops of even-numbered slots, on the commutator end of the armature. Cover the ends of the wires both at the start and the finish with rubber-tube insulation.

Make the connections to the commutator, as shown in the diagram for this purpose, Fig. 13, which represents the commutator and the end of the armature behind it, as viewed from the commutator end of the armature shaft. Make the connections under the heads of the machine screws at the inner end of the commutator, and solder the screw head, wire, and commutator segment together. Care must be taken that the segments are not soldered together in this process. All the connections must be made very carefully, as a slight error in this phase of the work will prevent the proper operation of the generator. The commutator must be set on the shaft so that its segments are centered on six alternate slots of the armature, and then clamped by means of the nuts. By beginning with the starting end of the wire in slot No. 1 it may be observed that each of the starting ends is soldered to the inner screw in the commutator segment in advance of the slot. The starting end in slot No. 1 is soldered to segment M; the finishing end of this coil in slot No. 2 to segment N, etc. The finishing end of the wire in each coil is soldered to the commutator segment behind the slot. For example: the finishing end in slot No. 2 is soldered to segment N; that in No. 12 to O, etc. Give the armature and windings a thorough coat of shellac and permit it to dry.

The generator may now be checked to see that all preliminary work has been done, and then assembled for testing. Place the armature in the tunnel and attach the bearings securely by means of the machine screws. Connect a battery of about 12 volts to the field for a minute, magnetizing the poles. Fit the brushes into place, and adjust them to the commutator. Turn on the battery again, and the machine should run as a motor. The commutator must then be given its final adjustment. If the commutator has not been set very accurately on the shaft, it may be necessary to adjust it slightly so that its segments are centered properly with coil-filled slots Nos. 10, 6, 2, 12, 8, and 4, as shown in Fig. 13. The armature should turn clockwise, when the observer is facing the commutator end. The speed on 12 volts will not be high because at least 20 volts are necessary to obtain full speed. This voltage is satisfactory for test purposes.

The generator is now ready to be run in its normal manner. Fix a pulley of suitable size to the extended end of the armature shaft, by means of a set-screw. The special local conditions will determine the size of pulley used. The generator should be run in the same direction as when it was tested by running it as a motor, as indicated in the assembly drawing, Fig. 9. The proper speed is about 2,000 r. p. m., although it should generate satisfactorily, though not to full capacity, at less speed. At full speed it should generate 25 to 30 volts and four amperes. Both bearings should be kept well oiled. Wipe the commutator with a rag dipped in vaseline to keep it bright and clean. The brushes should be set only tight enough to make a satisfactory contact and collect the current.

Producing a Blue Finish on Steel

Polished-steel objects may be given a blue finish by placing them in heated charcoal. The surfaces of the metal must be very smooth and clean. The charcoal is powdered and placed in a box made of steel or iron plate. The steel to be blued must be taken out from time to time and dusted with finely powdered whiting. The color should be observed, and when a dark blue is obtained, the work should be permitted to cool, then cleaned and oiled.

⟡Provide a special file for filing babbitt, and oil it slightly to prevent the metal from sticking.

Removing a Plug from Casting

A steel plug, hardened and fitted to a drive fit into a large casting, was to 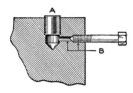 be removed, and the method shown in the sketch was devised for the purpose. A hole was drilled into the side of the casting to a point just below the plug A. The cavity was filled with white lead and oil, and a cap screw, B, was driven into the threaded hole. The result was a miniature ram, which drove the plug out easily without injuring it.—William T. Hummele, Buffalo, N. Y.

Cornice Rigging to Support Ladder Scaffold

Painters, and others who must work on scaffolds supported from the roofs or cornices of buildings, are familiar

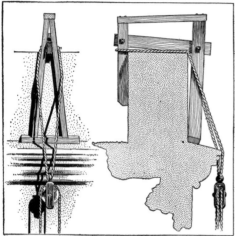

The Framework is Strongly Supported on the Wall and Makes the Use of Hooks Unnecessary

with the difficulty of providing a simple and safe means of attaching the tackle at the roof. The support shown in the illustration is made of 2 by 4-in. stock and fits firmly over the upper edge of the wall. Its front portion consists of an A-shaped frame which bears on the cornice and carries braces near the top. The frame may be made adjustable to various thicknesses of wall by boring additional holes for the bolts in the cross braces. The upper pulleys are supported on ropes secured about the framework.—H. W. Hart, St. Paul, Minn.

Forging Renews Worn Socket Wrenches

The square sockets of wrenches frequently become worn, and instead of repairing them, the tools are thrown aside. A number of such wrenches were picked up in a shop and the sockets renewed as follows: A piece of steel was ground to a square cross section of the original size of the socket, and the wrenches were heated over a forge fire. The worn edges were

hammered over this core, and when the wrench was smoothed and polished, the socket end was hardened. The wrenches were as serviceable as new ones.

Sawing Wooden Wheels, or Disks, on Band Saw

It was desired to saw a considerable number of wooden disks of the same diameter, and the following method, as shown in the illustration, was used with success: The disks were to be 10 in. in diameter. A smooth board, ⅞ in. thick, 8 in. wide, and long enough to reach across the table of the saw, was procured and clamped securely into place, as shown, after a nail had been driven barely through it so as to project at the center of the upper side and opposite the cutting edge of the saw. The point of the nail was exactly 5 in. from the saw. The stock was cut into square pieces of slightly more than the desired diameter. One of the pieces was placed on the board and pressed down on the nail so that it could be turned on the point. By turn-

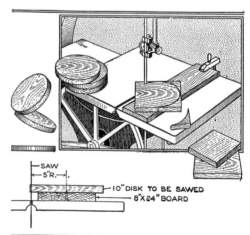

The Disks are Cut of Uniform Size without Marking Out Each Piece Separately

ing the piece of wood carefully, a disk was sawed out, having a smooth circular outline. Duplicates were made quickly in the same manner.—Edwin R. Mason, Danville, Ill.

Shop Apron with Convenient Spring Belt

Workmen in shops, as well as other persons who must wear an apron occasionally, are familiar with the nuisance of tying and untying apron strings, especially since they are easily broken in handling heavy objects. The use of an apron with a spring of band iron at the top instead of tie strings is quite convenient. The spring is curled slightly outward at the ends and may be slipped about the body quickly. It is not easily broken, and if given the proper tension insures that the apron will remain in place.

Device for Removing Small Shafts or Arbors

Experiencing difficulty in removing arbors and shafts from small gears and similar constructions in the workshop, I made a frame for removing them, as shown in the sketch. A piece of steel, 3 in. 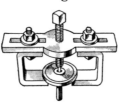 wide, 10 in. long, and ¾ in. thick, was provided with a ½-in. hole, at its center, tapped with a 12-gauge thread. Slots, 2½ in. long and ½ in. wide, were cut in the plate as shown, and a machine screw fitted to the threaded hole. Two pieces of steel, ½ in. thick, 1½ in. wide, and 5 in. long, were forged to a U-shape, and holes bored through their upper ends, to fit bolts clamped through the slots in the upper piece. An opening was left between the lower ends of the U-shaped pieces, and in this the gear, or other object from which a shaft or arbor is to be removed, is placed. By applying pressure on the center screw by means of a wrench, the shaft may be forced from the gear. The device may be made in various sizes.— W. C. Loy, Rochester, Ind.

⟪Rivets should be cut off before being inserted into place, so that just enough metal is available for proper riveting.

Tongs for Grasping Screws in Starting Them

It is often desired to place screws in corners where the hand cannot reach, and the device shown in the sketch was made and used successfully for this purpose. Strips of iron were twisted and forged at the ends to form tongs. The jaws were cut as indicated, and the two outer portions of each 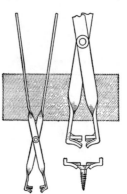 were bent down to receive the head of the screw while gripping it. It was possible by the use of this device to place screws in many places where there was barely room for a long screwdriver.

Lathe Center with Interchangeable Points

Lathe centers are frequently burned by persons inexperienced in the operation of such a machine, and occasionally even an experienced workman may have this trouble. The center shown in the sketch, with a point that is removable, was devised for use in a shop where boys were taught to operate lathes, and proved economical. It consists of two main parts: The shank A is turned to fit the taper of the lathe spindle, and the point B is turned to fit a 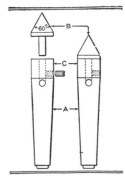 socket in the end of the main portion. A setscrew is provided in the straight portion, C, of the shank, and a hole is drilled to make removal of the point easy. When the point is burned, it may be replaced quickly by a new one.

Arm Pincushion Carried on Bicycle Clip

A tailor devised the arm pincushion shown in the sketch so that he would

have pins at hand while fitting garments or working in various parts of the shop. The device was made by fitting a pincushion into a cup and fastening it to an ordinary trouser clip worn by bicyclists. The cushion is carried on the left arm.—Mrs. Avis G. Vestal, Chicago, Ill.

Sorting Tray for Nails, Screws, and Bolts

Instead of throwing away stray bolts, screws, and other small pieces used in the workshop, a good plan is to place them in a tray for miscellanies from which they may be sorted conveniently. A tray for this purpose may be made of a wooden or metal box, about 2 in. deep, 6 in. wide, and 12 in. long. One corner of the bottom should be provided with a small opening covered by a slide, and the upper corner above it should be covered with a triangular section. In sorting the material it is poured from the small opening into the hand and distributed into several receptacles. The triangular covering at the corner prevents the contents of the tray from spilling while being sorted.

Utilizing the Heat in a Fireplace for a Radiator

A room in which there is a fireplace is usually quite comfortable close to the fire, but is likely to be cold near the far corners, especially in cold weather when a strong wind is blowing. There is much waste heat in a fireplace, and to utilize it under such conditions, I installed the radiator and hot-water heating system shown in the sketch. The piping is ¾-in., and is connected with standard fittings.

The grate in the fireplace was made of pipe and fittings, as shown, to fit into the opening, which will, of course, vary, hence no dimensions are given. The cold-water supply was arranged in a corridor adjoining and the pipes connected to the radiator and the grate under the floor, as shown. The circulation of the water is indicated by the arrows.—W. S. Wilson, Cascades, Canada.

A Grate of Pipe was Built in the Fireplace and Made Part of a Hot-Water Heating System by Which Parts of the Room Remote from the Fire were Heated

Patching the Printing Surfaces of Woodcuts or Type

A method which I employ almost daily in the shop for repairing wood type, large poster wood engravings, etc., when a miscut is made, and which could be used on wood in many instances where a smooth surface is desired over a patch, is as follows: Fill the holes with hot sealing wax, and when it is cold and hard put some lubricating oil on it and rub the surface down with a piece of pumice stone. The result will be a smooth, level patch, which can be worked like the wood surrounding it.—L. L. Pazourek, Cleveland, Ohio.

Old Kitchen Boilers Used for Well Casing

A farmer made use of old kitchen boilers for well casings, thus adding another to the many uses to which these cumbersome tanks have been put. They were cheaper than the well casing he had intended to use, and, it is asserted, will last longer. The boilers were removed to a shop in a wheelbarrow, as shown in the photograph reproduced, and the ends were removed by cutting the rivets. They were then butted end on end, and a band of strap iron was riveted on them, as shown. In this form they were lowered into the well, bored by a well driller. Boilers of this type are hard to dispose of, and they were taken

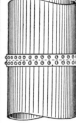

The Old Boilers were Gathered in a Dumping Ground and Used by a Farmer for Well Casings

from a city dumping ground and shipped to the farmer in sufficient number for his well.—John Hoeck, Alameda, Calif.

Gang Tool for Shaper in Machine Shop

The base of a column, which was too wide to be planed in a shaper by ordinary methods of using the machine,

The Base of a Column was Planed Satisfactorily by the Use of the Gang Tool Braced as Shown

was handled satisfactorily by means of a gang tool, as shown in the photograph reproduced. The base was set up in the shaper and supported by a jack. The center of the work was considerably to one side of the center of the ram, so it was necessary to extend the tool holder farther on one side of the tool post than on the other. The base of the column was cored, and the pressure on the cutting tools was not the same during the entire length of the longest cut. In order to prevent the bar supporting the tools from springing under these conditions, the support shown was clamped behind it and fixed to the front of the ram.—Harvey Mead, Scranton, Pa.

Preventing Frosting of Auto Panes in Winter

The gathering of frost on the windshield of an automobile in cold weather is dangerous. Alcohol added to the cleansing water will aid in preventing the forming of frost. If the shield, and other windows in the car, do not need cleaning apply a coating of three parts alcohol and one part glycerin, and rub it to a polish. This is especially useful in closed automobiles, and may be applied to show windows.

Scraper for Joints in Brickwork

Scraped joints are in general favor for brickwork, and the best appearance results only when the joints are uni-

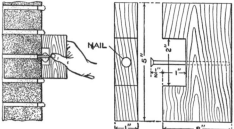

The Joints are Scraped Neatly and Uniformly by Means of the Homemade Scraper

form in depth. The tool shown in the sketch affords a simple means of gauging and smoothing the joints. It is made of a block of wood, 1 by 3 by 5 in., notched at one side, and having a 16-penny common nail driven into it at the notch. It is used in scraping the joints, as shown in the sketch at the left.—Ernest Greenhalgh, Indianapolis, Indiana.

A Soft-Face Hammer

It is frequently desirable, when it is necessary to pound soft metals like brass or finished metal work, to use a hammer which has a soft face, that is, a face which will not damage or mar the surface pounded. Hammers with babbitt-metal heads are regularly manufactured for this purpose and are very convenient, but an improvised soft-face hammer can easily be arranged as suggested in the sketch. First a piece of leather belting is cut as shown

at A. The strip is arranged on the hammer head as shown at B. The hole H must be large enough so that the hammer handle will slip through

it. The leather protective strip is fastened by driving a tack through the leather and into the hammer handle. When pounding on objects that should not be marred, the blow is delivered with the side of the hammer head protected with the leather.

Gauging Automobile-Body Dashes

In assembling sheet-metal shrouds on wooden frames of automobile bodies, trouble was experienced in setting the dash at right angles to the bottom of the body. As the dash is part of the shroud, the latter was clamped in place, and then tested for alinement with a large try-square, its perpendicular edge set against the dash. This method required consid erable time and, especially on piece work, proved unsatisfactory. The problem was solved by having all the assembling forms carefully planed up and leveled. Then a triangular frame was made, with three pins of the same length projecting out on one side at each of its corners. The top edge of this frame was carefully made at a right angle to the plane of the pins, and then a small spirit level was fastened to it, as shown in the sketch. In

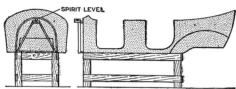

The Triangular Frame is Placed against the Dash and the Test for Alinement Made

testing the dash, the triangular frame is held up against it, two of the pins at the bottom, and the third in the center at the top. By observing the level, the position of the dash may be determined quickly, and proper adjustment made.

⁅Before putting on a tire casing, wipe it out carefully with a moist rag, to insure that the inner tube will not be damaged by dirt or sand lodged in the casing.

Portable Trolley and Tackle for Freight Transfer

By JOHN W. SHANK

RAPID and economical loading and unloading of merchandise freight between platforms and railroad cars was accomplished by fitting a portable trolley and tackle into the cars and above the adjoining platform, as shown in the sketch. Heavy packages and crates of goods ordinarily requiring the use of a truck are handled in this way with ease. A sling, or grabhook, is fixed around the load, which is raised from the floor by means of the multiple-pulley block and rope. The rope is locked and the load transported to its immediate destination on the loading platform or in the freight house.

The trolley is supported by means of tongs set into grooves cut in the ridge pole of the car roof, as shown in the detail sketch at the right. The hooks which support the trolley are of forged steel, curved as shown, to fit the trolley wire or rail, and to give clearance for the passage of the hanger. The trolley rail is built up of sections of round iron rod, jointed with a tongue and groove at each joint, and bolted to the hooks with flat-head bolts, as shown in the detail sketch at the left. The rigging may thus be "knocked down" for convenient removal. The curved sections at the turns in the rail are similarly jointed to the main trolley rail, a sup-

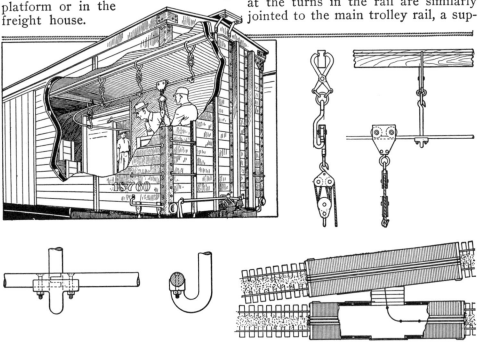

This Portable Rigging for the Handling of Package Freight Saves Time and Physical Energy of the Workmen

porting hook being set at each joint, about 4 ft. apart. The upper sketch shows the device in use in a freight car, and below is shown the use of the rigging between two freight cars, on adjoining tracks.

Tool for Boring Large Holes in Wood

It is sometimes necessary to cut large round holes through heavy flooring, wooden partitions, or wooden

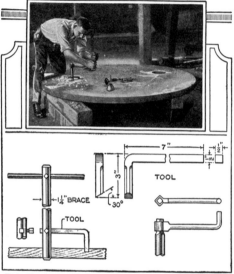

This Tool was Made to Bore Large Round Holes in a Tank Cover, and Has Many Uses

tank covers. With a saw it is difficult to cut a smooth circular hole, and a more accurate tool is required. Such a tool, designed to cut holes 5 to 12 in. in diameter, is shown in the illustration, and is made as follows: Heat a bar of tool steel, ½ by ½ by 10 in., to a cherry red; bend it at a right angle, 3 in. from one end, and temper it. The brace is made from 1¼-in. round bar stock, and its length should suit the work to be done. Drill a ½-in. hole through the bar, 4 in. from one end, squaring it afterward with a file, so that the tool may pass through with a snug fit. Perpendicular to this hole, drill and tap a hole for a ⅜-in. setscrew. At the other end of the brace, drill a ½-in. hole, and fit a round-bar handle through it.

To cut a 10-in. hole, for instance, through a wooden floor, bore out a 1¼-in. hole in the exact center of the circle laid out. Then set the tool so that it will be 5 in. from the extreme cutting edge to the center of the brace, and cut out the disk in the center. In the photograph reproduced, holes are being bored in a hard-maple cover, 3 in. thick, for a large tank. As these holes had to be accurate within a small fraction of an inch, they could not be sawed out, and the above described tool was designed and used with excellent results.—K. M. Coggeshall, Webster Groves, Mo.

Kinks in the Care of Spark Plugs

The failure of a spark plug is one of the most frequent troubles with the automobile engine, hence the autoist should know what to do when this occurs. When the spark plug misses, or fails to fire, the engine is out of tune or balance. This condition is instantly noticed by the irregular vibration set up in the car, and by the loss of power. Generally the trouble is caused by the plug becoming short-circuited through the collection of carbon on the porcelain of the plug. This is termed sooted or dirty, and is caused by several conditions. The carburetor may be out of adjustment, giving too rich a mixture, or there may be too much oil in the cylinder. These possible causes should be looked into if the trouble is chronic.

If the plug is found to have a black

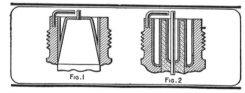

Typical Sections of Spark Plugs, Showing How Carbon Collects on Surface, Causing a Short Circuit

coating clean it thoroughly so that the porcelain is white, and the points quite clean. It will make cleaning easier if the plug is soaked in wood alcohol. Then take a sharp-pointed tool, a knife answering very well, wrap a piece of rag around it, and scrape the plug all over, getting down into the recesses.

There are various types of plugs, the most common being the porcelain, shown in Fig. 1. The inclosed type of plug will fire longer without the need of cleaning, but it is hard to clean, as it has to be taken apart. When a plug is taken apart, great care must be taken to see that the porcelain is not broken, and when reassembling it, all the joints must be made gas-tight. Fig. 2 shows another type of plug, the possibility of short-circuiting by carbon deposit being indicated.

The modern plug is so made that it will not come apart, and, while it is a little harder to clean the individual parts when they cannot be handled separately, it is not so much trouble in the long run, as it is hard to put the other type together again properly. The insulator of a plug sometimes cracks, and even though it be but a minute crack, it must be thrown away, as the carbon seeps in quickly, and the plug will not fire.

When buying new plugs be sure to get the type that is made for the particular engine to be fitted. In addition to the numerous special plugs, there are two sizes of hexagons in use, one $7/8$ in. across flats, and the other $1\frac{1}{8}$ in. across. It is annoying to find that the spark-plug wrench will not fit the new plug intended for use, especially so when one cannot get at the plug to turn it with an adjustable wrench. It is a good plan for the autoist to carry an extra set of spark plugs, so that in case of failure on the road the bad one may be replaced without the necessity of cleaning plugs until the return to the garage is made.

Movable Scaffold for Building and Painting

The supports for a scaffold shown in the illustration will be found more convenient in many cases than the use of a ladder, or of brackets fastened to the side of a building, to provide a support for workmen. They are made of 2 by 4-in. stuff, and should be arranged so that the lower ends are slanted away from the building sufficiently to pre-

These Supports for a Scaffold Are More Convenient than the Use of a Ladder, Especially for Work at a Comparatively Low Height

vent their slipping, and if desired, for use on smooth footings, braces which can be spiked down may be fastened to the lower ends of the supports.— James R. Townsend, Itasca, Tex.

Casters on Footboard for Use in Auto Repairs

One of the footboards in an automobile may be converted into a convenient device for use in repairing or examining the under parts of the machine. The board is fitted 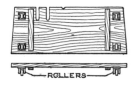 with four casters, as shown in the sketch, and these enable the workman to rest on the board and shift easily under the car. The device is always available, as it is fitted into its place in the floor of the car when not in use otherwise.—Louis S. Niper, Beach Park, Conn.

A Nonsagging Board Gate

The usual method of bracing a gate built up of boards is to fasten horizontal cleats across it, one near the top and another near the bottom, and a third diagonally between them, forming a Z-shape. This is often unsatisfactory in that the gate sags easily by strain in use, as well as from its own weight. A better method of disposing the braces is shown

in the sketch. This was tried out with success, the gate withstanding unusual strain. The lower brace is placed horizontally across the boards and well nailed. The upper brace extends diagonally downward and is notched into an intermediate brace, which in turn is notched into the lower one. The hinges are fastened to the edge, at the left of the sketch.—C. F. J. Charliss, Houston, Tex.

Spring Aids in Valve Grinding

In grinding gas-engine valves, it is imperative that the stems be lifted frequently from the

seating in the cylinder to insure an even distribution of the abrasive material. If the valve is not lifted from time to time, the emery or carborundum dust and oil are apt to form in small pellets, producing deep grooves in the valve head and seat, which are hard to remove by grinding. The usual method is to lift the valve stem with one hand, while oscillating it with the other. A coil spring of moderate tension, placed under the valve head, as shown in the sketch, will lift it automatically whenever the pressure is released from the grinding tool. Only enough pressure to keep the valve head seated, against the resistance of the spring, should be applied.—Victor W. Pagé, Bristol, Connecticut.

Inexpensive Traffic-Light Post

A traffic-light post that is practical and inexpensive is shown in the sketch.

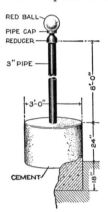

It is set in a concrete base providing the "isle of safety" and a 10-in. red-glass light globe is supported on an 8-ft. section of 3-in. iron pipe. The connections are made with standard reducers, and the globe is fitted into a 4-in. pipe cap. The wiring is conducted to the globe through a conduit connecting with the post. The pipe cap which holds the globe is drilled and tapped for small machine screws, which hold the globe in place.—H. G. McQueen, Dow City, Ia.

Skidding a Heavy Boiler or Machine

The moving of a heavy boiler or a large machine without the use of special appliances is sometimes a difficult task. A good way to handle this job is to build a wooden cradle around the object to be moved and mount this on two heavy wooden runners, resting on a well-greased plank. A few other greased planks should be in readiness so that when a couple of teams are hooked to the cradle and it starts to move, the planks can be laid as required just in advance of the runners. The planks may be used repeatedly.—James Skelton, Toronto, Can.

A Sanding Drum for the Wood Shop
by Charles A. King

A WIDE range of woodwork to be smoothed may be handled to advantage on a sanding drum like that shown in the illustration. It is of simple construction and can be made easily even in a small woodworking shop, the only special fittings required being the shaft, flanges, bearings, and collars. These are readily available from machinery-supply houses, or may be obtained from old machine parts. This machine was used in a job shop for the sanding of ordinary building trim, elaborate bank fittings, and even for high-grade furniture. Flat work, curved pieces of a radius larger than that of the drum, and the edges of stock may be sanded on it, by the use of the table or the edge-sanding rest. The drum revolves in the direction indicated by the arrow at a speed of 600 revolutions per minute. It is driven by a 3-in. belt over a 10-in. pulley, set on the shaft, and an idle pulley provides for shutting off the machine temporarily.

The single table above gives greater freedom of use, and was determined upon after two tables had been tried. Care must, of course, be exercised in sanding work so that the operator may not be endangered by the drum. It is desirable, also, to provide a drive that will leave the top of the drum and the table free from obstructions, and permit the operator convenient access in handling large pieces. The table serves merely as a rest for the stock as it passes over the drum.

The drum is supported in a frame made of hard wood. The legs are of 2½ by 4-in. stock, braced by 2 by 4-in. pieces, mortised into them, and pinned at the joints with ⅝-in. maple pins. The members A, which carry the drum shaft, are of 2½ by 4-in. stock, and are fixed to the legs by mortise-and-tenon joints, as shown in the side view, Fig. 2. The edge-sanding shelf B extends slightly beyond the members A, as shown, and should be set carefully on wedges, so that the center of a ⅞-in. board will extend on a line with a radius of the drum, as indicated by the dotted line at B. To insure accurate edge-sanding on stock of other thicknesses, it is necessary to build up on the shelf so that the edge will not be "out of square."

The table C is built up on a frame of 1¾ and 2½ by 4-in. stock, fastened at the joints with lag screws, as indicated in Fig. 2, at D and at E. The brace at E is shouldered into the side rails of the table, and its lower edge is beveled to accommodate the drum. The table is braced against the rear legs with 2 by 2-in. pieces, fastened with lag screws. It is 2 ft. 7½ in. from the floor, and the upper edge of the drum projects ½ in. above it.

The drum is carried on a 1⁷⁄₁₆-in. shaft, keyed to flanges, J, Fig. 4, which in turn are fixed to the drum ends G, with screws. The shaft rests in split bearings, set into the supporting member A. Side motion of the shaft in the bearings is prevented by collars between the flanges and bearings, and set collars, F, Fig. 1, on the ends of the shaft. The body of the drum is built up on the drumheads G, which are of two layers, cross-banded to insure great strength, necessary at the considerable speed of operation. The sanding surface is built up of small strips, H, cut so that their edges are in line with radii of the drum end. The pieces of the drumhead must be fastened together firmly with screws or bolts, riveted so that the nuts cannot become loosened accidentally. Cut the drumheads out approximately to

The sandpaper is drawn taut and clamped in place by means of the clamping strip K, shown in Fig. 5. The

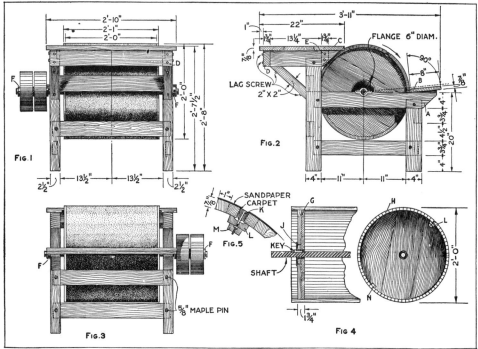

This Sanding Drum Has a Wide Range of Usefulness and can be Made Readily in the Wood Shop at Small Outlay

their finished size. Cut the keyways in the bearings of the flanges and mount the flanges upon the drumheads. Then turn the heads down carefully to their exact finished diameter, which is 1 ft. 10¼ in., if the staves of the drum are made ⅞ by 1 in. To do this, set them on the shaft together at one end, keying them, and apply the power by means of the pulley and belt. End motion of the shaft is prevented by the use of the set collars F, which are brought up against the bearings. Place the ends in position and nail the staves in place, setting the heads of the nails carefully, or countersink the screws, if this form of fastening is used. The staves should be of pine or whitewood, fitted tightly, and glued in place as they are fastened.

The sanding surface of the drum is covered with a layer of Brussels carpet, and the sandpaper is placed over this, the carpet providing a cushion.

strip is fitted into a groove so that, when the carpet and sandpaper layers are in place, the upper surface of the strip is just below the surface of the drum, never above it. The strip should be tapered only very slightly, if at all, the sides of the groove being parallel with those of the strip. The lower edge is rounded to prevent tearing the sandpaper. The strip is held in place by flat-head bolts screwed into nuts set in a strip M, fixed to the inner side of the drum. The bolts can thus be released from the outside by means of a screwdriver. They are held snugly in the strip L, being only loose enough to be turned without difficulty.

The clamping device must be counterbalanced by a strip on the opposite side of the drum, as at N, Fig. 4. The clamping device as well as this strip must, of course, be fastened in place before all of the staves are glued finally. They may be fastened temporarily with screws, and glued in place when the balance strip and clamping strip are in position. The clamping strip and its bolts should then be removed and a strip of the same thickness as those used for the drum should be fixed into place in the groove. The surface of the drum must next be turned smooth, using the machine as a lathe, and removing only as much stock as is necessary. The strip in the groove prevents the breaking of the edges at that point. The surfacing of the drum must be done with great care, for if it is not straight and true, the sandpaper will bubble and crack before it is worn considerably. The ends of the staves should be trimmed off to the proper length by turning. The drum should be in perfect balance to insure good results, and, if necessary, holes may be bored in the heavy side of the drumheads, or weights fastened securely to the lighter side, to correct fault on this score.

The carpet backing for the sandpaper is stretched over the drum and nailed into the clamping groove. The sandpaper is stretched over it, sufficient length being allowed to permit the sandpaper to pass under the clamping strip and against the opposite side of the groove. Slots are cut in the sandpaper to accommodate the bolts in drawing them up firmly. The first sheet of sandpaper should be fitted carefully, and others may be patterned from it. It is desirable to stretch the sandpaper over the drum on a damp day, as it will contract with dry weather, giving a better sanding surface. The paper should never be moistened in applying it, as this ruins it for use in sanding. For ordinary work No. 2 sandpaper is used, and for smoother finishes finer grades may be applied. The machine may be given an oil finish or painted a suitable color. A convenient method of fixing it to the floor is by the use of angle irons.

Exhaust Fan for Workbench Aids in Removing Dust

Before painting iron castings, or secondhand machinery, it is necessary to remove the rust and foreign substances from the surface. During the cleaning process, the detached rust particles, floating about in the air, are inhaled by the workman, lodge in his eyes, and settle on his clothing. This metallic dust is also injurious to the bearings of machinery which may be near by, to say nothing of its settling on finished or wet painted surfaces. A simple suction device was fitted to a workbench, as shown in the sketch, to eliminate these bad features.

The workbench was constructed with an iron grating for the working surface, instead of the usual board top. An air-tight, boxlike inclosure was then built below the grating, with the bottom sloping downward. At one side an exhaust fan, driven by an electric

Dust from Cleaning of Castings is Drawn Away through the Grating in the Top of the Bench, Thus Protecting the Workman

motor, was set, and the inlet side connected with the bench inclosure. The exhaust from the fan was piped outside the building. With the fan in operation, castings are placed on the grating and brushed or sandpapered without inconvenience to the workman. The dust and rust particles are drawn downward through the grating. Such a bench is suitable for use in the removal of old coats of paint, to clean up machinery parts, or even to finish the surface of woodwork. If chipping or grinding is done, it will be necessary to put up a back stop, as shown, to keep small particles from flying across the room and injuring other workmen.

Portable Electric Drill Used as Drill Press

Many shops are provided with a portable electric drill, which is a necessity for certain kinds of work, but not

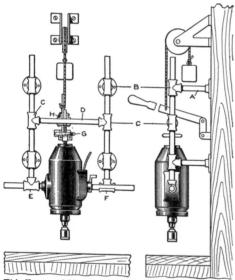

This Frame of Pipe and Fittings Enlarged the Range of Usefulness of a Portable Electric Drill Needed Only Occasionally

used often. The frame shown in the illustration was made to fit a drill of this type, and extended its usefulness to the many kinds of work ordinarily done on a small drill press. Most of the parts of the support and mechanism were made from pipe and fittings. The machine is fixed to a frame of wood, which supports a table on which the work is rested. The wooden support may be arranged so that it can be moved without taking the drill and fittings from it. The drill is supported in a frame which is raised and lowered by means of a lever, fixed to a counterweight.

Four standards, A, made of a section of 1-in. pipe, a flange, and a tee are fixed to the wooden frame. The frame of pipes and fittings which carries the drill is made of pipe of an outside diameter to slide closely in the tees, B, of the standards. Tees, C, are fixed solidly to the center brace D, and the sections of pipe joined to them. The shaft of the drill is rested in a tee, E, and in the tee F, which is cut open so that the shaft may be removed readily. The drill is held securely between the brace D and its bearings by means of the handwheel G, operating on a threaded rod set into a lug on the lower side of the brace.

The handle and its fittings are made of strap iron. The range of the drill is limited by the movement of the handle, which is fitted to the brace D by means of a shoe, H, in which it slides. The counterweight cord is fixed to the handle and passes over a pulley set in a bracket above the pipe frame.—W. A. Ready, Boston, Mass.

Substitute for a Small Printing-Press Roller

The roller on my printing press became so marred that it could not be used with satisfaction, so I made one which was quite efficient. It can be

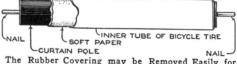

The Rubber Covering may be Removed Easily for Cleaning and Renewed Cheaply When Worn

cleaned easily and was made of materials which are easily obtained. I sawed a piece of curtain rod to the proper length and drove a nail into each end as a bearing, cutting off the head. Several layers of soft paper were pasted around the roller, as shown in the sketch, and the inner tube of a bicycle tire was then fitted over the roller. The rubber tube can be removed quickly and cleaned, or renewed if desired. Hand rollers may also be made in this way by fitting a handle on the nails at the ends of the roller.—P. F. Harper, Danville, Va.

Soldering Patches on Tanks or Large Objects

The soldering of patches on tanks and other objects that cannot be taken to the workshop readily is often difficult. The following method overcomes most of the objectionable features: First shape a patch by pressing a piece of tin somewhat larger than the opening, with the ball of a hammer, leaving a small flange around the edge. Tin both the patch and the part to be soldered; fill the hollow in the patch with melted solder and permit it to cool. Then using a pad, or heavy glove, place the patch in the hand, melt the solder with the soldering copper and apply the patch. Sweat it into place in the usual manner.—Charles Straughan, Sprague, Wash.

Automobile Gear-Box Repair

Trouble was experienced on the gear box of an automobile in that the grease leaked, as shown in Fig. 1. The boss at the left, as indicated in Fig. 2, was tapped, and a brass plug was inserted to cover the end of the shaft. This necessitated shifting the locking screw, as shown in Fig. 2. The tapped hole formerly necessary for the locking screw was plugged. A leather washer was fitted at the end plug to insure a tight joint.

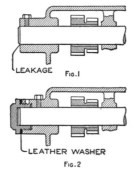

LEAKAGE   Fig. 1

LEATHER WASHER
Fig. 2

Portable Safety Platform for Telephone Linemen

To provide utmost safety in handling telephones on private lines when carried over the same poles as are used for electric-power wires, a simple and effective portable safety platform was devised, as shown in the illustration. It is constructed of wood, about 1½ in. thick, 14 in. wide, and 18 in. long, cut out at the inside edge to suit the average standard pole for heavy line service, and insulated with rubber or other suitable material. Two straps are attached to the platform at the inner side to reach around the pole, and are provided with a strong buckle for ready and substantial fastening. A spike driven into the pole serves to keep this support in place. At the outside edge, two heavy leather straps are also provided to carry the weight of the operator on the platform.

SPIKE
BUCKLE
LEATHER STRAP
SPIKE
BUCKLE
LEATHER STRAP
18"

The platform is ordinarily used about 2 ft. above the grade, to suit the regulation height of the telephone attached to the pole by means of a strap at a point about 9 ft. above the ground. This platform proved of great value in eliminating the constant danger of electric shock when using the private telephone lines of light and power companies, sometimes exposed to contact with high-voltage transmission lines.— L. R. W. Allison, Newark, N. J.

⟨Caliper a bored hole at several points in its length, as the size at the opening may be misleading.

Oil-Burning Blowtorch for Sheet-Metal Work

The torch shown in the illustration was designed for use in railroad shops on boiler, tank, freight-car, and other heavy sheet-metal work. By means of it a powerful flame may be directed on a limited area. The device is simple in construction, convenient in operation, and comparatively light. The oil fuel is admitted through the upper pipe, at the right, and the air for the blast through the lower pipe, the flow being controlled by ⅜-in. globe valves. The pipes are braced near the torch and form a strong grip for the operator. The torch proper is a coil of ¼-in. wrought-iron pipe, fixed into a brass collar, having holes through it, as shown in the detail sketch, and covered with a 2½-in. wrought-iron pipe, from which the flame is projected.

The upper sketch shows the general-assembly drawing of the torch; the details are shown in the lower sketches. The cover for the coil is 11 in. long over all. One end of it is fitted with a brass plug, shown in detail at the center, below. Inside of this plug is a second brass plug, shown at the right, and into this are fixed the supply tube and the coiled pipe. The dotted lines in the upper view show how the flame

heated to the proper temperature for ignition in passing through the coil, and the flame passes out through the center of it.

Cutting Threads without Tap or Die

Requiring a thread on a small piece of copper wire and a nut to fit it, I found that no tap or die was available. A piece of spring brass was drilled to a size slightly smaller than the wire, and a small rat-tail file was forced into it by gradual turns and then withdrawn with a rotary motion, forming threads. This nut was turned onto the tapered end of the wire, and being slightly harder than the copper in the wire, cut a satisfactory thread.—Thomas A. Hancock, Los Angeles, Calif.

Preserving Stove Linings

The fire-brick lining of a stove will last much longer and give better service if promptly jointed with fire clay. When the new fire bricks are placed in the stove, set them with the clay, which is mixed to a mortar with water. Burn a few sticks of wood, taking care not to heat the stove too rapidly, and the clay will soon harden. The lining usually begins to deteriorate at the joints, and by filling them with fire clay, the latter may be removed and a

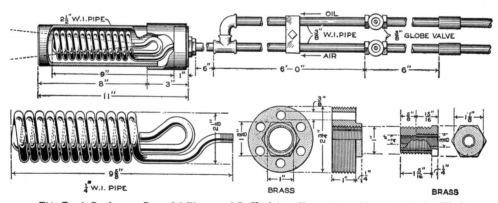

This Torch Produces a Powerful Flame and Is Useful on Heavy Sheet-Metal and Boiler Work

is forced from the end of the coil, which is also shown in detail. It is 9⅝ in. long and 2⅛ in. diameter. The oil is

new layer inserted when it has pitted or cracked badly.—L. E. Fetter, Portsmouth, N. H.

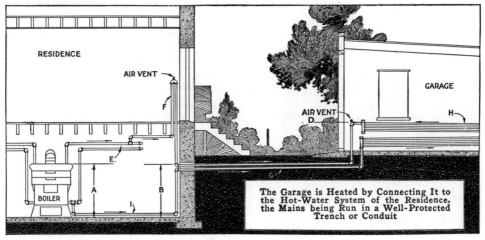

RESIDENCE

AIR VENT

F

BOILER

E

A   B

AIR VENT
D

GARAGE

H

G

The Garage is Heated by Connecting It to the Hot-Water System of the Residence, the Mains being Run in a Well-Protected Trench or Conduit

Heating a Garage from Residence Hot-Water System

The heating of a home garage in winter is a problem that confronts not a few motorists, and the method suggested in the sketch has been found practicable for utilizing heat from the residence heating system for this purpose. The chief difficulty encountered was that the top of the boiler in the basement was too high to permit the flow pipe to be run underground to the garage. In other instances the boiler may be situated so that a pipe extending across the cellar as required would be much in the way. These difficulties were overcome by the installation shown in the diagram.

The flow main to the garage was connected to a flow main, E, in the cellar leading directly from the boiler at the top. The pipe then passes through the floor, forming the loop F, which is provided with an air vent. From this, the pipe passes down to below the grade of the ground outside and into the tile, or other suitable trench, leading to the garage. The top of the loop F must be at least 3 ft. above the intake at D, and more is desirable if convenient to provide it. The circulation to the garage depends in a large measure on the height to which the loop rises. The distance B must not be more than 18 in. less than the distance A.

Run the pipe in the trench as close to the surface as it is possible to do and still provide adequate covering and protection. The arrows indicate that the pipes grade up toward the heads of the former. The main connects with the coils in the garage, as shown, flowing into the upper coil, which is in turn connected with the lower one at the extreme end, not shown. The return main G also is laid in the trench and grades up as indicated by the arrow. It passes through the wall and into the cellar below the flow main and then drops to the floor and returns to the boiler. The return pipe I need not be below the center line of the return tapping on the boiler, unless there are doorways, or other obstructions, making it necessary to drop it to the floor as shown. It must not, however, be connected to any other return pipe at a height above the center line of the return tapping. The loop F and the coil H should be freed of air by means of the vents.

Jig for Cutting Hard Lubricating Grease

In order to cut hard grease into disk-shaped pieces, about ½ in. thick and 1⅞ in. wide, the jig shown in the sketch was devised in a railroad shop. The principle involved may be used for a variety of similar purposes with slight adaptation. The grease is shipped in barrels and prepared for use by pressing it through a die to form it into long sticks, 1⅞ in. in diameter. These are placed in the jig

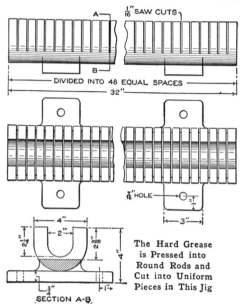

The Hard Grease is Pressed into Round Rods and Cut into Uniform Pieces in This Jig

and cut to uniform lengths, each piece weighing one ounce. The pieces of this size are used for the grease cups of locomotive driving rods. The device consists of a casting of iron provided with legs by which it is bolted down. It is 4 in. high, 8 in. wide, and 32 in. long. The guide slots are cut with a saw, cutting a kerf 1/16 in. wide. The inside of the jig is finished to make it easy to clean.—J. K. Long, Renovo, Pa.

Eliminating Pounding in Gasoline Engines

Pounding in a gasoline engine can, in almost every case, be attributed to a loose part within, particularly the various bolts. A careful examination should be made immediately, the bolts and nuts of the connecting-rod bearings, the main-shaft bearings, the bolts that connect the flywheel to the crankshaft end, and other fittings being closely inspected. A loose bolt on a flywheel rotating at great speed, is particularly dangerous, and should be remedied at once.

Safety Device for Wheelbarrow

When a wheelbarrow is pushed through a narrow passageway the hands of the laborer may be painfully injured by striking against the door jambs. To overcome this, nail a block of wood on each handle of the wheelbarrow just in front of the grip. The block should be tapered from the front end.—Victor E. Carpenter, South Bend, Ind.

Double-Shaft Universal Joint

The universal joint shown in the sketch provides for the use of one shaft within the other, permitting the two sections to be at an angle to each other while in operation. Other features are that the shafts may be run at different speeds, in the same or opposite directions, or one shaft may be run while the other is stopped. The outer shaft is a tube having a fork at the end adjoining the large ring at the universal joint. The forks are mounted on this ring with screws, as shown. The inner shaft is solid and the forks at the end are mounted on a solid steel ball, in the same relation to each other as are the larger forks, mounted on the ring. While largely an experimental device,

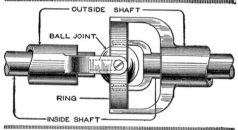

This Universal Joint Houses One Shaft within Another and Has Experimental Interest for Power Transmission

it has interesting possibilities for application to machinery and power transmission.—James O. Tow, Columbia, Missouri.

❦ Electric fans are used for the drying of motion-picture films. The films are wound on large drums which are revolved steadily while the current from the fan is played upon them.

Garden Seats of Concrete

By EDWARD A. KRUEGER

[This article details the making of two garden seats and gives designs for four others. Information on the various materials, surface finishes, and the mixing of concrete is given in pamphlets furnished gratis by manufacturers of Portland cement.—Editor.]

THE making of cement products is especially practicable for the home worker in that the materials required are inexpensive and easily procured; with reasonable care, excellent results may be obtained, even by a novice. The permanence of concrete, properly mixed and placed, commends it as a constructive material for many objects of use and ornament exposed to the elements.

A garden seat like that shown in Fig. 1, without the paneling on the edges, involves first the making of a plain box form for the top slab. This may be used for the making of two or more supports by nailing partitions in the form, as shown in the sketch and detail drawing, Fig. 2. A smaller form is required for the foundations, which are cast in molds separated by partitions. Make a rectangular form, having inside measurements of 18½ in. by 8 ft., and 3½ in. deep, for the top slab. Build up the platform for the form of ⅞-in. flooring, and smooth the top surface to give a good finish to the concrete. Cut the end pieces squarely, 18½ in. long, and fit them between the sidepieces. Screws, 12-penny common nails, or bolts, as shown in Fig. 2, may be used to hold the form together. Square the form and nail strips across the upper edges to prevent the weight of the concrete from forcing out the sides. Toenail it in place on the platform, clean the interior, removing nails or other obstructions, and smooth off rough parts with sandpaper. Fill any irregularities in the inner surfaces of the form with plaster of Paris, and permit it to dry. Apply one or two coats of shellac to the inside of the form, to protect it from the moisture. When the shellac is thoroughly dried, apply a uniform coat of linseed oil to the mold and the form is ready for the concrete. If many slabs are to be made with a mold, soak the wood thoroughly in crude oil before making the form.

If the form for the supports is made from new stuff, the process of construction is similar to that described. Set the partitions squarely, 15 in. apart from face to face, nailing them as shown. If the form for the top slab is used for the supports, clean it, and apply fresh coats of shellac and oil for each successive use. The weight of the top slab is usually sufficient to hold it in place. If desired, bolts may be cast into the upper edges of the supports and fitted into holes in the top slab, as shown in Fig. 3.

The top slab is reinforced with heavy wire mesh, or with ¼-in. round iron rods. The latter extend lengthwise of the slab, set on 3-in. centers, and crosswise on 10-in. centers, their ends being 1½ in. from the adjacent edges of the slab. They should be wired together to form a mat, or wired to light wire mesh. The reinforcing is placed 1 in. from the lower side of the slab, as shown in the working drawings, Fig. 1. It is important, therefore, that the upper side of the slab be marked when the form is removed, as the reinforcing is less effective if the slab is inverted.

If bolts are used in the supports, set wooden pegs of the proper size at

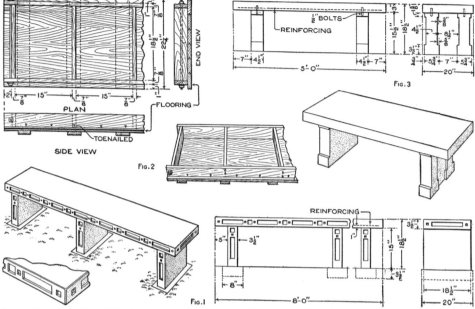

Plain Slabs of Uniform Width, Paneled if Desired, are Used for the Seat Shown in Fig. 1. That Shown in Fig. 3 Involves the Use of Special Forms for the Shaping and Paneling of the Supports

corresponding points in the bottom of the mold.

Prepare the concrete mixture and pour the mold as follows: Mix thoroughly a batch of concrete just sufficient to fill the mold, using one part of Portland cement to three parts of coarse, clean sand, a 1:3 mixture.

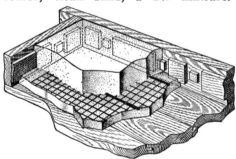

Fig. 4
The Method of Making the Edge Panels and of Reinforcing the Top Slab

Fill the mold uniformly to a depth of 1 in. and set the reinforcing into place, as shown in Fig. 4. The concrete should be wet enough so that water will rise to the surface with slight

tamping. Fill the mold, tamp the concrete, especially around the edges, and jar it to force the mixture well into the corners. Level the surface with a straightedge, and finish it carefully with a trowel. The edges may be rounded slightly with an edger or struck off at a slight bevel, using the trowel. The supports are made similarly, but without reinforcing. The edges are left square.

Permit the filled mold to remain at least 48 hours, when the sides of the form may be removed. The slab must not be moved from the platform, on which it was cast, for at least a week. If the edges are chipped or corners broken away, patch them by moistening the broken parts and filling the irregularities with the mixture. The slab should be moistened two or three times a day while "curing," and should not be exposed to heat, to a drying wind, or to the sun. Set the foundations, leveling them with great care, and mount the supports on them, set in a course of cement mortar. Set the top slab into place, upon courses of cement mortar, if no bolts are used.

These Garden Seats and Benches of Simple, Dignified Design may be Made by One of Fair Mechanical Skill at Small Outlay. They Add to the Comfort and Beauty of the Home Grounds, and Are of Substantial Construction, to Withstand the Elements

2857

The advantage of using bolts is that the seat may be taken down readily and moved to a new setting.

Possibilities for simple ornamental

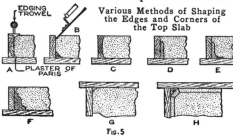

Various Methods of Shaping the Edges and Corners of the Top Slab

EDGING TROWEL

A — PLASTER OF PARIS

FIG. 5

treatment of this garden seat and slight variation in the finishing of the corners and edges are shown in Figs. 5 and 6. Finishing of the edges of the top slab in curved, straight-line, and molded forms are shown in Fig. 5. The use of a plaster-of-Paris fillet in the lower corner of the mold, and the rounding of the upper edge with an edging tool, are shown at A. The beveling of the lower edge by means of a triangular wooden fillet and the striking off of the upper edge with a trowel are shown at B. Views of the filled mold from above, the corners shaped with fillets, are shown at G and H.

The paneling of the edges of the plain slabs, as shown in Fig. 1, relieves the severe outline and adds a touch of

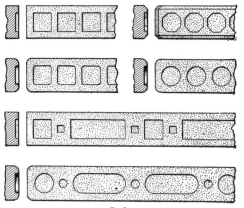

FIG. 6
Several Panel Treatments of the Edges, the Panels and Corners Designed to Harmonize in Each Case

individuality. The panels are ⅜ in. in depth and are made by nailing blocks into the form, as shown in Fig. 4. Bevel their edges slightly to produce

"draft" for the easy removal of the form, as indicated in the cross sections in Fig. 6. To insure that the concrete is cast around these blocks, press the mixture into the corners as the mold is filled. Several forms of panels are shown in Fig. 6, the edges of the slabs being shaped to harmonize with them.

New constructive elements are introduced in the forms for the garden seat shown in Fig. 3. The top slab is made 3 in. thick, 20 in. wide, and 5 ft. long, by the process described for the first seat. The supports are 4½ in. thick, and in their simplest form may be made with a cap and base effect, on the edges only. The working drawings and sketch show pilasters, ½ in. thick, on the outer sides, produced by panel-

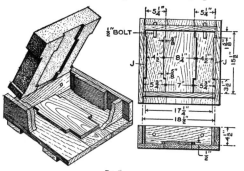

FIG. 7
The Form is Built Up Accurately and the Mold Poured. The Sides of the Form are Removed, the Support being Shown in Diagrammatic Relation to the Form Only

ing the surface. The detailed construction of the form for the supports is shown in Fig. 7. Make the form with inside dimensions of 15½ by 18½ in. Make two strips J, ⅝ in. thick, with a ⅜ by 1⅝-in. rabbet at the upper end, and nail them to the sides of the form, as shown. Make a piece ½ by 8¼ by 15½ in. for the panel mold. Rabbet the upper corners ⅜ by 1⅝ in., and the lower ones ⅝ by 3½ in. Bevel the edges on the sides and at the rabbets to give "draft." Nail the panel carefully into place in the bottom of the mold, centering it to make the pilasters of the columns each 4½ in. wide. Fix the sides into place with screws. Round off slightly all sharp corners, and set the nails, filling the holes with plaster of Paris. Smooth the inside of the mold, and clean, shellac, and oil it. Set the bolts which join the top slab and the support into the upper end of the form, and the mold is ready to be poured. Fill the mold with a 1:3 mixture of Portland cement and coarse, clean sand, and proceed in general as in the making of the slabs for the first seat.

Air-Pump Blower Driven by Punch Press

The pump shown in the sketch was devised for blowing away punchings of a light material and for keeping the parts of the dies clear. The pump was fastened to the shaft of the press by means of the shouldered bolt A, fixed in place with two nuts, as shown. The plunger of the pump B was fastened to the shoulder of A, and the body of the pump was inserted in a clip, C, fixed to the side of the press. The clip was made in the form of an oarlock and bolted to a flange, D. The latter was fixed to the punch press with flat-head screws. The rubber hose connected to the lower end of the pump is just long enough to reach the dies. The pump may be removed from the clip easily

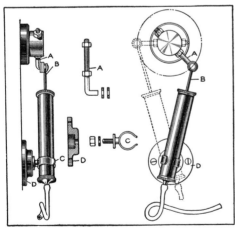

The Pump is Fixed to the Side of the Punch Press so That It is Operated Automatically, and Is Removable by Reason of the Clip C

and released at the shoulder of the bolt A, for use in the ordinary fashion.—George P. Kuhne, East Rutherford, N. J.

Device for Tying Parcels

The wire clip shown in the illustration was devised for use in tying parcels temporarily, and is especially

The Cord is Fastened to One End of the Device and is Passed Quickly around the Parcel and Locked at the Hook

convenient for bundles of letters and other small objects. It is bent from a piece of wire to the shape shown, and one end of the tying cord is clamped in the folded portion of the wire. Starting from this point of fastening, the cord is passed around the parcel, hooked to a small projection at the center of the device, passed at right angles around the parcel and clamped under the hook as indicated. The round loop is used in grasping the device and steadying it while the cord is drawn rapidly into place. The cord is released quickly by removing it from the hook, and the device, with cords of various lengths, may be prepared and kept on hand for repeated use.—E. E. Burnham, Amite, La.

Remedy for Noisy Telephone Bells

In a large office where each desk has its individual telephone the repeated ringing of the various call bells is annoying. Especially is this true if the telephone bells are highly pitched. To eliminate this feature, a large concern, which owned its telephones, had the bells slotted twice with a hacksaw. A metallic, unobjectionable buzzing sound results when the operator rings a station.

Garden Dump Cart of Varied Uses

The cart shown in the illustration gives better service than a wheelbarrow, and was made from materials gathered in the barn and home workshop. The fact that it can be tipped to dump off loads readily, as shown in the illustration, makes it handy for hauling dirt for the garden and tennis court, and the transporting of sod.

On the lawn it carries tools, grass, and water. In the garden and orchard it is used to carry fruit, vegetables, and other products, its width being such as to fit conveniently between the rows.

The cart was made by cutting off the rims and spokes of an old set of buggy wheels, and nailing double barrel hoops on them. These were covered with old bicycle tires, affording a good protection when the cart is used on lawns. A wooden axle was provided and the braced handle fitted to one end at a height convenient for pulling or pushing the cart.—E. R. Smith, Walla Walla, Wash.

Spinning a Cranky Engine

After overhauling and tightening the bearings of a marine engine, it was found necessary to crank it by other means than by hand. The only available power was an automobile, one rear wheel of which was jacked up, the other three blocked, and the motor mounted on skids, placed as shown in the sketch. Its flywheel was set in contact with the tire of the raised

wheel of the automobile. By engaging the clutch gently, the cranky engine was caused to operate, and in a few minutes was running on its own power.

Locking Four Drawers with Plate Hasp

It is sometimes not practicable to provide separate locks for several adjacent drawers, and under these circumstances the plate hasp shown in the sketch was used with satisfaction. A staple riveted into a plate was fastened to the strips between the drawers, and

a square plate having a suitable slot cut in it was fitted over the staple. A small lock secured to the staple locks the drawers effectively.—Joseph Prophet, Pittsfield, Mass.

Shifting-Fork Repair

The shifting fork on an automobile gear box broke at one of the prongs, and a new one was made to replace it, as shown in the illustration. A piece of strip steel was bent to the same shape as the broken prong, and a portion was cut out of the shank

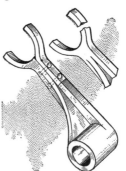

of the fork into which the strip was fitted. Two $\frac{3}{16}$-in. flat-head rivets were used to fix the prong in place. The repaired fork has given satisfactory service under hard usage.

¶Graphite and oil will arrest cutting in bronze bearings when oil alone proves ineffective.

Drum in Table Top for Listing Merchandise Sales

A clerk in charge of daily-sales reports found that much time was used in sorting over the twelve forms required, even though cards of different colors were provided. Heavy stock was necessary for the cards because of the wear on them. By the installation of a homemade revolving drum, set in the top of a table as shown, the work was done in one-half the time formerly required, and the cards were discarded in favor of forms printed on thinner paper.

The device was made as follows: Two flat-rimmed wheels were used as the foundation for a drum built up of laths. The drum was mounted on an axle and this in turn supported at its ends in lugs bolted to the framework of the table. The upper portion of the drum was exposed through an opening in the table top, and the blank forms were inserted on the drum, which was covered with several layers of wrapping paper. The drum was revolved easily to get at the various forms to

SIDE VIEW   FRONT VIEW

Economy of Time and Blank Forms was Effected by the Use of This Drum, in Listing Sales

which reference was made hundreds of times each day in keeping check on the quantity of stock disposed of.—John P. Lyons, Chicago, Ill.

An Electrical Water Gauge

The house water-supply tank on the twelfth floor of an office building was a source of trouble to the engine crew in the basement, because of its small size, and the variable rate at which the water was used. An electrical indicating device was constructed, as shown, in which the consecutive lighting of 5-cp. lamps, located in the engine room, denoted the water level in the tank in units of 1 ft. The tank was tapped close to the bottom and a piece of 1-in. pipe inserted with locknuts

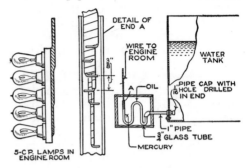

Engineers in the Basement were Enabled to Note the Height of Water in a Tank on the Twelfth Floor by Means of This Device

and rubber washers; an ell and a nipple were placed on the end of the pipe. One end of an S-shaped glass tube was made water-tight in the nipple by means of plaster of Paris. Six wires, taped together, having ½ in. of the insulation removed from the end of each, and bent at right angles, were taped to the other end of the tube. Mercury was then placed in the first bend of the tube, and oil in the second bend. When the device was connected to the tank the resulting water pressure forced the oil into contact with the mercury, balancing a column of mercury against a column of water. The oil provided an insulation between the mercury and the tank, and maintained its position because it is lighter than mercury or water, and mixes with neither.

The contacts for the various lamps were made through the longer wire, which was submerged in the mercury. As the water level became higher in the tank, the mercury was forced to a correspondingly higher position, making contact for the lamps in order. The distance between the wires is ⅜ in. A pipe cap, drilled with a $\frac{1}{16}$-in. hole, was placed on the end of the pipe in the tank, to prevent the surge of the water from disturbing the mercury. The glass tube was supported by felt pads in a hinged-cover box.—E. E. Stevenson, Los Angeles, Calif.

Holder for Examining Drawings

Unnecessary wear on drawings, or blueprints, and considerable inconvenience are often caused in drafting rooms and elsewhere when drawings must be referred to repeatedly, on various parts of a set, or roll. The device 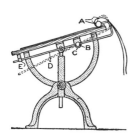 shown in the sketch is a holder that may be fixed to the drafting table, or other convenient place, for examining drawings, and prevents wear as well as makes consultation of the drawings easy. A wooden cylinder, A, 1½ in. in diameter, and as long as is necessary for the drawings, is supported on two ⅜-in. rods, which are fixed to the bar B. The latter is supported by two brackets C, fastened to the under side of the drawing board. A rod, D, is fixed to the bar B and extends to a convenient point at the front of the drawing board, or table. The hook E holds the rod D in position. To release the drawings, unhook rod D and move it downward, pivoting on B, as shown by the dotted lines. The rod D should be so arranged that when it is in the hook E, the proper pressure to hold the drawings is given to the cylinder A.—H. P. Morgan, South Norwalk, Conn.

Motor Cylinder Repaired with Copper Strip

One of the cylinders of an automobile was scored badly the full length of the stroke by the loosening of a wrist pin. There was not time to have the cylinder rebored, so an emergency  repair was undertaken with success, as follows: The cylinder was dismounted and a channel was cut in the shape of a dovetail, as shown in the sketch, extending from the end of the cylinder to the other end of the scored portion. The channel was made to the depth of No. 18 gauge sheet metal, and the bottom of it was rounded to conform to the curve of the cylinder. A strip of copper was wedged into the channel, as shown, and riveted into place. The surface was then dressed down to the proper curve and scraped smooth. The strip must be curved slightly, as indicated in the sketch at the right, in order to fit into the channel. Nearly the full power was obtained from the cylinder.—Logan E. Anderson, Cove, Ore.

Sanding Block for Interior Trim and Floors

Sandpapering, especially on large surfaces, such as floors, or door and window casings, etc., is a 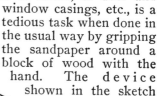 tedious task when done in the usual way by gripping the sandpaper around a block of wood with the hand. The device shown in the sketch provides a convenient method of applying the sandpaper and is especially useful, by reason of the handle, in reaching casings and other woodwork at a considerable height above the floor. The sandpaper is gripped in the block by inserting it under the piece fastened in the top with screws.—Guy E. Waite, Ottawa, Ill.

Notch in Wick Improves Lamp Flame

A railroad brakeman who had an unusually bright light in his lantern explained that it was due to the care given the wick. He cut a small notch at the center of the edge of the wick, causing the flame to have a notched outline at its top. This gave relatively more light than the flame from a wick cut square across.—C. E. Drayer, Cleveland, Ohio.

Fence Extension at Tidewater Stream

By B. FRANCIS DASHIELL

PREVENTING stock from passing around the end of a fence between adjoining fields at a tidal-river bank proved difficult until the fence extension, shown in the sketch and the diagram, was built. It adapts itself to the varying heights of the water, and may even be used in a lake, or a river of not too swift current and with little floating debris, to meet the varying depths of the water in different seasons.

A fence of woven wire, graded down to the bottom to keep out smaller stock, was built to extend a short distance from the shore line at low water. A post was set, about 25 ft. beyond the last fence post, so that it projected above the surface at high water, and was guyed strongly. A slide rod of round iron was fitted to

The Barbed Wire is Supported by Floats and Accommodates Itself to the Changing Water Level

each of these posts, as shown in the diagram, being made long enough in each case so that the ends extended beyond the limits of the water's vertical movement. A barbed wire was fitted with suitable floats of wood, and provided with rings to engage the slide rods. It was stretched into place as shown, and was made free to float easily with the change in the water level.

Planting Bulbs Conveniently

To set out a large number of bulbs is quite a job, especially when they are to be planted in a lawn which should not be injured. I used a 2-in. iron pipe about 2 ft. long, with the end ground sharp, to cut the holes for the bulbs. A mark was painted on the pipe, 4 in. from the cutting end, so that

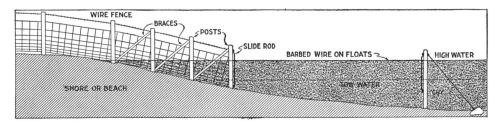

Sectional Diagram Showing the Arrangement of the Fence, Posts, and the Barbed-Wire Barrier

I could easily drive it down to the proper depth. After the bulb was dropped in the hole the earth was replaced by rapping the pipe. This necessitated only a slight cutting of the lawn.—A. E. Holaday, Naugatuck, Connecticut.

Sharpening Scissors on a Grinding Wheel

Scissors may be sharpened quickly and effectively on a grinding wheel,

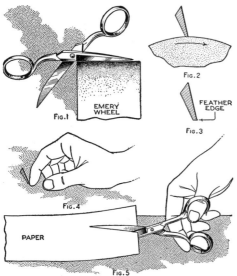

FIG.2

FEATHER EDGE

FIG.3

EMERY WHEEL

FIG.1

FIG.4

PAPER

FIG.5

The Blades are Ground to a Feather Edge, and This is Removed by Cutting Carefully into a Piece of Paper

and this method is especially useful where several pairs are to be put into shape. Hold the scissors on the wheel, as shown in Fig. 1, the direction of the wheel being as indicated in Fig. 2. A feather edge, or extension, will be produced, as suggested in Fig. 3. Test the edge to make certain that a slight feather edge is ground throughout the cutting edges of both blades. This may be done by passing the finger nail along the edge, as in Fig. 4. Then remove the feather edges by using the scissors in cutting paper; apply oil to the edges before closing them or using them in this manner. The feather edges will be removed smoothly, leaving a sharp cutting edge.—R. B. S., Philadelphia, Pa.

Hinged Drawer Front Is Convenient

A large drawer in a bench was used for tools of various sizes, and it was difficult to remove those placed in the back of the drawer. As a result most of the tools were placed in the front part, often making it inconvenient to open the drawer. The front of the drawer was arranged to swing forward on hinges, and compartments were provided so that the tools had to be put in carefully. This increased the usefulness of the drawer and made it easier to get at the tools.—Charles C. Brabant, Detroit, Mich.

Hood on Chimney Increases Draft

Large smokestacks are often provided with an arrangement near the top to increase the draft. I devised the one shown in the illustration for use on a residence chimney, and it gave good results. A hood of sheet metal was built around the top of the chimney, flaring out to a spread of 15 in. from the bricks, and with an opening of about 3 in. at the upper end. The resulting draft through the hood has a tendency to draw the air and smoke up out of the

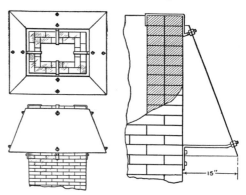

This Hood on a Chimney Increases the Draft and Tends to Overcome Down Draft

chimney, counteracting down draft.—James E. Noble, Toronto, Ont., Can.

ⅭDraftsmen will find a strip of string solder convenient as a spline for laying out irregular curves.

Hardening Small Carbon-Steel Tools

Special care must be taken in the tempering of small tools of carbon steel. A small gas furnace, inclosed, with a chamber for the heating of the tools, is desirable, but a coal or coke fire properly banked is satisfactory. The fire must be burned down to a bed of live coals, and it is best to insert a section of tubing into the fire to protect the tools from the direct blast. The quenching heat may be determined accurately by instruments, but where these are not available, the use of a magnet is suggested. When the magnet no longer has an attraction for the steel being heated at the part in the fire, the proper point for quenching may be determined by permitting the steel to remain in the fire a few moments longer. The point at which the magnet ceases to attract is about 1,425° F., and the best heat for tempering is 10° above that temperature.

Cracked and damaged tools in the hardening process frequently result from the failure to relieve the strain on the steel after quenching, and the moment that it has cooled sufficiently to harden. While still grasping the tool in the cooling bath, the instant that the tremor from the sudden plunge stops, the piece should be withdrawn quickly, and permitted to cool in the open air. The steel will still be too hot to hold in the hand. This is only necessary, of course, when the steel is not to be drawn to temper on the original heating.—A. Dane, Pottstown, Pa.

Saving a Fallen Tree at a River Bank

Continued high water softened a river bank in a park, so that several trees toppled over into the water for want of good root anchorage. A willow at one point was especially desirable, and it was brought back to its former position by the method described. High up on the trunk, well out over the water, a threaded eyebolt, B, was sunk into the tree, and a good bearing secured by means of a large washer screwed down tightly with a nut. This afforded a hold for a double

A Fallen Tree at a River Bank was Raised and Braced by the Method Shown

block, while a single block, A, was roped to a near-by tree. Then tackle was adjusted between the blocks, and the free end thereof hitched to a triple set of blocks and tackle, C and D, secured to a tree at some distance from the river bank. This gave a good purchase, and a horse hitched to this second tackle could exert a very heavy pull upon the fallen tree. By careful work the tree was brought to its former position without a mishap. The raised tree was permanently tied to the tree that held the single block by means of stout wire connecting the eyebolt G, in the former, with an eyebolt, H, sunk into the latter. This wire I was run through the eyes in four strands and twisted to the proper tension with a stick, J. The tree was also anchored to the base of a near-by elm.—C. L. Meller, Fargo, N. D.

❦Make it a rule to reset the tailstock on a lathe immediately on completing a taper job.

Gravity Water System for a Summer Cottage or Camp

By G.E. Kastengren

T HE gravity water system described in this article and shown in the illustrations was built for a summer home in the Olympic Mountains. The principles underlying its construction, and the general details, may be used directly or with slight adaptation in various other mountain or rolling-hill regions, or other places where a suitable flow of water is available. The source of the water supply was a small spring-fed creek, with a minimum flow of 15 gal. a minute, and situated at an elevation of 800 ft. above the house to which the water was conducted, as shown diagrammatically in the large illustration. The water is conveyed a distance of 1,440 ft. and is stored in a 25-bbl. oak cask, obtained from a brewery for $15. This was set at an elevation of 92 ft. above the house, on a strong platform built of logs, across

Detail of the Sections, Showing the Method of Joining Them at the Ends

a gully, about 4 ft. deep and leading almost directly to the house. This made unnecessary a great deal of excavation otherwise essential, as an excellent trench was thus provided for the pipe line. The water is conveyed from the intake to the tank by means of a flume, constructed as shown in the detail sketch. Views of the flume and of the tank are shown in the photographs reproduced in the headpiece. A pipe line conducts the water from the storage tank to the house.

Galvanized-iron pipe, secondhand, was obtained for the pipe line and other pipe sections and fittings, 2-in. and 1½-in. pipe being used. It was conducted from the bottom of the tank, as shown, and joined with the usual unions. At the end near the house, a 1½-in. nozzle was placed, for fire protection and sprinkling. The joints were made with various fittings to accommodate the line to the ground, with a minimum of supports. A globe valve was fitted at the outlet from the tank and a ladder was provided in lieu of a depth gauge in the tank.

To convey the water from the intake to the tank, I devised a flume of the special type shown in detail, and it proved well suited to the conditions. It leads through a heavy forest of fir and cedar, and occasional windfalls, especially during the winter, are likely to break parts of it. It was therefore necessary to construct the flume so that it could be repaired easily and quickly. It is made in sections of 16-ft. length. They are not nailed together, but the lower end of each rests on the upper end of the next section below, and a broken section may thus be quickly replaced. Since the area for the passage of the water would be reduced considerably at the joints if they were set together as originally made, portions were cut away by beveling the adjoining ends, as shown by the dotted curves in the detail sketch. The lower edge of the cover was beveled to a distance of about 3 in. at the upper end of each section. The upper edges of the trough were beveled similarly at the lower end of each section. The ends were telescoped, as shown, and the covers of the adjoining sections set to cover the joints on top. The lower portion of the flume was made of two strips, one 1 by 4 in. and the other 1 by 5 in., nailed together, and a calking string was inserted in the joint. The cover board is 1 by 6 in., and serves to brace the sections. It is nailed down and further reinforced by galvanized-wire stays, tightened around the sections as shown. No difficulty was experienced with the sagging of the sections as the cover and trough, joined rigidly, form a strong hollow beam. The capacity of the flume is about that of a 3-in. pipe, and 20 board ft. of lumber were required for each section.

The sections were all built at the house and carried to their places over a hastily broken trail. The work was planned systematically so that all of the pieces were cut first, and the similar parts and processes handled at the same time. The most difficult part of the work was the carrying

of the sections to their destinations, and in this work it is well worth while to make a fairly good trail.

The plans for this system include extension of the pipe line 250 ft. up the hill with 2½-in. pipe, con-

The Water is Conducted by a Wooden Flume from a Spring to the Storage Tank, and Then to the House by a Pipe Line

nected to a larger tank there. This will give a head of 255 ft., for the development of 500 watts of electric current, during the hours when lights or power are needed. A minimum flow of 25 gal. a minute is available for this purpose. The cask will be used in this arrangement as formerly, a ¾-in. pipe line being installed to conduct the water to the house. This will not interfere with the power line by reason of the use of a regulating valve, opened only when water is needed for the cask. The cost of this installation, exclusive of labor, was $109, and the investment has increased the utility of the place immensely, and enhanced its value probably $800. A valuable consideration also is the added security of the wooden buildings from the danger of fire.

Snow-Melting Device for Roofs

When three feet of snow fell in a region unaccustomed to heavy snow-

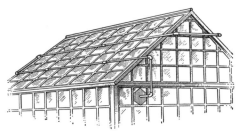

Damage to Glass Roofs was Avoided by Melting the Snow in a Heavy Snowfall as It Drifted on the Roof

falls much damage was done and several roofs collapsed under the strain. Many glass-roofed greenhouses suffered. The owner of several such buildings saved his property from damage by further snowfalls by extending the steam pipes that heated the interior, through the roof, as shown in the illustration. With a good head of steam in the boilers, he kept the pipes hot, and as fast as snow drifted on the glass roofs it melted away.

Reboring a Large Gear without Machinery

It was desired to rebore a gear, 40 in. in diameter, fitted to a 2-in. shaft, to fit a $2\frac{1}{8}$-in. shaft,

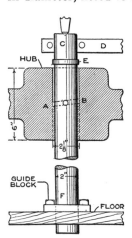

and the local shops were not equipped with machinery suitable for this work. The rigging shown in the diagram was set up, and the job completed in a short time with success, and without the use of ordinary boring, or special, machinery. The gear was placed on two strong shop horses, and bolted to the floor, leveled carefully, so that the bored bearing in it was vertical. A hardwood block was bolted to the floor directly below the bearing hole, and a 2-in. hole was bored into it. Strong braces were set against the gear. A vertical boring shaft was fitted to the bearing hole as follows: A 2-in. shaft, C, was bored to fit a $\frac{5}{16}$ by $2\frac{1}{8}$-in. piece of tool steel, tempered and ground, and set at an angle, as at A-B, so that the end A became a cutter. The lower end of the shaft was set in the hole at F, which extended through the floor. The inclination of the cutter gave the cutting edge a $\frac{1}{16}$-in. lead, and the hole was bored true by centering the cutting bar at the beginning of the cut. A ring, E, $2\frac{1}{8}$ in. in diameter, was fitted on the shaft and acted as a follower. Power was applied on the arm D, 5 ft. long.—L. M. Drake, Daytona, Florida.

Push Button Varies Tone of Electric Horn

In residential sections the loud blast from an electric automobile horn is an unnecessary nuisance, but on long

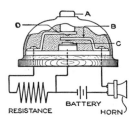

stretches of country road, at sharp turns, or in crowded, noisy city streets a penetrating blast is often desirable. A push button designed to control the horn's tone at the operator's will can be constructed easily, as indicated in the diagram. The usual push button A has a contact point, C, and a spring-brass strip, B. When the button A is pushed downward, C and B make contact, and a circuit is established through the battery and horn. A second brass strip, D, similar to B, is added, and placed above B. A small resistance is then placed in series between C and D. The amount of this resistance can be determined by experiment. The horn is operated as follows: A pushes D against B, and a high-resistance circuit through the battery and the horn is established. The horn then gives the subdued tone. A slightly harder push on A will bring B in contact with C, cutting out the resistance, and impressing full battery voltage on the horn. A full-toned warning will thus result.—K. M. Coggeshall, Webster Groves, Missouri.

Straightedge Arched for Leveling Concrete

When troweling the surface of a concrete walk, or similar area, many of the strokes start or end in the center of the panel. Care is necessary to prevent the center from becoming lower than the edges, forming a lodging place for water. If the straightedge, used to strike off a level surface before troweling, is arched, a level walk will be more easily obtained. The arching of the under side of the straightedge gives a slight crown, and subsequent troweling brings the surface down to a level.—J. J. O'Brien, Buffalo, N. Y.

Preventing Back Draft in Fireplace

If a fireplace smokes, or does not "draw" properly, the cause may usually be found in that the portion known as the choke is too large. To remedy this quickly and at slight cost a false back is provided in the fireplace, as shown in the sketch. A sheet of tin plate is fastened to the back wall, a few inches above the hearth level, and extended upward, on a slight forward curve, to a point about 2 in. above the lower edge of the facing. This sheet should be the full width of the back wall. At the lower edge it is nailed to the mortar and at the top it is fastened to a cross rod. Cut the sheet the width of the back wall of the fireplace, and of a length corresponding to the vertical distance to be covered, allowing 1 in. to be used for a loop on the cross rod. A right-angle turn of 2 in. is then made on each end of the rod, which is 4 in. longer than the width of the fireplace, forming a springing resistance against the walls. The lower edge of the apron is then nailed, the sheet of

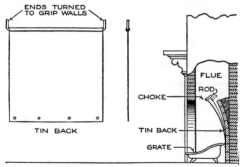

The Draft in a Fireplace may be Regulated to Prevent Smoking by Means of the Adjustable Sheet-Metal Guard

metal being curved as shown. The opening into the flue can thus be reduced in size as desired, by moving the cross rod, care being taken to create just the necessary draft to prevent smoking.—Charles Alma Byers, Los Angeles, Calif.

Indicator Holder with Five Positions

Having purchased an indicator, I found that I needed a number of attachments to make any considerable use of it. These were expensive, so I made the holder shown in the illustration, and was able to do many kinds of work with it. It has five positions for the indicator, as shown by the numbering on the sketch. The holder was made of a ⅜ by ⅜ by 1½-in. strip of machine steel. The holes in it were tapped to fit a thread by means of which it was supported in its various

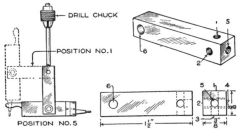

This Simple Holder Enlarged the Usefulness of an Indicator without Special Attachments

positions. The holder is fastened to the indicator by means of a thumb-screw set in hole No. 6.—Arthur Whittier, Norwood, Mass.

Safety-First Alarm System for Shops

In emergencies it is often desirable to stop the machinery in a shop quickly, and, if the establishment is a large one, a signal arrangement between the engine room and the shop is practical. Serious accidents or loss of life may thus be averted. A simple arrangement which any workman could use in an emergency is shown in the sketch. The box with its code lettered to be seen at a distance should be located so that it may be reached quickly, and painted a conspicuous color.—J. R. Minter, Washington, Ind.

Auxiliary Vise Jaw for Holding Irregular Pieces

A block of hard wood, shaped to match the upper end of the vise jaw and pivoted at the center, as shown in the sketch, will add to the usefulness of many vises. The block will adjust itself to pieces of unequal width and will save needless wear on the vise, as the block may be quickly renewed when worn out.

Anchor Bent from Round Bar

A form of anchor that can be made easily from a bar of round iron is shown in the sketch. The original was made of 2-in. bar iron, but the method of forming the anchor can be applied to smaller stock for use on a rowboat or other small craft. The ends of the rod

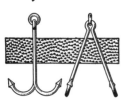

are heated and upset by striking them on the end. They are then pointed as shown, and the bar is bent into shape with an eye at the top to fit a ring.— J. Harger, Honolulu, H. I.

Electrical Ground Made of Flowerpot

A ground suitable for wireless apparatus, lightning arresters, and similar electrical devices, may be made quickly as shown in the sketch. The heavy copper wire of the ground is fitted into a large flowerpot, and a wire is fixed to its end to hold it in place. The bottom of the pot is covered to a depth of about 1 in. with cement. Rock salt is then poured in and a disk of sheet zinc is imbedded in it in contact with the wire. A 1-in. layer of cement is poured in on top. Salt will draw moisture and for this reason a ground made as described will give good results. The clay flowerpot tends to hold the moisture.—A. Gemmill, Ansonia, Conn.

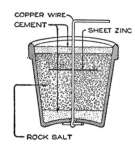

Rodent-Proof Support for Corncrib

To prevent the inroads of rats and mice, and, at the same time, provide a substantial support, a foundation for a corncrib was made of 8-in. tile set in concrete, as shown in the sketch. The tile was placed with the flange down, and a ½-in. iron rod was imbedded in the concrete with which it was filled. A galvanized-iron cap was fitted over the top and the iron rod passed through it to form a substantial fastening for the sills of the crib.—R. W. Smith, Minneapolis, Minn.

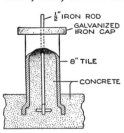

Adaptation of Motorcycle for Home and Shop Use

By J. H. SEEGER

A MOTORCYCLE that is used only for transportation or pleasure jaunts is not giving the fullest service to its owner. By providing suitable rigging and devices, all easily made in the home workshop, I use my motorcycle the year round, for a large variety of home and shop duties. The arrangement shown in Fig. 1 permits the use of the engine for driving a cooling fan, an emery grinder, and an ice-cream freezer. Many other home and farm machines may be driven similarly. The work of wash day made lighter by the use of the motorcycle engine is shown in Fig. 2, and a detail of the driving pulley in Fig 3. The machine fitted to a truck for use on railroad tracks is shown in Fig. 4. The vehicle is not impaired for its ordinary use, and the devices used with it are quickly disconnected.

The installation for the grinder and freezer was made in the shop. The grinder is a handy shop machine and is driven at great speed and with sufficient power for most ordinary grinding. The fan on the opposite spindle of the grinder is used to cool the engine when it is used for continuous duty on work other than the driving of the grinder. If it is desired to cool the engine while grinding, the fan should be incased for the safety of the operator. The freezer, or other light machine, such as a churn, is connected to a line shaft by gearing. Other suitable means of transmitting the power are readily installed. The drive pulley on the engine is 4½ in. in diameter, and the pulley on the line shaft 13 in. The drive pulley was supported by braces of strap iron, fixed to the engine as shown in the detail view.

In connecting the engine to the washing machine and the wringer, it is necessary to gear the speed down considerably, hence large pulleys are used, and a further reduction made between the line shaft and the pulleys on the shafts of the wringer and the washing machine. The pulley below the machine is 10 in. in diameter. In all of these arrangements, the motorcycle

FIG. 1
Grinder, Fan, and Ice-Cream Freezer Driven by a Motorcycle Engine, the Speed Adjusted by Pulleys and Gears

must be mounted on a strong rear-wheel stand, or other rigid frame, from which it may be released easily. If necessary, the frame may be bolted to the floor, as in the workshop installation. The sprockets, chains, and other

FIG. 2
The Work of Wash Day Made Lighter by the Belting of Motorcycle to the Washing Machine and Wringer

machine parts used, were picked up from old machines, separators, farm tools, and similar devices, at practically no expense.

The car for use on railroad tracks is of simple construction. It will carry three workmen, and operates smoothly and speedily, even in bad weather. Three flanged wheels, like those commonly used on small hand cars, were used. An iron bar, fitted with a small roller bearing against the inner side of the rail, guards the motorcycle from slipping off the rail in taking a curve.

FIG. 3

The rear wheel only comes into contact with the rail, and furnishes satisfactory traction with the ordinary rubber tire. It can be raised to operate the engine, without traveling, by the usual stand. The car and the framework supporting the carrying rack are arranged to be set up or removed quickly for use with the motorcycle,

FIG. 4

Motorcycle Rigged to Run on Railroad Tracks and Accommodating Three Persons

by bolt fastenings. This enables the rider to travel a part of his journey on rail, and the rest over roads, in an emergency.

⊂A piece of heavy cardboard, about 6 in. square and having a ½-in. hole through it, is useful in locating splinters or small particles of foreign matter in the hand. Hold the hand in front of a strong light and locate the splinter by observation through the opening.

Focusing and Caring for Headlights

The adjustment of headlights should be made at night and without interference from other light. The vehicle should be headed toward a wall, or other similar surface, with the lamps 10 ft. from it. If the lamps are properly focused, the light thrown on the surface will be in the form of a circle, about 3 ft. in diameter, and having a very bright spot in the center, 3 or 4 in. in diameter. When this is not the case, the lamps are out of focus and should be moved forward or backward in the reflectors. If they are too far back, the rays of light will diverge, so that a large area is illuminated, but the light will be unsatisfactory for driving; if they are too far away from the reflectors, the rays of light will converge, so that there will be excellent light, a few feet ahead of the car, but not satisfactory for driving.

An adjustment of the lamps for maximum illumination on a point 150 ft. from the car will give good results for general driving. The two reflectors should be so adjusted that they will throw their light directly ahead of the car, and slightly toward the ground. Lamps having concentrated filaments are desirable, as a better focus is possible, in that the light is confined to a small spot. If the reflectors are dirty, they may be cleaned by rubbing them lightly with a piece of fine cotton dipped in alcohol. Rub from the outer edge toward the center or the reverse, never around the reflector.—P. D. Norem, Chicago, Ill.

Wire Substitute for Latticework

Fine galvanized-iron wire mesh may be used with good effect to replace old-style wood latticework in inclosing the lower portions of a porch, stairs, or similar places. It makes a satisfactory appearance, and if well painted, will last longer than wood. It is also easily fitted and fastened in place. Climbing plants are afforded a good hold, and the fine mesh keeps out small animals. —James M. Kane, Doylestown, Pa.

Motor Attachment and Brake for Sewing Machine

A small battery motor using a current of about six volts was fitted to a sewing machine and provided with a brake and pedal, as shown in the sketch. The arrangement gave thorough satisfaction and was constructed in a short time, with materials readily available. The motor was bolted to a wooden base, which was in turn connected to a block support with a strap hinge. A stop was provided to keep the base in a horizontal position, and a coil spring was fitted under it, to hold it down, except when the foot is pressed upon the pedal. The motor was belted to the pulley on the end of the spindle of the machine, and a brake pad of wood was fitted to the base, to engage the flywheel. The pedal is connected to the back end of the base with a hinge, and pressure upon it, in front of its pivotal point, causes the base and motor to be raised, releasing the belt and bringing the machine to a quick stop by the action of the brake. The machine may thus be stopped without shutting off the current to the motor, but a small switch should be mounted near the operator to control the current supply. A small trans-

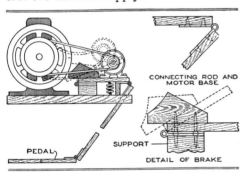

The Motor is Controlled by Pressure on the Pedal, the Brake at the Same Time Acting on the Flywheel

former may be used to reduce 110-volt lighting current, or it may be supplied by a storage battery.

❡Always joint a saw to insure a straight cutting edge before filing the teeth.

Adaptable Jig for Turning Pulleys in a Lathe

After several castings for light pulleys had been broken while attempting to turn them up in a lathe by the com-

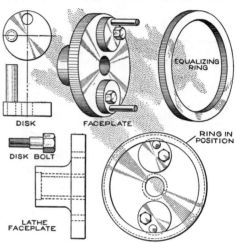

The Eccentric Disks and the Ring Equalize the Strain in Turning Up Light Pulleys in a Lathe

mon method of mounting them on an arbor and faceplate with a stud, the device shown in the sketch was made, and proved satisfactory. A faceplate was turned up and threaded to fit the lathe spindle. Two disks provided with studs, set close to their edges as shown in the detail sketch, were fixed to the faceplate with machine bolts, so as to pivot easily. They were mounted eccentrically. An equalizing ring was made and fitted over the disks and studs, as shown. The operation of turning up the pulleys was then carried out as follows:

The pulley was mounted on an arbor and placed on the faceplate so that each of the studs rested against a spoke, with the ring in position. The pressure of the spokes against the studs forces them against the ring, which equalizes the strain, giving a uniform pull on opposite sides of the pulley. The faceplate may be used for various sizes of pulleys, by drilling and tapping holes at suitable distances from the center, to accommodate the studs. Three disks for very light pulleys may also be used.

Roofed Watering Tank of Concrete

A large concrete watering tank, having a frame superstructure over it, was found practical on an Iowa farm. Its

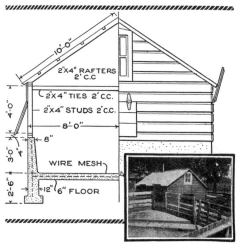

The Concrete Watering Tank was Built at the Center of the Barnyard, Giving Access to Stock in the Various Sections

large size enabled the farmer to use plenty of water in spite of adverse weather when the windmill could not be operated. The roof over the water kept it cool in summer, and aided in keeping the water supply pure. The original was made 16 by 20 ft., but the method of construction may be applied readily to smaller tanks.

A strong foundation of concrete, having a 24-in. footing and a 12-in. wall, tapering to 8 in. at the top of the tank, was poured in forms and served as the tank proper. The 6-in. floor and the walls were reinforced with heavy wire mesh. The tank was made to extend 3 ft. above the floor level, and bolts were set into the top of it, to provide a fastening for the frame portion. The lat-

ter was made of 2 by 4-in. material, with double pieces for the sills. The rafters and other details are of standard construction. Windows were set in the gables, for light and ventilation, and several doors, to be raised in opening them, were fitted in the sides and ends. The sides and ends were finished with matched siding, set horizontally.

The openings are spaced in relation to the fenced parts of the barnyard, so that each type of cattle has separate access to the tank. The tank was set in the center of the adjoining sections of the barnyard for this purpose.

The top of the concrete wall should be leveled carefully, to provide a satisfactory foundation for the frame structure. The tank should be finished, especially inside, with a smooth coating of a creamy mixture of cement and water, three days after pouring the concrete in the forms, the latter being removed at that time. The intake and overflow pipes must, of course, be provided for when the forms are set up.

Platform Facilitates Taking Down of Automobile

A platform used in an automobile factory, and which has practical applications for use in repair shops and garages, is shown in the illustration. After the car has been tested and certain parts removed it runs onto the platform and down the incline, where it drops onto a truck, resting on its axles. The car uses its own power in this process, and the same platform is used to unload the chassis when it is painted and ready for the body, the process being reversed.

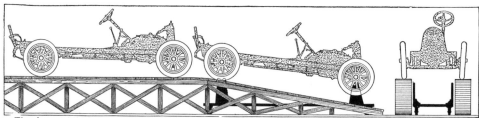

The Automobile is Run onto the Platform by Its Own Power and Set on the Truck for Taking Down before Painting the Chassis

Indoor Air Supply for Furnace Heating Systems

Many hot-air furnace heating systems provide for two sources of fresh-air supply. In moderately cold weather an outdoor intake is used while during severe cold spells, or when the wind is in such a direction that it blows into the intake, air is drawn from a duct in the basement. The air taken in from this source is not desirable, hence a better plan of using already warmed air is to take it from a duct connected with the front hall, rather than the basement.

A Book Fumigator and Sterilizer

Of recent years public libraries and schools have come to realize the danger of books as germ carriers. In larger institutions, special rooms and apparatus may be fitted up for this purpose, but in smaller ones, sterilizing books is a problem. The book fumigator shown was designed so that an ordinary carpenter could make it at moderate expense, and is suitable for use in a large room without incommoding the occupants.

Excessive and continued heat provides a fairly certain method of sterilizing a book, but this treatment is so severe that the bindings are usually injured. If the books are placed as shown, in a suitable cabinet, with the covers spread apart so that the leaves swing free, and are then subjected to a strong fumigating gas overnight, excellent results may be obtained. The fumigator consists of a closely fitted cabinet, divided vertically by a central partition. The two doors are paneled, and each one carries two strong crossbars. Instead of being hinged directly to the cabinet each hinge is fastened to a square block, which in turn is hinged to the sides. This arrangement permits the doors being forced against a strip of felt extending around each door casing. The method of clamping the doors is shown. When not in use, the bars stand vertically. If more pressure is required,

give these bars one or more half turns to the right. The inside space should be closely papered and the exterior

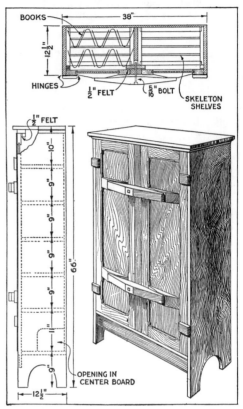

The Books are Arranged in the Cabinet with Leaves Exposed for Thorough Fumigation

varnished, or shellacked. The shelves may be made adjustable, greatly increasing the utility of the cabinet.

To provide the fumigating gas, place a few spoonfuls of formaldehyde solution in a saucer, and just before closing the doors drop a little permanganate of potash or chlorinated lime into the solution, which will immediately generate a powerful germicidal gas. The common sulphur torch or formaldehyde generator involving a flame should not be used.—John D. Adams, Phoenix, Ariz.

¶Gasoline and kerosene used in mixtures should be kept well stirred because the kerosene will otherwise settle.

Base for Swage Block

The usefulness of a swage block is considerably increased if it is set upon a strong and easily portable base. In

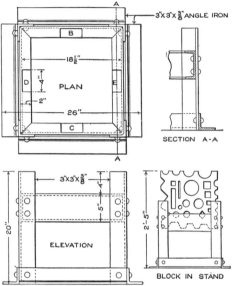

This Strong Frame Increased the Usefulness of the Swage Block

many shops this tool is set on a wooden block, or placed upon any makeshift available. I devised the base shown from 5-in. channel bars and 3 by 3-in. angle iron. The channel bar was mitered at the corners to form a frame, as shown in the plan. Four legs were riveted to it and braced at the bottom with angle iron. Portions were cut out of the upper flange of the channel bar, as at B, C, D, and E, to fit the block, in two positions. When it is desired to use it in a horizontal position, the block is rested on the channel-bar frame.—A. E. Dowden, Worcester, Mass.

Storage Areas Marked on Floors

The method used in a large warehouse to keep the piles of stored goods from encroaching on the aisle space is as follows: A white 2-in. stripe is painted on the floor bordering the space which must be kept clear, such as trucking aisles, approaches to fire exits, and valves controlling the automatic sprinkler system. Special attention is called to valves by lettering the name on the floor with a large arrow pointing to the valve.

High-Speed Foot-Power Grinder

An old bicycle wheel, weighted with a lead pipe around its rim, was used to provide a flywheel for the bench grinder shown in the sketch. The ratchet part of a coaster-brake bicycle hub was used for the axle and ratchet device. The axle was mounted in the brace at the end of the workbench, and the support for the grinder was set on the bench in line with the flywheel. A rope was used as a belt and runs in the grooved rim of the wheel. Holes were cut in the top of the bench to permit the rope belt to pass through. The ratchet device was arranged between the flywheel and the brace on the bench, a block being set against the brace to bring the ratchet out sufficiently to make room for the treadle. The latter was pivoted in the rear leg of the bench, and a section of bicycle chain fixed to it as shown, to act with the ratchet. A coil spring, like those used on doors, was fastened to the end of the drive chain and to the end of the treadle. The high gearing of the belt from the large drive pulley

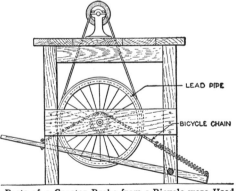

LEAD PIPE

BICYCLE CHAIN

Parts of a Coaster Brake from a Bicycle were Used to Make This High-Speed Grinder, Fitted to the End of the Workbench

to the small one on the grinder gives great speed, which is desirable in a small grinder of this type.—N. Michels, Chicago, Ill.

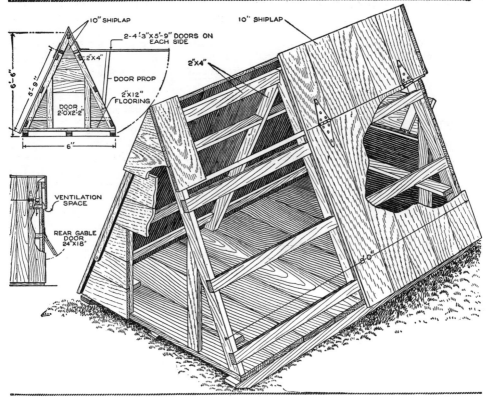

This Portable Hog House may be Constructed Readily in the Farm Workshop and Provides a Clean, Well-Ventilated Shelter

An Individual Hog House

Farmers will find the individual hog house shown in the sketch practical, since it is easy to build, and can be moved from place to place readily on the skids provided. The frame is built up of 2 by 4-in. stuff, braced with $\frac{7}{8}$-in. strips. Three A-frames give the main support to the house, and the cross braces are notched into them. It is 8 ft. long and 6 ft. wide, with a door at one end, and ventilating doors on the sides and the other end. The frame is covered with siding, shiplap, or plain $\frac{7}{8}$-in. boards. The floor is of heavy planks. The construction provides for ventilation spaces at the gables of the ends, as shown in the lower detail sketch. The side doors are hinged at the top and can be raised and set under props fastened to the ends of the house, permitting the air and sunlight to enter freely, and making it convenient to clean. Fenders should be built around the inside, about 8 in. above the floor, to protect the young shoats.—W. E. Frudden, Charles City, Iowa.

Drawing the Temper in Small Taps and Reamers

The proper way to hold a tap or reamer in drawing the temper is with the threaded, or fluted, end in a round pair of tongs, the squared end to the flame. Draw the tool to the proper degree at the point. When drawn to the proper color, quench it in oil or lukewarm water. This gives the cutting part of the tool the hardness necessary for standing up under the cut, and the shank the strength and toughness necessary to prevent breaking. For tapping cast iron, draw to a light straw, and for steel, to a light brown.

Powerful Wrench Used in Dismantling Large Pipe Line

In removing a line of about 4,000 ft. of 6-in. and 8-in. pipe with screwed joints which had been in place for

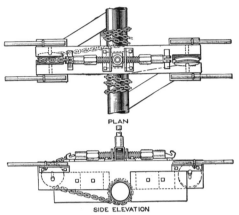

PLAN

SIDE ELEVATION

This Rigging Is Useful in Taking Down Pipe Structures and may be Adapted for Assembling Pipe

about five years, the pipe wrench shown in the illustration was rigged from a steamboat jack and a 12 by 12-in. timber, 6 ft. long. With this rig it was possible for one man to start the joints on 8-in. pipe. The device offers suggestion for use in joining or disassembling other large and small-pipe structures.

In operation, the wrench was placed astride the pipe, and centered over the coupling. Then the chains were given several turns around the pipe and over the sheaves at the ends, and hooked into the special hooks on the ends of the jack. The screw was given a few turns' hold in each sleeve at the start. Then, by means of the handle and ratchet, the chain was quickly tightened up and the joint broken, in most cases with a jump. The sleeves are kept from turning over by the short bars on the bottom of the hooks. The short diagonal pieces on each side rest against the pipe and take the pull of the chains. The handle used was about 3 ft. long. Two short pipe handles at each end provide means for carrying the device from place to place. For clearness, the chain is shown on one-

half of the sketch only, the other half being the same. This rig could also be used for tightening joints in pipe laying by reversing the chains and the diagonal pieces or braces.—E. C. Entler and James Ryan, Keokuk, Ia.

Solid-Tire Rubber for Making Heels

When the rubber-block tires on the motor trucks of a large company are renewed, the old tires are returned to the garage with the vehicle fitted. The workmen trim the rubber blocks to $7/8$ in. thickness on the band saw, cut them to the shape of rubber heels, and nail them to their shoes. These inexpensive heels afford much comfort, and are an aid to safety in that they give a more secure footing, and withstand heavy wear.—Theodore J. Becker, Kansas City, Mo.

Gauge for Plastering Trowel

Plaster, stucco, cement, and similar finishes applied in layers of uniform thickness, can be

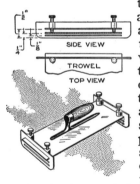

SIDE VIEW

TROWEL

TOP VIEW

applied quickly and easily with a trowel fitted with gauges like the homemade ones shown in the sketch. They are of $1/16$-in. sheet iron, and provided with slots to fit the ends of the trowel, so as to make the layer of plaster $1/8$, $1/4$, or $1/2$ in. thick, as desired. The gauges are fastened with knurled screws. After the roughing application is made, the surface of the plaster must be smoothed with a plain trowel to remove the tracks of the gauges.—Alfred J. Miller, Albuquerque, N. M.

❏Scissor blades may be kept at the proper tension by placing a small flat spring under the head of the screw which holds the parts together.

Title Stamp for the Drafting Room

Every draftsman well knows the tediousness of lettering in the drawing titles by hand. There is, also, an unavoidable lack of uniformity, when there are several draftsmen employed. A standard title, applied to the drawings by means of a hand stamp, shown in the sketch, and permitting of filling in to suit the particular job, overcomes these difficulties in a practical and efficient manner. The drawing for the title should be made three times the size of the zinc etching, which is to be made from it, and used in the stamp. Ordinary printing ink is used on the cut. A suitable base for the stamp is made of a piece of wood, 5 in. wide and 16 in. long. The lever, to hold the cut or type block, is 3 in. wide and 16 in. long, one end being hinged to the base. The type block is fastened to the lever with screws, as shown, and a piece of blotting paper is placed under the drawing when an impression is to be made. Ink is kept in a tube, and a small quantity spread on a piece of plate glass, from which it is worked onto the roller, and applied to the type block. The stamp applied to trac-

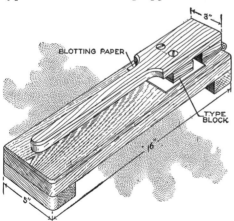

A Standard Type Block for the Titles of Drawings is Mounted in the Stamp for Convenient Application to Tracings:

ings will reproduce white on blueprints, and will be clean-cut, in distinction to the blurred appearance of titles printed with a rubber stamp.—E. E. Stevenson, Los Angeles, Calif.

Handy Containers for Distilled Water

Having use at times for a large quantity of distilled water and not wishing to go to the expense of purchasing

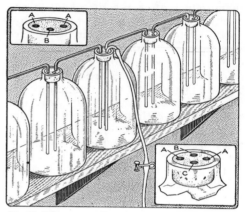

Distilled Water was Kept in Large Bottles Provided with a Siphon Tube

the amount of block tin necessary to line a tank sufficiently large, I hit on the following scheme: I had a number of 5-gal. bottles—the spring-water kind—and I fitted each of these with a three-hole cork; two of the holes, A, receive glass tubing, and the third, B, is plugged loosely with cotton, in order to allow the entrance of air and at the same time keep out dust. Each piece of glass tubing was bent in two right angles, and was of such a length that it reached to the bottom of each bottle and allowed the bottles to stand close together. When the first bottle was partly filled with distilled water, from a still, it was easy to run some into the second bottle by siphoning through the glass tube. Later on the water was conducted into the other bottles in order. They were placed on a shelf, and a glass tube, with rubber tubing and a pinchcock, conducted the water as needed from a fourth hole, C. This is an inexpensive means of providing storage for a large supply of water.—William G. Kennedy, Albany, New York.

❠Care in the handling of lathe centers will save regrinding them and prevent inaccuracies from damaged points.

Spring Stripping Attachment for Power Presses

By GEORGE P. BREITSCHMID

A FORM of stripper widely used on power punch presses, to remove the product after the dies have been applied, is that fixed to the die by means of four screws. Such a device was in use in a large manufacturing establishment using many presses, and proved costly from various considerations: The device was dangerous to the workman; caused great wear on tools; required that dies be frequently dressed, and made it impossible to see the work in process as readily as is desirable. Cost of production was high, and the profit of the operators was relatively low because their production quantity was kept down. By the introduction of the simple spring stripping device shown in the illustrations, together with jigs for the economical production of its many variations, a striking improvement was made in all of these points. The stripper consists of a flat steel plate, cut to provide clearance for the punch, and is shown fixed to the ram of the press in Fig. 1. The stripper, shown at A, has an opening at its center for a punch of oblong face, a slight clearance being provided all around its edge. The stock of the punch is fixed in the central opening of the ram B, and is clamped by means of the screws. A jig for boring and counterboring the stripper, for fastening it to the ram, is shown in Fig. 2; three views of a jig for marking the center opening with clearance for the punch are shown in Fig. 3, together with details of the adjustable handle.

The ram of the press B was first bored for two heavy screws, C, and counterbored at the top and bottom, the heads S of the screws being countersunk at the top and chambers provided at the bottom for $\frac{5}{16}$-in. square helical springs, D, of tool steel, $1\frac{1}{16}$-in. pitch, tempered. The latter are compressed between the collars E and the upper surface of their chambers, by the pressure of the ram in operation. They are adjusted by means of a steel rod,

inserted in the cross-bored sockets. The action of the springs upon the stripper, which is fixed to the lower ends of the large screws by means of smaller ones, is to thrust the punched work from the punch. The stripper is made of $\frac{3}{8}$-in. machine steel; the length is standard, 8 in., as shown in Fig. 1, and the holes in it are bored 6 in. apart on centers. The width may be suited to the dies.

The jig for boring and counterboring the strippers accurately and uniformly, so that they may be used interchangeably on various presses, is shown in Fig. 2. It consists of a metal base, F, to which are fitted clamps, G, held in place by screws. The clamps are adjustable at the slots in them, and the blank from which the stripper is to be made is fitted under the clamps, the ends of the blank being set against two stops, H. Hardened steel bushings, J, are fitted into the base as guides for the boring of the stripper. The smaller holes are bored on 6-in. centers, with the base inverted. The counterboring is done with the base in the position shown. The stripper is indicated by the dotted outline.

The jig for marking the opening in the stripper, through which the punch passes, and for allowing the necessary clearance of $\frac{1}{16}$ in. all around the punch, is shown in Fig. 3, in top, front, and side views.

The device consists of a base, K, carrying a vertical post, L, dovetailed to a vertical sliding member, M. The latter can be adjusted vertically and tightened in position by the threaded rod N, which is held firmly by the spring plate O. The plate is shown in detail at the upper part of Fig. 3.

In operation, the stripper, drilled by the use of the jig shown in Fig. 2, is fitted over the pins P, which fit snugly into the holes in the stripper. The sliding gauge Q is moved to hold the edge of the stripper, the jaw R being undercut to hold the stripper down as well as from the side. The punch S, inserted into its holder, or a split bushing if the punch has a small shank, is now be fastened into place on the ram of the press, as shown in Fig. 1.

The stripper is made of varying

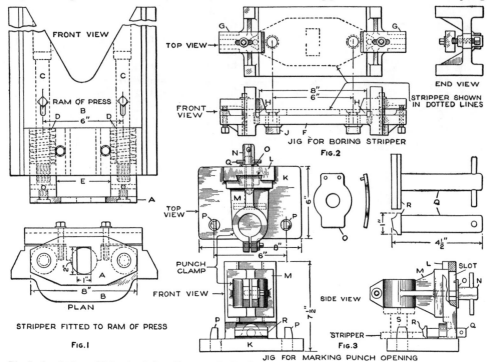

The Spring Stripper Makes for Safety, Economy in Production, and a High Grade of Work on Power Presses. Fig. 1 Shows the Stripper Fixed to the Ram of the Press. A Jig for Boring the Fastening Holes in the Stripper is Shown in Fig. 2, and a Jig for Marking the Clearance Hole for the Punch is Shown in Fig. 3, with Details of Parts

placed in the clamp of the sliding member M. It is lowered to rest upon the stripper blank, and, with a scriber, a line is scratched around the punch on the surface of the stripper. Clearance of 1/16 in. all around is allowed, and the clearance hole is drilled out and filed smooth. The stripper may widths to accommodate it to different jobs, but since the fastening holes and the length are standard, the jigs may be used for a large variety of work. The stripping attachment may be fitted to various types of punch presses, and is suitable for blanking, perforating, or bending operations.

Wall Crane for Small Shop or Garage

In garages and machine shops where it is necessary to handle heavy machine parts, a small crane saves much time and effort. The illustration shows a wall crane, built largely of 2-in. pipe and fittings, that can be made readily, and has a wide range of use if properly located on the shop wall. The dimensions may be varied to suit special conditions, and a length of about 10 ft. for the arms is satisfactory. This size will lift objects weighing up to 1,000 lb. with safety. The arms of the bracket are fitted at their upper and lower ends into tees, to form a right angle, and to give a fastening at the top for the brace, which is an iron rod. It is fixed at its upper end to a plug screwed into the tee, and at its lower by bolting it to the turned-up end of the horizontal member. The vertical support is carried at its lower end in an elbow, and near its upper end in a tee, fitted into a flange and bolted to the wall. A suitable trolley and tackle may be pro-

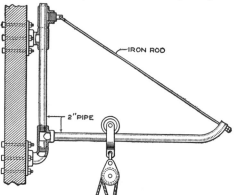

IRON ROD

2"PIPE

This Wall Crane, Made of Pipe and Fittings, will Carry a Load Up to 1,000 Pounds, if Carefully Made

vided either by making the pulleys and fittings or purchasing them.—Thomas W. Benson, Philadelphia, Pa.

Truck Arranged for Hauling Long Stock or Ladders

Under traffic laws in various localities, vehicles are not permitted to carry long articles that extend over 5 ft. at the rear, without hanging on a danger signal. To overcome this, and for convenience in handling long beams, lumber, etc., a transportation company fitted its trucks with doors in the front end, permitting long pieces to be passed through and extend along the radiator, as shown in the illustration. This helps

Beams, Planks, and Other Long Objects are Carried Conveniently by Reason of the Door

to balance the load and prevents it from dragging along the road.—J. C. Grindell, St. Louis, Mo.

Repairing Ratchet on Steering Post

On account of the severe wear on the steering-post ratchet of a "jitney" driver's automobile, he was forced to devise a method of using the worn ratchet in an emergency. He wound a heavy brass wire around it, the wire resting in each of the cogs. The follower engaged the wire just as it had the ratchet teeth, and the repair was so satisfactory that it was unnecessary to replace the part.

Cap for Screwdriver Reduces Marring of Work

The slipping of a screwdriver from the slot of a screw being fastened into a finished surface usually results in a severe injury to the finish. This condition was met in automobile work in putting screws into highly finished surfaces on bodies and other fittings. The screwdriver, shown in the illustration in several forms, was devised for the purpose of overcoming this, and proved quite satisfactory. The lower end of the screwdriver, in the simplest form, was ground as shown at the left, and a sleeve fitted over it, as shown above. The sleeve was made fixed for certain kinds of work, and movable on a pin and spring for work requiring this adjustable feature. The screw is driven in the usual manner. For larger screws, the sleeve was enlarged at its lower end, as indicated in the lower sketches. The device is useful also in driving screws in rough work, enabling the workman to work quickly with less danger of the driver slipping from the slot.—Charles C. Brabant, Detroit, Mich.

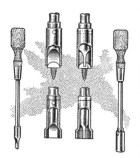

❡Draw enameled wire between a folded piece of sandpaper to remove the insulation.

A Rustic Four-Square Shelter House

By H. A. HOOPER

CHIEF among the advantages of the type of square summer house, or shelter, divided by diagonal partitions is the increased seating capacity. Shelter is afforded from the sun and elements under varying conditions in one or more of the sections. Each of the four sides affords entrance to a shelter, and has relative privacy from the adjoining sections. Several houses of this kind were built on a golf course and proved useful and popular.

This construction may be used for houses of various sizes, that shown in the illustration being 16 ft. square, about 30 in. from the ground to the floor, and with 8-ft. corner posts. The height from the lower edge of the roof to the peak is 4 ft., and the eaves have an overhang of 2 ft., giving added protection. Rustic timbers and smaller limbs were used for the structural portions of the house. The supports for the seats and the latticework under the floor were made similarly, of lighter stock. The partitions extend

This Shelter House Has a Relatively Large Seating Capacity and Affords Added Protection by Reason of the Partitions

to the height of the eaves, and are supported at their junction by a post. Standard mill stock may, of course, be used throughout the structure, if desired.

Proper Insulation of Splices

A properly insulated splice should last as long as any portion of the insulation. Apply the tape while the splice is still hot from soldering. Rubber tape should be put on first, to a thickness according to the voltage which is to be carried. Then apply friction tape as firmly as possible, and heavy enough to withstand wear. The tape should extend on the actual insulation at either side of the plug, otherwise there is a tendency for the wire to break at these points. On small work it is advisable to tear the tape into strips of not more than ½ in., for the best finish. A "whipping," made by winding twine tightly and evenly around the splice for the full length of the tape, is desirable to produce a high-class finish. Insulation varnish, or shellac, should be applied, but not while the work is at all damp.—W. B. Baruch, Charlestown, Massachusetts.

Radial Pivoted Arm for Shop Light

I recently installed a swinging light which reaches nearly all parts of the shop. It was made by supporting a long rod, $\frac{7}{8}$ by 3 in. at the thickest portion and tapering toward

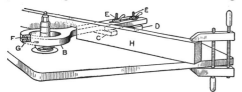

The Radial Arm is Swung Easily to Various Parts of the Shop and the Light Adjusted on the Wire

the ends, as shown. The arm was set in two brackets suspended from a circular turntable, pivoted at the middle on a bolt. The latter was fixed through a square plate which was fastened to the ceiling joists with screws. The cord for the electric light was carried on insulators which slide along a wire fixed to the lower edge of the radial arm.—R. E. Brown, Portland, Ore.

Safety Spring for the Variety Wood-Molding Machine

The spring shown in the sketch is a safety device, and also satisfactory in preventing vibration, and in holding

This Safety Spring Reduces Vibration and Is Adjustable to a Variety of Work

the face of the work closely against the table top. It is adjustable to various thicknesses. The block C should be about $\frac{1}{8}$ in. thicker than the piece to be fed into the machine, while the piece D should be enough thicker to insure that the under side of the head of the spring is practically parallel with the table top when the knives are cutting. The wing nuts E hold the spring firmly in contact with the blocks. The adjusting screws, at E, are threaded into the table.

The spring B should be made of from $1\frac{1}{8}$ to $1\frac{3}{8}$-in. hard wood. The diameter of the circular opening is slightly larger than the extreme diameter of the knives. The neck of the spring should be from 2 to 4 in. wide, and must give a firm pressure. End adjustments are made by the slot, at E, extending to the end. A spline, F, is glued into the rim of the spring, as shown in the section, at G, to strengthen the short grain of the wood. The lower side, at G, is rounded to permit the work to enter easily; the inner edge is flat, and the under side of the head is waxed to make feeding easier. For heavy work, the piece H extends from edge to edge of the table, and is clamped at both ends. The groove in H fits the neck closely, but with sufficient play to permit the spring to move vertically without undue friction.—Charles A. King, East Kingston, N. H.

Repairing a Short-Circuited Armature Section

To locate a short-circuited armature section, pass a current from a dry cell, or storage battery, through the armature, using the brushes of the machine. Using a low-reading voltmeter—a millivoltmeter if possible—touch its lead wires to one pair after another of adjacent commutator bars. A zero deflection of the voltmeter indicates a short-circuited section.

It will be noticed, at periodic intervals in passing around the commutator, that the voltmeter deflection reverses, and that just before this transition point the deflection is less than normal. This merely indicates a passage from one pole to another on the

The Use of This Frame Enables One Man with a Team of Horses to Transplant Trees of Considerable Size

winding. On a four-pole armature, for instance, there will be four such reversals of the meter deflection. Switching of lead wires is all that is necessary to make the meter read in the right direction.

If a short circuit is found, clean out the spaces between commutator bars, to be certain no small bits of metal or copper dust are responsible. Failing thus to locate the trouble, carefully lift out the coil connected to the bars to which the short was traced, and repair any breaks in the insulation. Shellac and silk ribbon are the best materials for this work. Apply the ribbon smoothly, coating it thoroughly.

A broken circuit in the winding itself may be located by connecting a battery through an ammeter to two metal strips, held apart by a piece of wood, at such a distance that they will touch adjacent commutator bars. Holding this device against the commutator, turn the armature slowly by hand. A reduced deflection of the ammeter indicates a broken or open-circuited winding. The only resort, in case of open circuit, is to lift out the damaged coil, solder the ends together, reinsulate, and replace the wire in the slots.—K. M. Coggeshall, Webster Groves, Mo.

Transplanting Large Trees

Trees of considerable size may be transplanted for shade, or decorative, purposes by one man with a team of horses, by the use of the frame shown in the illustration. It is made of 4 by 4-in. timbers, spiked together. A trench is dug around the tree, and the roots cut free, taking plenty of earth with them, as shown in Fig. 2. To get at the lower roots it is desirable to haul the tree to the position shown in Fig. 3, by means of a guy rope hitched to the team. If the tree is too large to be lifted clear of the ground by means of the frame, it may be skidded to a stoneboat, as indicated in Fig. 3. The frame is lashed to the trunk of the tree, and its lower ends set on blocks. A rope is fixed to it near the top, and the tree may be raised to drop on the stoneboat, by driving the team slowly forward. The frame may be used to set the tree into a pit at its new location, by using the frame in the reverse direction. The tree should be guyed to make it plumb, and the earth filled firmly around it, as shown in Fig. 4.— J. G. Allshouse, Avonmore, Pa.

⟪Chalk sandpaper on the back to prevent it from slipping in the hand.

Wrench Adapted Easily for Many Uses

The ordinary monkey wrench, with a few alterations and additions, may be made to serve many purposes other

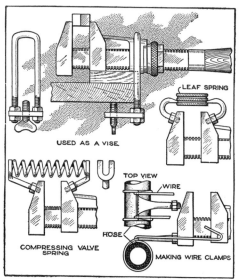

By the Addition of a Few Simple Attachments the Wrench Is Available for Several New Duties

than that of a wrench and hammer, by utilizing the adjusting feature as a tension screw. It is particularly desirable for automobile purposes, saving both weight and expense. The sketches show a few of the possibilities by providing threaded holes and attachments. If the jaws of the wrench are hardened, it is necessary to anneal them. If the knurled sleeve is not already hexagonal, it is advisable to flatten the sides so as to obtain gripping surface.

An attachment which converts the wrench into a small vise was made as shown. The detachable bracket is provided with a thumbscrew for securing it to the running board of an automobile or other projecting edge. An attachment of 7/16-in. rod for converting the wrench into a valve-spring compressor is shown at the left. Attachments used in separating the leaves of an automobile spring to insert lubricants are shown at the right.

An attachment for the making of wire bands or clamps for radiator hose,

bands about buckets, garden-hose connections, etc., is also shown. The sliding jaw has a 3/16-in. hole drilled through it and a pin inserted, which projects about 1/4 in. on either side. The chisel-shaped attachment is grooved for holding the wire. A strong tension by means of the knurled sleeve, before finally drawing up the loop, is desirable.—George A. Luers, Washington, D. C.

Care of Automobile Steering Connections

The leather boots necessary to protect the steering joints of an automobile from mud and water should be given careful attention. Old grease should be removed from the joints when necessary, and the boot cleaned. The joints should be greased thoroughly, and a strip of linen, 3 in. wide, used as an inner covering to retain the grease. The boot is placed over this cloth covering, thus keeping it clean for lacing. The inner covering may be discarded when the joint is again greased.—Alexander Bollerer, New Britain, Conn.

Faucet Tap for Large Cans

Oil cans shipped to an undeveloped region were not provided with a suit-

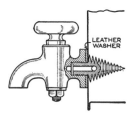

able tap, and it was found inconvenient to run off the oil from a plugged hole. The faucet tap shown in the sketch was devised, and proved convenient. A tapered screw was fitted to the faucet, and inserted through the end of the can by driving in the point and then turning the faucet until it was set tightly. A leather washer was provided to make a close joint. When the can is emptied, the faucet is quickly removed by unscrewing the threaded point, and may be used repeatedly.—Gus Hansen, Peachland, Can.

INDEX TO VOLUME XIV

SHOP NOTES FOR 1918

Advertisement, Novel Window......... 2792
Advertising, Inexpensive Lantern Slides for 2744
Air Motors, Safety Throttle for........ 2767
Air-Pump Blower Driven by Punch Press 2859
Air-Pump Lift, Locomotive.............. 2728
Air Supply for Blowpipe, Automatic.... 2756
Air Supply, Indoor, for Furnace Heating Systems........................ 2875
Alarm System, Safety-First, for Shops.. 2870
Alining Wheels of a Sidecar or Automobile 2792
Anchor Bent from Round Bar.......... 2870
Anchor-Plate Pockets, Machinery Foundations with........................ 2803
Anvil, I-Beam......................... 2801
Arbor, Improved Emery-Wheel......... 2815
Arbors, Small Shafts or, Device for Removing 2839
Arm Pincushion Carried on Bicycle Clip 2840
Arm, Radial Pivoted, for Shop Light.... 2884
Armature Section, Repairing Short-Circuited 2884
Ash Disposal, Elevated Bin Makes Convenient 2813
Auditorium, Large, Sounding Board for 2786
Auto Panes, Preventing Frosting of in Winter 2841
Auto Repairs, Casters on Footboard for Use in 2845
Auto Tires, Outdoor Rack for.......... 2691
Auto Top, Keeping Down Saves Gasoline 2802
Automatic Exhaust Heater............. 2688
Automatic Fire Damper in Ventilating Duct 2690
Automobile Axle, Rear, Eliminating End Thrust on............................ 2822
Automobile-Body Dashes, Gauging...... 2842
Automobile Brake Shoes, Reversing for Wear 2698
Automobile Cone Clutch, Oiling........ 2728
Automobile Drain Cocks, Long Wrench for 2793
Automobile-Engine Cooling System, Cleaning 2799
Automobile Gasoline Tank, Vent Cover for 2752
Automobile Gear-Box Repair........... 2851
Automobile Jacks Save Tires.......... 2729
Automobile, Keeping Warm in Winter.. 2827
Automobile or Sidecar, Alining Wheels of 2792
Automobile Pedal, Leather Cover for... 2808
Automobile, Platform Facilitates Taking Down of........................... 2874
Automobile, Pointers on Cleaning and Polishing 2686
Automobile Polish, Paraffin............ 2739
Automobile Radiator, Eliminating Rattle of............................. 2735
Automobile Radiator, Painting......... 2687
Automobile Radiator, To Prevent Spilling Water on When Filling.......... 2703
Automobile, Secondhand, How to Judge 2750
Automobile Spring Inserts to Prevent Squeaking 2685
Automobile Steering Connections, Care of 2886
Automobile Steering Post, Watch Fitted to 2745
Automobile, Stretching Fence Wire with 2810
Automobiles, Homemade Bumper for.... 2722
Auxiliary Vise Jaw for Holding Irregular Pieces 2870
Average Table for School Grades....... 2757

Babbitt Bearings, Making Oil Grooves in 2802

Babbitt Metal, Making Smooth Castings in 2704
Babbitting Split Bearings in One Operation 2774
Baby Cab, Truck for When Indoors.... 2704
Back Draft in Fireplace, Preventing... 2869
Back-Firing, Carburetor, Remedy for.. 2710
Bag, Fruit Picker's, Minimizes Damage to Product 2764
Ball-Bearing Tailstock Center.......... 2734
Band Saw, Sawing Wooden Wheels or Disks on 2838
Bar-Lead Molds 2758
Bar, Round, Anchor Bent from........ 2870
Barn Doors, Sliding, Eccentric Catch for 2769
Barn, Wing-Joist Frame............... 2828
Barnyard Crane and Trolley for Silage Feeding 2763
Base for Swage Block.................. 2876
Bathtub, Dust Cover for.............. 2785
Battery Room, String Solder Replaces Copper Wire in........................ 2798
Battery, Storage, How to Make........ 2693
Beach Device—Water Joy Wheel....... 2726
Bearing Wheel for Gate............... 2752
Bearings, Remedy for Overheating..... 2689
Bearings, Split, Babbitting in One Operation 2774
Belt Dressing 2691
Belt Ends, Trimming, for Lap Joints... 2731
Belts, Counteracting Static Electricity in 2746
Belts, Machine, Kink for Lacing........ 2816
Bench, Portable and Collapsible........ 2718
Bench-Vise Handles, Noiseless Rubber Tips for 2822
Bending and Polishing Brass Tubing... 2752
Bending Rails or Bars, Simple Method of 2704
Bicycle Clip, Arm Pincushion Carried on 2840
Bin, Coal Chute Built into............ 2830
Bin, Elevated, Makes Ash Disposal Convenient 2813
Bit Brace Used on Chuck Wrench...... 2732
Block-and-Tackle Hoist for Cellar..... 2765
Block Protects Sawyer's Hands from Splinters 2704
Blower, Air-Pump, Driven by Punch Press 2859
Blowpipe, Automatic Air Supply for.... 2756
Blowpipe, Self-Acting 2826
Blowtorch, Oil-Burning, for Sheet-Metal Work 2852
Blue Finish on Steel, Producing....... 2837
Blueprint Drier for Indoor or Outdoor Use 2725
Blueprints That will Not Fade........ 2758
Boiler, Heavy, or Machine, Skidding.... 2846
Boiler, Old, Watering Trough Made of.. 2684
Book Fumigator and Sterilizer......... 2875
Boot Scraper, Safety, for a Doorstep... 2692
Boring Large Holes in Wood, Tool for.. 2844
Bottles, Rapid Method of Labeling..... 2710
Box Corners, Brass, Made of Square Tubing 2685
Box, Light, Hinge for................. 2768
Brace for Gatepost, Underground...... 2793
Brace, Twisting Wire with............. 2739
Brake-Band Support, Adjustable....... 2733
Brake-Lever Rod Guide............... 2814
Brake, Motor Attachment and, for Sewing Machine 2873
Brake Shoes, Automobile, Reversing for Wear 2698
Brass Box Corners Made of Square Tubing 2685
Brass, Brush Finish for............... 2688
Brass Tubing, Bending and Polishing.. 2752
Brickwork, Scraper for Joints in....... 2842
Brush Finish for Brass................ 2688

Brushes, Improving Commutator Contact at 2764
Buggy-Top Braces, Tools Made of 2797
Building and Painting, Movable Scaffold for 2845
Bulbs, Planting Conveniently 2863
Bumper for Automobiles, Homemade ... 2722
Bumper, Spring, for Motorboat Landings 2795
Bushing Avoids Marring of Work in Lathe Dog or Chuck 2825
Bushing, Hard-Rubber, Made without Lathe 2812
Buttonhook, Improvised 2702

Cable Clamp for Large-Conductor Terminations 2712
Cable Fastening, Leaded Socket for 2742
Camp Stove, Gasoline 2699
Camp, Summer Cottage or, Gravity Water System for 2866
Cans, Large, Faucet Tap for 2886
Canvas Tool Bag 2773
Cap for Screwdriver Reduces Marring of Work 2882
Cap Keeps Dust Out of Carburetor 2730
Capacity of Wash Boiler, Finding 2735
Carbon-Steel Tools, Small, Hardening.. 2865
Carburetor Back-Firing, Remedy for ... 2710
Carburetor, Cap Keeps Dust Out of.... 2730
Carburetor, Electric Light Warms in Winter 2808
Cartridge Fuses, Renewing 2733
Casters on Footboard for Use in Auto Repairs 2845
Casting, Removing a Plug from 2837
Castings, Smooth, Making in Babbitt Metal 2704
Cellar, Block-and-Tackle Hoist for 2765
Center Drill, Combination, Milling Small Slots with 2768
Center, Hollow, for Re-Turning Spindles 2716
Chain-Rivet Extracting Tool 2814
Chain, To Prevent from Rattling 2691
Chair Legs, Spring-Cushioned 2724
Charging Periods, Lights behind Storage Batteries Indicate 2813
Chimney, Hood on Increases Draft 2864
Chuck Wrench, Bit Brace Used on 2732
Clamp Enables One Man to Nail Siding Readily 2831
Cleaning and Polishing an Automobile, Pointers on 2686
Cleaning Paint on Engines 2690
Clip Board for Shop Orders 2705
Clip for Pocket Scale 2812
Clock, Dutch 2697
Cloth, Weights for Drying Large Pieces of 2769
Clothes Washer, Sanitary 2734
Clothesline Post 2739
Coal Chute Built into Bin 2830
Coil Spring to Reinforce Rubber Tube 2710
Colony Poultry House 2701
Commutator Contact at Brushes, Improving 2764
Compass Adapted for Making Lettering Guide Lines 2758
Concrete Foundation Fitted to Machine Base 2756
Concrete, Garden Fountain and Basin of 2707
Concrete, Garden Seats of 2855
Concrete, Roofed Watering Tank of 2874
Concrete, Straightedge Arched for Leveling 2869
Concrete, Tamper Made of 2692
Conduit Pipes, Time-Saving Kink in Bending 2715
Conduits, Pulling Wires into 2718
Cone Clutch, Automobile, Oiling 2728
Containers, Handy, for Distilled Water. 2879
Cooling System, Automobile-Engine, Cleaning 2799
Copper Strip, Motor Cylinder Repaired with 2862
Copper Wire, String Solder Replaces in Battery Room 2798
Core-Drier Pattern for a Manifold 2719
Corking Painted Ironwork 2692
Corncrib, Rodent-Proof Support for 2870
Cornice Rigging to Support Ladder Scaffold 2838

Counter Advertising Matter, Tray for.. 2812
Countersink, File Used as 2697
Coupling, Temporary Shaft 2689
Cover for Mortar 2734
Cover for Washing Machine 2753
Crane and Trolley, Barnyard, for Silage Feeding 2763
Crane, Wall, for Small Shop or Garage. 2881
Crankshaft-Turning Fixture 2722
Cranky Engine, Spinning 2860
Cross Disk on Faucet Stops Splashing.. 2738
Curtain Fixture, Holder for 2714
Curved Signs, Lettering for 2721
Curved Surface, Patching Veneer on.... 2724
Cutter, Reel and, for Sandpaper and Emery Cloth 2811
Cutters, Gang Machine, Oiling 2755
Cutters, Tool Holder with Set of 2717
Cutting Hard Lubricating Grease, Jig for 2853
Cutting Threads without Tap or Die... 2852
Cylinder, Motor, Repaired with Copper Strip 2862

Dashes, Automobile-Body, Gauging 2842
Detachable Lamp Hanging 2714
Dial-Glass Casings, Steam-Gauge, Removing 2702
Dies, Obtaining Sharp Impressions from 2718
Dismantling Large Pipe Line, Powerful Wrench Used in 2878
Display Board for Gas Brackets 2755
Distances, Short, Testing Judgment of. 2808
Distilled Water, Handy Containers for.. 2879
Dock Railing, Removable 2685
Door, Hinge Plates and Escutcheon for 2831
Door, Old-Style Closet, Glass Panels in. 2721
Door with Loose-Pin Hinges, Securing. 2721
Doors, Handle for Cellar or Floor 2808
Double-Pipe Runs, Straps to Fit 2793
Double-Shaft Universal Joint 2854
Draft, Hood on Chimney Increases 2864
Drafting Room, Title Stamp for 2879
Drafting Table for Full-Size Detailing and Large Drawings 2766
Drafting Table Made of Pipes and Fittings 2825
Drain Cocks, Automobile, Long Wrench for 2793
Drawer Front, Hinged, is Convenient... 2864
Drawers, Four, Locking with Plate Hasp 2860
Drawing Pen Used as Emergency Forceps 2725
Drawing the Temper in Small Taps and Reamers 2877
Drawings, Holder for Examining 2862
Drawings, Rack for Filing Vertically... 2796
Dressing, Belt 2691
Drill, Portable Electric, Used as Drill Press 2850
Drill Press, Portable Electric Drill Used as 2850
Drill Press Used as a Vertical Miller... 2810
Drilling Radial Holes, Adjustable Jig for 2832
Drills Made from Hacksaw Blades 2786
Drum in Table Top for Listing Merchandise Sales 2861
Dry Batteries, Trouble Lamp Operated by 2745
Dry-Battery Sets, Maintenance of 2752
Dump Cart, Garden, of Varied Uses 2860
Dust, Cap Keeps Out of Carburetor 2730
Dust Cover for Bathtub 2785
Dust, Exhaust Fan for Workbench Aids in Removing 2849
Dust in Sand, Apparatus for Removing. 2827
Dust, To Prevent Entering Flywheel Bearing of Marine Engine 2685
Dutch Clock 2697

Eccentric Catch for Sliding Barn Doors. 2769
Economizer, Gasoline Fuel Strainer and 2741
Economy in Platinum or Other Wiring.. 2735
Electric Drill, Portable, Used as Drill Press 2850
Electric Flatirons, Curbing Borrowers of 2698
Electric Horn, Push Button Varies Tone of 2868
Electric-Lamp Board of Sheet Metal... 2686

Electric Light Warms Carburetor in Winter 2808
Electric Plant, Mountain-Stream....... 2747
Electrical Finder for Submerged Metal Objects 2821
Electrical Generator, Building......... 2833
Electrical Ground Made of Flowerpot.. 2870
Electrical Water Gauge................ 2861
Electromagnet Used to Place Letters in Score Board 2729
Emery Cloth, Sandpaper and, Reel and Cutter for 2811
Emery-Wheel Arbor, Improved......... 2815
End Guards for Plug Gauge............ 2768
End Thrust on a Rear Automobile Axle, Eliminating 2822
Engine, Cranky, Spinning.............. 2860
Engine, Portable, Solid Foundation for.. 2745
Engines, Cleaning Paint on........... 2690
Escutcheon, Hinge Plates and, for Door 2831
Exhaust Fan for Workbench Aids in Removing Dust 2849
Exhaust Heater, Automatic............ 2688
Exit Lights That Illuminate........... 2698
Experimental Purposes, Glass Prisms for 2724
Expressman's Signal Flag, Order Holder on 2703
Extracting Tool, Chain-Rivet.......... 2814

Fan Ducts, Sound Deadener for........ 2766
Farm Sale Pavilion.................... 2770
Farm Seed-Corn House................. 2736
Farm Shop and Garage................. 2681
Faucet, Cross Disk on Stops Splashing. 2738
Faucet Top for Large Cans............ 2886
Faucets, Safety Key for............... 2730
Fence Extension at Tidewater Stream.. 2863
Fence Posts, Metal Points for........ 2768
Fence Posts, Removing Easily......... 2816
Fence, Stairs for Climbing over....... 2824
Fence Wire, Stretching with an Automobile 2810
Ferrule for Tool Handle Made of Hose Coupling 2821
File Used as Countersink.............. 2697
Fire Damper, Automatic, in Ventilating Duct 2690
Fireplace, Heat in Utilized for a Radiator 2840
Fireplace, Preventing Back Draft in... 2869
Fixture, Crankshaft-Turning 2722
Fixtures, Hand-Operated Wire-Forming 2817
Flash Lamp, To Prevent from Short-Circuiting 2684
Floor Vibration under Scale Platform, Overcoming 2802
Floors, Interior Trim and, Sanding Block for 2862
Floors, Plank, Jackscrew Used in Laying 2798
Floors, Storage Areas Marked on...... 2876
Flowerpot, Electrical Ground Made of.. 2870
Flywheel Bearing of Marine Engine, To Prevent Dust Entering................ 2685
Focusing and Caring for Headlights... 2872
Footboard, Casters on, for Use in Auto Repairs 2845
Forceps, Emergency, Drawing Pen Used as 2725
Forge Fire Adapted for Heating Soldering Iron 2741
Forging Renews Worn Socket Wrenches 2838
Foundation, Concrete, Fitted to Machine Base 2756
Foundation, Solid, for a Portable Engine 2745
Fountain and Basin of Concrete, Garden 2707
Frames, Old, Gilding.................. 2767
Freight Transfer, Portable Trolley and Tackle for 2843
Frosting of Auto Panes in Winter, Preventing 2841
Fruit Pickers' Bag Minimizes Damage to Product 2764
Fumigator and Sterilizer, Book........ 2875
Funnel, Emergency 2706
Furnace Heating Systems, Indoor Air Supply for 2875

Gang Tool for Shaper in Machine Shop. 2841
Garage, Farm Shop and................ 2681

Garage, Heating from Residence Hot-Water System 2853
Garage, Wall Crane for Small Shop or. 2881
Garden Dump Cart of Varied Uses..... 2860
Garden Fountain and Basin of Concrete 2707
Garden-Hose Reel Inclosed in Wall Cupboard 2744
Garden Seats of Concrete.............. 2855
Gas Brackets, Display Board for........ 2755
Gas Burner, Noisy, Silencing........... 2768
Gas Engines, Starting Large........... 2739
Gas-Stove Burner, Safety Spring for.... 2738
Gaskets, Packing, Templates for Cutting 2792
Gasoline Camp Stove.................. 2699
Gasoline Engine, Kink in Overhauling.. 2824
Gasoline Engines, Eliminating Pounding in 2854
Gasoline Fuel Strainer and Economizer. 2741
Gasoline, Keeping Auto Top Down Saves 2802
Gasoline-Supply Indicator, Automatic.. 2740
Gasoline Tank, Automobile, Vent Cover for 2752
Gate, Bearing Wheel for............... 2752
Gate, Nonsagging Board............... 2846
Gatepost, Underground Brace for...... 2793
Gauge for Cutting Packing-Box Stock.. 2799
Gauge for Spacing Steel-Marking Punches 2825
Gauge, Homemade Pipe................. 2687
Gauges, Snap 2742
Gauging Automobile-Body Dashes...... 2842
Gear-Box Repair, Automobile.......... 2851
Gear, Large, Reboring without Machinery 2868
Generator, Electrical, Building......... 2833
Gilding Old Frames.................... 2767
Gland Nut, Water-Pump, Holding...... 2730
Glass Panels in Old-Style Closet Door... 2721
Glass, Plane, Concave Mirror Ground from 2796
Glass Prisms for Experimental Purposes 2724
Glass Stopper, Loosening Tight......... 2794
Gravity Water System for a Summer Cottage or Camp..................... 2866
Greenhouse, Wind Indicator for....... 2772
Grinder, High-Speed Foot-Power....... 2876
Grinding Wheel, Sharpening Scissors on 2864
Grip, Auxiliary, for Valve Handle...... 2740
Ground Fill, Hastening the Settling of. 2765
Guard to Prevent Entangling of Reins. 2733

Hacksaw Blades, Drills Made from...... 2786
Hacksaw, Cutting Wide Slots with...... 2762
Hammer, Soft-Face 2842
Handle for Cellar or Floor Doors...... 2808
Hanger Bolt, Substitute for........... 2794
Hard Spots on Lathe Spindle, Removing 2698
Hardening Small Carbon-Steel Tools... 2865
Hauling Long Stock or Ladders, Truck Arranged for 2882
Headlights, Focusing and Caring for.... 2872
Heat in Fireplace, Utilizing for a Radiator 2840
Heating a Garage from Residence Hot-Water System 2853
Heels, Solid-Tire Rubber for Making... 2878
High-Speed Foot-Power Grinder........ 2876
Hinge for Light Box................... 2768
Hinge Plates and Escutcheon for Door. 2831
Hinged Drawer Front is Convenient.... 2864
Hog House, Individual................. 2877
Hogs, Self-Feeder for................. 2723
Hoist, Block-and-Tackle, for Cellar..... 2765
Hoist, Simple Combination-Lever....... 2732
Holder for Curtain Fixture............ 2714
Holder for Examining Drawings....... 2862
Holes in Sheet Metal, Device for Punching 2812
Holes, Large, in Wood, Tool for Boring. 2844
Home and Shop Use, Adaptation of Motorcycle for 2871
Home Workshop, Woman's...2775, 2781, 2787
Hood on Chimney Increases Draft...... 2864
Hoop for One-Man Truck.............. 2687
Horn, Brass, Repairing Slide on........ 2756
Hose Coupling, Ferrule for Tool Handle Made of 2821
Hot-Water System, Residence, Heating Garage from 2853
House, Farm Seed-Corn............... 2736

Hydroplane for Carrying Line across a Stream 2680
I-Beam Anvil 2801
Impressions, Sharp, Obtaining from Dies 2718
Indicator and Tool Holder............. 2740
Indicator, Automatic Gasoline-Supply.. 2740
Indicator Holder with Five Positions... 2869
Individual Hog House................. 2877
Indoor Air Supply for Furnace Heating Systems 2875
Insulation, Nippers for Removing from Wire 2822
Insulation of Splices, Proper.......... 2883
Insulation on Wires, Testing through.. 2767
Insulation, Removing Quickly......... 2729
Interchangeable Points, Lathe Centers with 2839
Interior Trim and Floors, Sanding Block for 2862
Irregular Pieces, Auxiliary Vise Jaw for Holding 2870

Jack, Improvised Lifting.............. 2801
Jacks, Automobile, Save Tires.......... 2729
Jackscrew Used in Laying Plank Floors 2798
Jig, Adaptable, for Turning Pulleys in a Lathe 2873
Jig, Adjustable, for Drilling Radial Holes 2832
Jig for Cutting Hard Lubricating Grease 2853
Joint, Inexpensive Universal........... 2680
Joints in Brickwork, Scraper for....... 2842
Joist-Boring Machine, Homemade...... 2823
Judgment of Short Distances, Testing.. 2808

Key-Ring Riveter 2812
Keyseater, Portable 2690
Kink, Time-Saving, in Bending Conduit Pipes 2715
Kinks in Use of Tire Patches.......... 2765
Kitchen Boilers, Old, Used for Well Casing 2841
Kitchen Stove, Soot Scraper Aids Water Heating in 2758

Labeling Bottles, Rapid Method of...... 2710
Lacing Machine Belts, Kink for........ 2816
Ladder Scaffold, Cornice Rigging to Support 2838
Lamp Flame, Notch in Wick Improves. 2862
Lamp, Hanging, Detachable........... 2714
Lantern Slides, Inexpensive, for Advertising 2744
Lap Joints, Trimming Belt Ends for.... 2731
Lathe, Adaptable Jig for Turning Pulleys in 2873
Lathe Center with Interchangeable Points 2839
Lathe Dog or Chuck, Bushing Avoids Marring of Work in.................. 2825
Lathe Fixture—Spindle-Turning Device Effects Large Saving................. 2759
Lathe, Sander Attachment for.......... 2815
Lathe Spindle, Removing Hard Spots on 2698
Lathe, Tail Center in, Prevents Loosening of 2730
Latticework, Wire Substitute for....... 2872
Lawn, Sprinkler for Narrow Strips of.. 2753
Leak, Pipe, Temporary Repair for..... 2802
Leather Cover for Automobile Pedal... 2808
Lettering for Curved Signs............ 2721
Lettering Guide Lines, Compass Adapted for Making 2758
Level, Plumb-Bob, Quickly Made...... 2722
Leveling Concrete, Straightedge Arched for 2869
Lever Holds Planer Tool Block on Backstroke 2811
Lifting Jack, Improvised.............. 2801
Lifting Rig for Heavy Wheels or Pulleys 2751
Lights behind Storage Batteries Indicate Charging Periods 2813
Lights, Exit, That Illuminate.......... 2698
Line, Hydroplane for Carrying across a Stream 2680
Load Scale for Trucks................. 2689
Locking Four Drawers with Plate Hasp 2860
Locknut, Quickly Made................ 2739

Lockstitch Sewing Awl................ 2794
Locomotive Air-Pump Lift............. 2728
Loosening a Tight Glass Stopper....... 2794
Lubricating Grease, Hard, Jig for Cutting 2853
Lug, Drilled, Soldering on Sheet Brass.. 2769

Machine Base, Concrete Foundation Fitted to 2756
Machine Belts, Kink for Lacing........ 2816
Machine, Heavy Boiler or, Skidding..... 2846
Machine Shop, Gang Tool for Shaper in 2841
Machine-Thread Cleaner, Wire Spring.. 2794
Machinery Foundations with Anchor-Plate Pockets 2803
Machinery, Reboring a Large Gear without. 2868
Manifold, Core-Drier Pattern for....... 2719
Marble or Granite, Polishing........... 2754
Marine Engine, To Prevent Dust Entering Flywheel Bearing of............ 2685
Marring of Work, Cap for Screwdriver Reduces 2882
Mechanics, Improved Tool Box for..... 2731
Merchandise Sales, Drum in Table Top for Listing 2861
Metal Objects, Submerged, Electrical Finder for 2821
Metal Patches, Setting Screws in Making 2799
Metal Points for Fence Posts........... 2768
Miller, Vertical, Drill Press Used as.... 2810
Milling Small Slots with Combination Center Drill 2768
Mine Tunnel, Ventilating.............. 2809
Mirror as a Shop Tool................ 2711
Mirror, Concave, Ground from Plane Glass 2796
Molds, Bar-Lead 2758
Mortar, Cover for.................... 2734
Mosaic Finish with Paint and Varnish.. 2758
Motor Attachment and Brake for Sewing Machine 2873
Motor Cylinder Repaired with Copper Strip 2862
Motorboat Landings, Spring Bumper for 2795
Motorcycle, Adaptation of, for Home and Shop Use 2871
Mountain-Stream Electric Plant........ 2747
Movies, Making a Waterfall for........ 2705

Nail Set, Keeping Point of in Shape.... 2813
Nails, Screws and Bolts, Sorting Tray for 2840
Names, Long List of, Device Facilitates Handling 2821
Nippers for Removing Insulation from Wire 2822
Noiseless Rubber Tips for Bench-Vise Handles 2822
Noisy Telephone Bells, Remedy for..... 2859
Nonsagging Board Gate............... 2846
Notch in Wick Improves Lamp Flame.. 2862

Oil-Burning Blowtorch for Sheet-Metal Work 2852
Oil Grooves in Babbitt Bearings, Making 2802
Oil Tray for Screw Cutting............ 2739
Oil-Well Pump Signal................. 2706
Oiler, Safety-First Shaft.............. 2706
Oiling an Automobile Cone Clutch...... 2728
Oiling Gang Machine Cutters.......... 2755
Oiling Sheet Metal for Stamping or Punching 2715
Oiling Straddle-Milling Cutters......... 2715
Order Holder on Expressman's Signal Flag 2703
Overhauling a Gasoline Engine, Kink in 2824
Overheating of Bearings, Remedy for.. 2689

Packing-Box Stock, Gauge for Cutting. 2799
Paint and Varnish, Mosaic Finish with. 2758
Paint on Engines, Cleaning............ 2690
Paint, Sulphate-of-Zinc 2793
Painted Ironwork, Corking............ 2692
Painting an Automobile Radiator....... 2687
Painting, Building and, Movable Scaffold for 2845
Panels, Glass, in Old-Style Closet Door. 2721
Paper Holder for Desk or Workbench.. 2725
Paraffin Automobile Polish............ 2739
Parcels, Device for Tying............. 2859

Patches, Soldering on Tanks or Large Objects 2851
Patching the Printing Surfaces of Woodcuts or Type........................ 2841
Pattern, Core-Drier, for Manifold....... 2719
Photography, Sensitized Paper for......'2716
Pincushion, Arm, Carried on Bicycle Clip 2840
Pipe and Fittings, Press Made of........ 2729
Pipe Gauge, Homemade................. 2687
Pipe Leak, Temporary Repair for....... 2802
Pipe Line, Large, Powerful Wrench Used in Dismantling 2878
Pipe Rack, Portable.................. 2730
Pipe, Truss for Long Span of........... 2741
Pipe Wrench, Emergency.............. 2811
Pipes and Fittings, Drafting Table Made of 2825
Piston Rings, Obtaining Long Wear Out of 2773
Planer Tool Block, Lever Holds on Backstroke 2811
Planting Bulbs Conveniently........... 2863
Plastering Trowel, Gauge for......... 2878
Plate Hasp, Locking Four Drawers with 2860
Platform Facilitates Taking Down of Automobile 2874
Platform, Portable Safety, for Telephone Linemen 2851
Platinum or Other Wiring, Economy in 2735
Plug Gauge, End Guards for........... 2768
Plug, Removing from Casting........ 2837
Plumb-Bob Level Quickly Made........ 2722
Pocket Scale, Clip for............... 2812
Polish, Paraffin Automobile........... 2739
Polishing Marble or Granite........... 2754
Portable Keyseater 2690
Portable Trolley and Tackle for Freight Transfer 2843
Positions, Five, Indicator Holder with.. 2869
Post, Clothesline 2739
Post, Inexpensive Traffic-Light........ 2846
Poultry House, Colony................. 2701
Pounding in Gasoline Engines, Eliminating 2854
Power Presses, Spring Stripping Attachment for 2880
Preserving Stove Linings............. 2852
Press Made of Pipe and Fittings........ 2729
Pressure Regulator, Automatic......... 2731
Printing-Press Roller, Small, Substitute for 2850
Printing Surfaces of Woodcuts or Type, Patching 2841
Prisms, Glass, for Experimental Purposes 2724
Protection, Stream-Bank 2724
Pulley, Enlarging for Emergency Use... 2822
Pulleys, Adaptable Jig for Turning in a Lathe 2873
Pump Connection, Sound-Proof........ 2813
Pump Operated by Distant Windmill... 2831
Pump Signal, Oil-Well................. 2706
Punch for Making Fiber Washers..... 2706
Punch Press, Air-Pump Blower Driven by 2859
Punches, Steel-Marking, Gauge for Spacing 2825
Punching Holes in Sheet Metal, Device for 2812
Push Button Varies Tone of Electric Horn 2868

Rack for Filing Drawings Vertically... 2796
Rack for Raising Crossbar on Vaulting Standards 2807
Rack, Outdoor, for Auto Tires......... 2691
Radial Holes, Adjustable Jig for Drilling 2832
Radial Pivoted Arm for Shop Light.... 2884
Radiator, Automobile, Eliminating Rattle of 2735
Radiator, Utilizing Heat in Fireplace for 2840
Railing, Removable Dock.............. 2685
Rails or Bars, Simple Method of Bending 2704
Ratchet on Steering Post, Repairing.... 2882
Rattle in Wood Turning, Silencing.... 2751
Razor Handle, One-Piece.............. 2714
Razor Strop, Improving............... 2742
Reboring a Large Gear without Machinery 2868
Record Map, Keeping Up to Date...... 2692

Reel and Cutter for Sandpaper and Emery Cloth 2811
Reel, Garden-Hose, Inclosed in Wall Cupboard 2744
Regulator, Automatic Pressure........ 2731
Reins, Guard to Prevent Entangling of. 2733
Remedy for Overheating of Bearings... 2689
Renewing Cartridge Fuses............. 2733
Repairing Slide on Brass Horn......... 2756
Residence Hot-Water System, Heating Garage from 2853
Reversing Automobile Brake Shoes for Wear 2698
Revolving Tool Rack.................. 2801
Rheostat, Motor-Starting, Trouble Signal for 2774
Riddling Sand, Easy Method of......... 2797
Rigging for Surface-Grinding Taper Cylinders 2746
River Bank, Fallen Tree at, Saving..... 2865
Riveter, Key-Ring 2812
Road Patching 2702
Rodent-Proof Support for Corncrib.... 2870
Rods, Small, Straightening in a Vise... 2703
Roller, Small Printing-Press, Substitute for 2850
Roofed Watering Tank of Concrete..... 2874
Roofs, Snow-Melting Device for........ 2868
Rope, Determining Strength of........ 2832
Rubber, Solid-Tire, for Making Heels... 2878
Rubber Tips, Noiseless, for Bench-Vise Handles 2822
Rubber Tube, Coil Spring to Reinforce. 2710
Rust under Molding on Screen Frames, Preventing 2703
Rustic Four-Square Shelter House...... 2883

Safety Block for a Bench Vise........ 2769
Safety Boot Scraper for a Doorstep.... 2692
Safety Device for Wheelbarrow........ 2854
Safety-First Alarm System for Shops.. 2870
Safety Key for Faucets................ 2730
Safety Platform, Portable, for Telephone Linemen 2851
Safety Spring for Gas-Stove Burner.... 2738
Safety Spring for the Variety Wood-Molding Machine 2884
Safety Throttle for Air Motors.......... 2767
Sale Pavilion, Farm.................. 2770
Sand, Apparatus for Removing Dust in. 2827
Sand, Easy Method of Riddling........ 2797
Sand Racks for Storage Batteries....... 2814
Sander Attachment for a Lathe........ 2815
Sanding Block for Interior Trim and Floors 2862
Sanding Drum for the Wood Shop...... 2847
Sandpaper and Emery Cloth, Cutter and Reel for 2811
Saving a Fallen Tree at a River Bank... 2865
Sawing Wooden Wheels or Disks on Band Saw 2838
Scaffold, Movable, for Building and Painting 2845
Scale, Load, for Trucks................ 2689
Scale Platform, Overcoming Floor Vibration under 2802
Scales, Small Steel, Making........... 2826
School Grades, Average Table for..... 2757
Scissors, Sharpening on a Grinding Wheel 2864
Score Board, Electromagnet Used to Place Letters in..................... 2729
Scraper for Joints in Brickwork....... 2842
Scraper, Sharpening for Heavy Cut.... 2703
Screen Frames, Preventing Rust under Molding on 2703
Screw Cutting, Oil Tray for........... 2739
Screw Eyes in Signboard, Preventing from Rusting 2796
Screw-Riveting Kink 2797
Screwdriver, Cap for, Reduces Marring of Work 2882
Screwdriver Grips Small Screws........ 2691
Screwdriver Handle, Nonblister........ 2711
Screws, Setting, in Making Metal Patches 2799
Screws, Tongs for Grasping in Starting Them 2839
Securing Door with Loose-Pin Hinges.. 2721
Seed-Corn House, Farm................ 2736
Self-Acting Blowpipe 2826

Self-Feeder for Hogs.................... 2723
Sensitized Paper, Preparing for Pho-
tography 2716
Settling of a Ground Fill, Hastening.. 2765
Sewing Awl, Lockstitch................ 2794
Sewing Machine, Motor Attachment and
Brake for 2873
Shaft Coupling, Temporary............ 2689
Shaft Oiler, Safety-First.............. 2706
Shafts, Small, or Arbors, Device for Re-
moving 2839
Shaper, Gang Tool for, in Machine Shop. 2841
Sharpening Scissors on a Grinding
Wheel 2864
Sharpening Scraper for Heavy Cut..... 2703
Shear, Rigid, Made of Snips........... 2699
Sheet Brass, Soldering Drilled Lug on.. 2769
Sheet Metal, Device for Punching Holes
in 2812
Sheet Metal, Electric-Lamp Board of... 2686
Sheet Metal, Oiling for Stamping or
Punching 2715
Sheet-Metal Work, Oil-Burning Blow-
torch for 2852
Shelter House, Rustic Four-Square..... 2883
Shifting-Fork Repair 2860
Shoes, Wrapping Pair of.............. 2690
Shop and Garage, Farm............... 2681
Shop Apron with Convenient Spring Belt 2839
Shop Light, Radial Pivoted Arm for.... 2884
Shop Orders, Clip Board for........... 2705
Shop, Small, or Garage, Wall Crane for. 2881
Shop Tool, Mirror as.................. 2711
Shop Use, Home and, Adaptation of
Motorcycle for 2871
Shops, Safety-First Alarm System for.. 2870
Short-Circuited Armature Section, Re-
pairing 2884
Short-Circuiting, To Prevent Flash
Lamp from 2684
Shovel, Preventing Snow from Clinging
to 2813
Show-Card Holder, Convenient......... 2773
Siding, Clamp Enables One Man to Nail
Readily 2831
Silage Feeding, Barnyard Crane and
Trolley for 2763
Silencing a Noisy Gas Burner.......... 2768
Skidding a Heavy Boiler or Machine... 2846
Slide on Brass Horn, Repairing........ 2756
Slots, Small, Milling, with Combination
Center Drill 2768
Slots, Wide, Cutting with Hacksaw.... 2762
Small Screws, Screwdriver Grips....... 2691
Snap Gauges 2742
Snips, Rigid Shear Made of............ 2699
Snow-Melting Device for Roofs......... 2868
Snow, Preventing from Clinging to
Shovel 2813
Socket, Leaded, for Cable Fastening.... 2742
Socket Wrench, Reducing Size of....... 2714
Socket Wrenches, Forging Renews Worn 2838
Soft-Face Hammer 2842
Soldering Drilled Lug on Sheet Brass.. 2769
Soldering Iron, Forge Fire Adapted for
Heating 2741
Soldering Patches on Tanks or Large
Objects 2851
Solid-Tire Rubber for Making Heels.... 2878
Soot Scraper Aids Water Heating in
Kitchen Stove 2758
Sootless Cap for Removing Stovepipes.. 2689
Sorting Tray for Nails, Screws and Bolts 2840
Sound Deadener for Fan Ducts......... 2766
Sound-Proof Pump Connection......... 2813
Sounding Board for Large Auditorium.. 2786
Spacing Steel-Marking Punches, Gauge
for 2825
Spark Plugs, Kinks in Care of......... 2844
Spigot, Worn-Out, To Repair.......... 2814
Spindle-Turning Device Effects Large
Saving 2759
Spindles, Hollow Center for Re-Turning 2716
Spinning a Cranky Engine............. 2860
Splashing, Cross Disk on Faucet Stops.. 2738
Splices, Proper Insulation of........... 2883
Splinters, Block Protects Sawyer's
Hands from 2704
Spools, Wire Straightener Made of..... 2807
Spring Aids in Valve Grinding......... 2846

Spring Belt, Convenient, Shop Apron
with 2839
Spring, Broken, Washer Makes Usable.. 2734
Spring Bumper for Motorboat Landings 2795
Spring, Coil, to Reinforce Rubber Tube 2710
Spring-Cushioned Chair Legs........... 2724
Spring Inserts, Automobile, To Prevent
Squeaking 2685
Spring, Safety, for the Variety Wood-
Molding Machine 2884
Spring Stripping Attachment for Power
Presses 2880
Spring, Tension, for T-Square.......... 2798
Springs, Winding Small Compression... 2767
Sprinkler for Narrow Strips of Lawn... 2753
Sprocket Made of Wooden Disk and
Staples 2773
Staining Streaked Wood Uniformly..... 2755
Stairs for Climbing over Fence......... 2824
Stanchion, Self-Locking Swinging...... 2810
Starting Large Gas Engines............ 2739
Static Electricity in Belts, Counteract-
ing 2746
Steam-Gauge Dial-Glass Casings, Re-
moving 2702
Steel, Producing a Blue Finish on...... 2837
Steering Connections, Automobile, Care
of 2886
Steering Post, Repairing Ratchet on.... 2882
Stock, Long, or Ladders, Truck Arranged
for Hauling 2882
Storage Areas Marked on Floors....... 2876
Storage Batteries, Lights behind Indi-
cate Charging Periods............... 2813
Storage Batteries, Sand Racks for...... 2814
Storage Battery, How to Make......... 2693
Stove, Camp, Gasoline................. 2699
Stove-Lifting Truck of Varied Uses.... 2816
Stove Linings, Preserving............. 2852
Stovepipes, Sootless Cap for Removing.. 2689
Straddle-Milling Cutters, Oiling........ 2715
Straightedge Arched for Leveling Con-
crete 2869
Straightening Small Rods in a Vise..... 2703
Strainer and Economizer, Gasoline Fuel. 2741
Straps to Fit Double-Pipe Runs........ 2793
Stream-Bank Protection 2724
Stream, Hydroplane for Carrying Line
across 2680
Stream, Tidewater, Fence Extension at. 2863
Strength of Rope, Determining......... 2832
String Solder Replaces Copper Wire in
Battery Room 2798
Stripping Attachment, Spring, for Power
Presses 2880
Substitute for a Small Printing-Press
Roller 2850
Sulphate-of-Zinc Paint 2793
Summer Cottage or Camp, Gravity Water
System for 2866
Support, Adjustable Brake-Band....... 2733
Support for Corncrib, Rodent-Proof.... 2870
Surface-Grinding Taper Cylinders, Rig-
ging for 2746
Surface Whiting for Laying Out Work. 2691
Swage Block, Base for................. 2876
Swing, Lean-Back, of Wood-Faced Angle
Iron 2711

T-Square, Tension Spring for........... 2798
Table Top, Drum in, for Listing Mer-
chandise Sales 2861
Tail Center in Lathe, Prevents Loosen-
ing 2730
Tailstock Center, Ball-Bearing......... 2734
Tamper Made of Concrete............. 2692
Tanks or Large Objects, Soldering
Patches on 2851
Tap or Die, Cutting Threads without... 2852
Taper Cylinders, Rigging for Surface
Grinding 2746
Taper Gauge, Adjustable.............. 2808
Taps and Reamers, Small, Drawing the
Temper in 2877
Telephone Bells, Noisy, Remedy for.... 2859
Telephone Linemen, Portable Safety
Platform for 2851
Temper in Small Taps and Reamers,
Drawing 2877
Templates for Cutting Packing Gaskets. 2792

Terminations, Large-Conductor, Cable Clamp for 2712
Testing through Insulation on Wires... 2767
Threads, Cutting without Tap or Die.... 2852
Throttle for Air Motors, Safety......... 2767
Thumbscrews, Special - Size, Quickly Made 2725
Tidewater Stream, Fence Extension at.. 2863
Time Variations of Watch Explained.... 2679
Tire Patches, Kinks in Use of.......... 2765
Tires, Automobile Jacks Save.......... 2729
Title Stamp for the Drafting Room...... 2879
Tone of Electric Horn, Push Button Varies 2868
Tongs for Grasping Screws in Starting Them 2839
Tool Bag, Canvas....................... 2773
Tool Box for Mechanics, Improved...... 2731
Tool for Boring Large Holes in Wood.. 2844
Tool Holder, Indicator and............. 2740
Tool Holder with Set of Cutters....... 2717
Tool Rack, Revolving................... 2801
Toolmaker's Vise 2762
Tools, Hardening Small Carbon-Steel.. 2865
Tools Made of Buggy-Top Braces....... 2797
Traffic-Light Post, Inexpensive........ 2846
Transplanting Large Trees............. 2885
Tray for Counter Advertising Matter... 2812
Tray, Sorting, for Nails, Screws and Bolts 2840
Tree, Fallen, at River Bank, Saving.... 2865
Tree Repairing, Simple................. 2800
Trees, Large, Transplanting........... 2885
Trolley and Tackle for Freight Transfer, Portable 2843
Trouble Lamp Operated by Dry Batteries 2745
Trouble Signal for Motor-Starting Rheostat 2774
Truck Arranged for Hauling Long Stock or Ladders 2882
Truck for Baby Cab Indoors............ 2704
Truck, One-Man, Hoop for............. 2687
Truck, Stove-Lifting, of Varied Uses... 2816
Trucks, Load Scale for................. 2689
Truss for Long Span of Pipe........... 2741
Tubing, Odd-Sized, Hammered from a Smaller Diameter 2715
Tubing, Square, Brass Box Corners Made of 2685
Turning Pulleys in a Lathe, Adaptable Jig for 2873
Twisting Wire with a Brace............. 2739
Tying Parcels, Device for.............. 2859

Universal Joint, Double-Shaft.......... 2854
Universal Joint, Inexpensive........... 2680

Valve Cage, Repairing................. 2714
Valve-Cap Wrench 2826
Valve Grinding, Spring Aids in......... 2846
Valve Handle, Auxiliary Grip for....... 2740
Valve Lifter, Keeping Clean............ 2718
Vaulting Standards, Rack for Raising Crossbar on 2807
Veneer, Patching on Curved Surface.... 2724
Vent Cover for Automobile Gasoline Tank 2752
Ventilating a Mine Tunnel............. 2809
Ventilating Duct, Automatic Fire Damper in 2690
Vertical-Pull Windlass 2716
Vise, Bench, Safety Block for.......... 2769
Vise Jaw, Auxiliary, for Holding Irregular Pieces 2870
Vise, Holding a Small, Irregular Piece in 2772
Vise, Straightening Small Rods in...... 2703
Vise, Toolmaker's 2762

Wall Crane for Small Shop or Garage... 2881
Wall Cupboard, Garden-Hose Reel Inclosed in 2744
Wash Boiler, Finding Capacity of...... 2735
Washer, Fastening upon Wood Without Screws or Nails...................... 2786
Washer Makes Broken Spring Usable.. 2734
Washer, Sanitary Clothes.............. 2734
Washers, Fiber, Punch for Making..... 2706
Washing Machine, Cover for........... 2753
Watch Fitted to Automobile Steering Post 2745
Watch, Time Variations of, Explained. 2679
Water Gauge, Electrical............... 2861
Water Heating in Kitchen Stove, Soot Scraper Aids 2758
Water Joy Wheel...................... 2726
Water-Pump Gland Nut, Holding....... 2730
Water System, Gravity, for a Summer Cottage or Camp..................... 2866
Water, To Prevent Spilling on Automobile Radiator When Filling.......... 2703
Waterfall for the Movies, Making...... 2705
Watering Tank of Concrete, Roofed..... 2874
Watering Trough Made of Old Boiler... 2684
Wear, Long, Obtaining, Out of Piston Rings 2773
Weights for Drying Large Pieces of Cloth 2769
Well Casing, Old Kitchen Boilers Used for 2841
Wheelbarrow, Safety Device for........ 2854
Wheels of a Sidecar or Automobile, Alining 2792
Wheels or Disks, Wooden, Sawing on Band Saw 2838
Wheels or Pulleys, Heavy, Lifting Rig for 2751
Whiting, Surface, for Laying Out Work 2691
Wick, Notch in Improves Lamp Flame.. 2862
Wind Indicator for Greenhouse......... 2772
Winding Small Compression Springs.... 2767
Windlass for Raising Wagon Boxes.... 2743
Windlass, Vertical-Pull............... 2716
Windmill, Distant, Pump Operated by.. 2831
Window Advertisement, Novel.......... 2792
Window Covering, Translucent......... 2772
Wing-Joist Frame Barn................ 2828
Wire-Forming Fixtures, Hand-Operated 2817
Wire, Nippers for Removing Insulation from 2822
Wire Rings, Making Small.............. 2794
Wire Spring Machine-Thread Cleaner.. 2794
Wire Straightener Made of Spools...... 2807
Wire Substitute for Latticework....... 2872
Wire, Twisting with a Brace............ 2739
Wires, Pulling into Conduits........... 2718
Wiring, Economy in Platinum or Other. 2735
Woman's Home Workshop...2775, 2781, 2787
Woodcuts or Type, Patching Printing Surfaces of 2841
Wood-Molding Machine, Variety, Safety Spring for 2884
Wood Shop, Sanding Drum for......... 2847
Wood, Streaked, Staining Uniformly... 2755
Wood, Tool for Boring Large Holes in.. 2844
Wood Turning, Silencing Rattle in...... 2751
Workbench, Exhaust Fan for Aids in Removing Dust 2849
Workshop, Woman's Home...2775, 2781, 2787
Wrapping a Pair of Shoes.............. 2690
Wrench Adapted Easily for Many Uses. 2886
Wrench, Long, for Automobile Drain Cocks 2793
Wrench, Powerful, Used in Dismantling Large Pipe Line..................... 2878
Wrench, Socket, Reducing Size of...... 2714
Wrench, Valve-Cap 2826

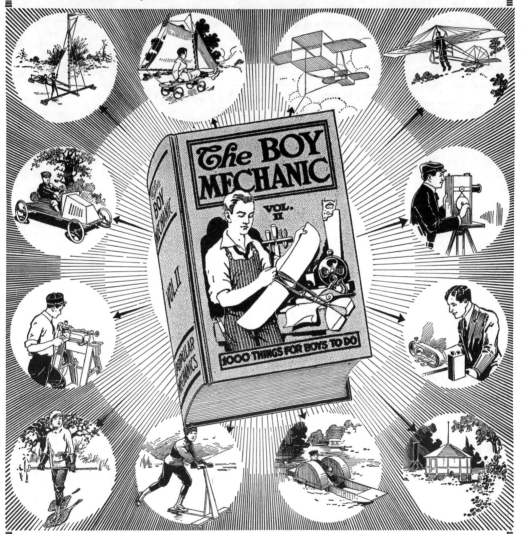

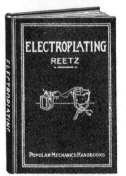